UKIYO-E
PAINTINGS
IN THE BRITISH MUSEUM

UKIYO-E
PAINTINGS
IN THE BRITISH MUSEUM

TIMOTHY CLARK

SMITHSONIAN INSTITUTION PRESS

WASHINGTON, D.C.

© 1992 The Trustees of the British Museum

Published in the United States
by Smithsonian Institution Press
470 L'Enfant Plaza, Suite 7100
Washington, D.C. 20560

Library of Congress Catalog Number 92–64231

ISBN 1–56098–243–8

Designed by Harry Green
Typeset by Wyvern Typesetting Ltd, Bristol
Printed and bound in Hong Kong by Everbest

PAGE 1   MORITOSHI, *Courtesan in a White Kimono*,
c. Kambun era (no. 3).

PAGE 2   Teisai HOKUBA, *Geisha on a Landing Stage in
the Snow* (detail), Tempō era (no. 121).

PAGE 4   Torii KIYOSHIGE, *The Actors Nakamura
Tomijūrō I* (right) and (?)*Ichikawa Ebizō II* (left) *in
'Momiji-gari'*, *c*. Hōreki era, before 1758 (no. 43).

CONTENTS

The Trustees of the British Museum

acknowledge with gratitude

generous assistance towards the

production of this book from

The Daiwa Anglo-Japanese Foundation

PREFACE

This is a catalogue of the 200 paintings in the British Museum by artists of the Ukiyo-e, or 'floating world', school. Entries are arranged broadly chronologically from the second half of the seventeenth to the end of the nineteenth centuries, though with some regard to grouping artists by sub-schools or lineages. A few examples of early seventeenth-century genre (*fūzoku*) painting which share similar themes have been included to establish the context from which Ukiyo-e paintings developed. Preparatory drawings for Ukiyo-e woodblock prints have not been included; neither have the unsigned brush studies done by Hokusai and his pupils. Osaka artists such as Tsukioka Settei and Ichiyōtei Yoshitaki who worked primarily in the Ukiyo-e idiom have been included, but *bijin* painters of the Kyoto Shijō school have not – these will be included in a future catalogue of paintings in all genres by this school. The catalogue concludes with two early works from the 1890s by Kaburagi Kiyokata, who once described himself as 'last painter in the Ukiyo-e line', and the Appendix contains a small group of forged works. The study of Ukiyo-e painting has been overshadowed in the past by that of the more easily collected woodblock prints. It is hoped that this catalogue will contribute towards the integrated study of Ukiyo-e school works in all media – paintings, prints and illustrated books.

Much of the information presented relies on the previous research of Japanese scholars, particularly as published in Narazaki Muneshige (ed.), *Hizō ukiyo-e taikan, vol. 1: Daiei Hakubutsukan I*, Tokyo, Kōdansha, 1987, and I would like to express my sincere thanks to the many authors involved in that project. I am heavily indebted, too, to Jack Hillier, Kobayashi Tadashi, Asano Shūgo and Naitō Masato who have shared with me unstintingly of their knowledge on numerous occasions and to Matsudaira Susumu who assisted with identifying the Kabuki signboards (nos 167–70). Kasuya Hiroki, Hayashi Nozomu, Robert Campbell, Lisa Spalding and Ōtsuka Yūzō gave their expert help in the difficult matter of deciphering and interpreting inscriptions and Christopher Cullen kindly checked the transliterations of Chinese. My thanks also to the various museums and individuals who provided photographs for the Introduction.

Colleagues in the British Museum's departments of Japanese Antiquities, Conservation (Eastern Pictorial Art Section) and Photographic Services have helped in numerous ways to realise this project, and I am grateful, too, to Teresa Francis and Deborah Wakeling for their helpful editing, to Harry Green for his expert design, and to Julie Young, who produced the book. Lastly, I should like to acknowledge with sincere thanks the timely intervention at the last moment of the Daiwa Anglo-Japanese Foundation with financial assistance that has enabled the catalogue to be considerably more useful than would otherwise have been the case.

INTRODUCTION

When an anonymous eighth-century Japanese artist was called upon to paint an image of Kichijōten (Mahadevi), goddess of beauty and fecundity, he portrayed her as the most lovely Tang court lady he could imagine – China was, after all, the well-spring of all 'high' culture at this time – dressed in stuffs and gauzes of the utmost refinement, and then further adorned her with the various iconographic attributes of the deity – a jewelled crown and necklace, flowing scarves and the 'wish-granting jewel' (*nyoi no hōju*) held out to the believer (fig. 1). Some 1,000 years later, about the year 1790, the 'floating world' (Ukiyo-e) artist Katsukawa Shunshō (?1726–92) was commissioned to paint a special portrait of the grand courtesan Hinazuru by a man who had been her loyal patron over many years: Shunshō was to paint her in her most sumptuous costume of a black surcoat embroidered with peacock feathers and turquoise brocade *obi* (sash) and then add the jewelled crown and necklaces, and the lotus flower pedestals of the Bodhisattva Kannon on her passage to rebirth in the Pure Land Paradise (fig. 2). As the fellow-reveller who inscribed the painting using the sobriquet 'Crazy-verse poet who has sported his way round the three capitals'[1] (Santo Yūreki Kyōkyaku) tells us, the old roué would gaze at the painting with nostalgic longing and compose poems to it, one of which reads: 'Even on an old man's body/that looks like a withered tree/this female Bodhisattva/makes flowers bloom.'[2]

Of course it is one thing to make a goddess into a beautiful woman and quite another to make a beautiful woman into a goddess (this says much about the secularisation of Japanese society in the intervening millennium), but appreciated for a moment on a purely formal level the two paintings have remarkably similar qualities to offer. The standard Far Eastern figure-painting techniques had been established by the Tang dynasty in China – the fine 'iron wire' outline in soot-black ink on a silk support, filled with meticulously layered natural dyes and mineral pigments often finished with gold leaf or pigment, the face almost always shown in three-quarter profile. In a very real sense the painters of the popular Ukiyo-e school who are the subject of this catalogue were the revivers of a sumptuous figure-painting tradition not used to such seductive ends in Japan since the court aristocracy had ceased to commission hyper-refined hanging scrolls of Buddhist deities in the early Kamakura period (1185–1333). During intervening centuries of warrior government the relegation of women to the margins of political and social life was not conducive to the painting of images of beauties.

The 'floating world' and the pursuit of pleasure

Following the victories of the Tokugawa clan in the Battle of Sekigahara in 1600 and the Osaka campaigns of 1615 and the restoration of nationwide peace under their hegemony after more than a century of ruinous wars, civilian culture began to revive and blossom in the rebuilt cities of Kyoto, Osaka and Sakai and in the new Tokugawa fortress capital of Edo (modern Tokyo). A small castle town in 1600, by 1700 Edo had become a bustling metropolis of more than a million, one of the largest cities in the world at the time, with a substantial population of merchants and artisans supplying goods and services to the military aristocracy who were required by the Tokugawa to maintain luxurious mansions surrounding the castle. With

Fig. 1
Anon., *Kichijōten*, 8th century. Yakushi Temple, Nara (National Treasure)

peace and increasing prosperity there quickly evolved a new distinctive culture of pleasure seeking, centring on the newly created brothel quarters of Yoshiwara (established in Edo in 1617), Shimabara (Kyoto, 1640) and Shimmachi (Osaka, Kan'ei era, 1624–44). In granting these quarters exclusive government licences the new rulers shrewdly sought to channel townsmen's energies into the time- and money-consuming courtship of courtesans and away from any possible political intrigue.

Another focus of passionate popular support was the Kabuki theatre. This had its origins in a kind of *risqué* revue led by Okuni, a former priestess from the Izumo Grand Shrine, performed each summer in the dry riverbed of the Kamō River in Kyoto during the decade from about 1603 to 1612. Okuni appeared in male drag wearing a huge gold sword and a crucifix (*kabuki-mono* meant at the time someone who paraded the streets dressed in outrageous costume), and led a troupe of girls in suggestive formation song and dance numbers, interspersed with simple dramas featuring Okuni and the ghost of her lover, Nagoya Sansaburō, who had been killed in a brawl. From these modest outlaw beginnings Kabuki flourished in spite of the various government attempts to suppress it – women were banned from performances in about the year 1629, and pretty boys in 1652 – becoming by the later seventeenth century a sophisticated dramatic art form employing the skills of leading playwrights, a host of acting 'dynasties' and commanding the total, unswerving support of the non-samurai classes in the cities.

Ukiyo (written with characters meaning 'sad world') was originally a pessimistic term conveying the Buddhist notion that this present desire-ridden world of illusion was a place of sadness and pain. In the later seventeenth century, however, the word was recoined (and rewritten with characters meaning 'floating world'), enjoying a healthy turn-about in meaning to become an epithet connoting a sense of 'fashionable', 'up-to-date', 'erotic'. Thus one could be a 'floating-world man' (*ukiyo-otoko*), take a 'floating-world hot bath' (*ukiyo-buro*), read a 'floating-world novel' (*ukiyo-zōshi*) and look at 'floating-world pictures' (*ukiyo-e*). The classic definition of the ethos of enthusiastic pleasure seeking was given by Asai Ryōi (d. 1691) in the preface to his *Ukiyo monogatari* ('Tales of the Floating World') of c. 1661:

> ... Living only for the moment, turning our full attention to the pleasures of the moon, the snow, the cherry blossoms and the maple leaves; singing songs, drinking wine, diverting ourselves in just floating, floating; caring not a whit for the pauperism staring us in the face, refusing to be disheartened, like a gourd floating along with the river current: this is what we call the *floating world* ...[3]

Genre painting and Ukiyo-e

Ukiyo-e grew out of earlier traditions of genre painting (*fūzokuga*). In the late sixteenth and early seventeenth centuries artists of the leading Kanō school were commissioned by military patrons to produce folding screens – often with sumptuous gold-leaf backgrounds – to decorate their mansions, showing a wide variety of genre scenes – panoramic views of Kyoto (later Edo), the antics of the *hoi polloi* at festival processions and fairs in the dry riverbed at Shijō in Kyoto (including scenes of early Kabuki), military sports such as dog-chasing, historic battles and merry-making in houses of pleasure.

Fig. 2
Katsukawa SHUNSHŌ, *The Courtesan Hinazuru as Kannon, c. 1790.* Private collection, Japan

Fig. 3
Torii KIYOMASU, *The Actors Ōtani Hiroji* (left)
and Ichikawa Danzō (right) *in an 'Armour-
tugging' Scene*, 1717. British Museum

Undoubtedly this explosion of interest in scenes of the world around them reflected confidence in the stability of the new order of peace and prosperity, as well as the materialistic tastes of new masters not necessarily educated in sophisticated classical imagery.

During the second quarter of the seventeenth century, however, as the numerous branches of the Kanō school under Kanō Tan'yū (1602–74) came to serve an increasingly bureaucratic function as painters in attendance to the Bakufu (the Tokugawa administration) and feudal aristocracy, Kanō painters were steered away from genre subjects towards more edifying classical Chinese subjects. Those painters who did continue to paint scenes from the 'floating world' dropped out of the official painting academy and operated as independent, generally anonymous 'city painters' (*machi-eshi*) catering to an ever-wider clientele in the merchant as well as samurai classes. It is to this period, roughly the Kan'ei era (1624–44), that we can place a group of screens showing *Fan Dancers*, a single elegant figure to each panel (no. 1). As the century progressed, painting formats shifted, correspondingly, away from large-scale screens to the smaller hanging-scroll, album and handscroll formats, which could be more quickly mass-produced, and subject-matter, too, gradually became more narrowly concentrated on the special world of the pleasure quarters that was of interest to middle-class patrons; on individual houses of pleasure; and finally on the figures of individual courtesans themselves, in hanging scrolls known as 'Kambun beauties' (*Kambun bijin*) after the Kambun era (1661–73) when most of these are thought to have been produced (nos 3, 4).[4]

It is best to see the shift from genre painting to Ukiyo-e as a process of gradual transition rather than trying to force discrete definitions for the two. However, certain overall trends can be identified which allow us at a particular point to say that Ukiyo-e has come of age: the adoption of the age-old process of woodblock printing to mass-produce 'floating-world' imagery cheaply – this had the effect of cutting the direct tie between artist and patron and permitting more rapid experimentation with new subjects; the emergence of individual masters – notably Hishikawa Moronobu (d. 1694) who after 1672 habitually signed his works; the palpable energy and excitement reflecting a new sense of cultural confidence and buoyancy on the part of the townsman class which these artists inject into their works in the budding Ukiyo-e style (for that is what it has become); and the emergence of a popular culture in Edo increasingly independent of the influence of Kyoto and Osaka. The great fire which destroyed most of Edo in 1657, and which must have destroyed much of the existing corpus of work in the nascent Ukiyo-e style along with it, makes the break seem sharper than it probably was, but by the 1660s the new style had reached the point of take-off into self-sustained development. It is no coincidence that the 'manifesto' of the 'floating world' by Asai Ryōi quoted above was published *c.* 1661.

Ukiyo-e paintings and prints

Although the adoption of woodblock printing to mass-produce 'floating world' imagery was of critical importance, it is nevertheless true that until about 1720 Ukiyo-e printmaking remained in a largely dependent relationship to Ukiyo-e painting. While masters such as Moronobu and Sugimura

Fig. 4
Kaigetsudō ANCHI, *Courtesan, c.* 1710–20.
British Museum

Jihei (worked *c.* late 1670s–1700) quickly learned to exploit the bold contrasts and potentiality for cropping the composition of the graphic medium to brilliant expressive effect, on the whole their choice of themes and formats was determined by painting practice. Here the issue is complicated by the very fragmentary survival of early paintings – no paintings are known by Sugimura, and where, for instance, are the great *painted* erotic works by Moronobu whose existence can be hypothesised on the basis of the works in this genre by his pupils (no. 11)? Moronobu and Sugimura's *printed* erotica certainly imitate the formats of handscrolls and albums, with their decorative borders, and Moronobu's designs for genre prints and illustrated books are often taken from larger compositions in handscroll, hanging-scroll and even screen format.

With the Torii school and Kaigetsudō atelier, the two main groupings of Ukiyo-e artists who dominated the late Genroku (1688–1704) to Shōtoku (1711–16) eras, the situation is even clearer. Not one of the great signboards (*e-kamban*) painted by Torii-school artists to hang in front of the Kabuki theatres for each new play survives from earlier than the mid-eighteenth century; and yet their large prints in the so-called *kakemono-e* (hanging-scroll) format, with their bold 'gourd-shaped legs and wriggling-worm line' (fig. 3), are surely based on the techniques used for such signboards and hint at how magnificent these must have been. Similarly, the now rare prints by artists of the Kaigetsudō atelier (fig. 4) in the same large format are essentially black and white versions of the paintings produced by Kaigetsudō Ando (worked *c.* Hōei (1706–11)–Kyōhō (1716–36) eras) and his followers (nos 21–3). In the past the history of Ukiyo-e has often been written as the history of the development of the woodblock prints of this school. With regard to the early period, in particular, it should be rewritten with paintings central to the account, or at the very least given parity with prints.

There is no easily demonstrable progressive development in the techniques of Ukiyo-e painting – the basic skills were already mastered by the eighth century – as there is in the case of the development of Ukiyo-e printmaking: two-colour prints after the early 1740s; full-colour printing after 1765. One is, nevertheless, always conscious of a healthy reciprocal influence and even rivalry between the sister media. This is particularly true after the perfection of full-colour printing techniques in 1765 which seemed to spur painters to ever-more subtle refinements of line and drapery decoration in the 1770s and 80s. Conversely, it is hard to imagine the lovely delicacy of the prints of Harunobu without the stylistic precursor of the paintings by the Kawamata group of artists (nos 45–6). The truth is, of course, that whilst there were some who did only paintings (Chōshun), particularly in the early period, and others who were indifferent or only occasional painters (Harunobu), in general most Ukiyo-e artists of merit were active in both media. The classic career pattern seems to have been for an established print designer to semi-retire in later years to cultivate his skills with the brush (Shunshō, Koryūsai, Eishi).

Technique

Ukiyo-e painters are very occasionally shown at work in prints or book illustrations. One of the earliest of these occurs in the two-volume illustrated

Fig. 5
Okamura MASANOBU, *Osan Painting*, from
Ehon fūga nana Komachi, 1740s. Gerhard
Pulverer Collection, Cologne

book *Ehon fūga nana Komachi* ('Picture Book of Seven Elegant Komachis') by
Okamura Masanobu (1686–1764), thought to have been published in the
1740s, in which Osan, granddaughter of the great Hishikawa Moronobu, is
shown putting the finishing touches to a painting of a standing beauty
(fig. 5). Osan was the daughter of Hishikawa Sakunojō Moronaga, who it
has recently been suggested was Moronobu's daughter.[5] The inscription on
the right of the illustration says that Osan succeeded Sakunojō as a painter
at the age of fifteen. The illustration shows that paintings (probably on silk
in this case rather than paper) were mounted on stretchers to be worked on,
and Osan is surrounded by an ink-stone and brushes to her right and trays
of pots of colour and a wide selection of flat and pointed brushes to her left.
The brazier would be necessary to heat some of the pigments during their
preparation. The pigments used in Ukiyo-e paintings have been extensively
analysed by Elisabeth West Fitzhugh at the Freer Gallery of Art, Washington, DC, who was able to identify eighteen different classes or types of
pigment, the most widely used being shell white, vermilion, red lead, an
organic yellow, malachite and azurite.[6]

For an extremely detailed record of the techniques of figure painting we
are fortunate to have an eye-witness account left by the English architect
Josiah Conder (1852–1920), who studied with the painter Kawanabe Kyōsai
(1831–89) between 1881 and 1889, included in his *Paintings and Studies by
Kawanabe Kyōsai*.[7] Kyōsai trained in the Kanō school and is generally classified as a Kanō painter. Nevertheless, he often painted hanging scrolls of
beauties in the *goku-saishiki* (detailed colouring) mode employed by Ukiyo-e
painters. In fact, many Ukiyo-e painters in the Edo period had studied with
Kanō teachers. Conder tells us that Kyōsai worked from preliminary
charcoal sketches which were tidied up into more finished 'preparatory
drawings' (*shita-e*) in ink outline.[8] Though painters of the Kyoto Shijō school
in the early nineteenth century often seem to have used charcoal under-

ABOVE Fig. 6
Katsukawa SHUN'EI, *Courtesan Tying her Obi*
(preparatory drawing), 1790s. Ōta Memorial
Museum of Art, Tokyo

ABOVE CENTRE Fig. 7
Katsukawa SHUN'EI, *Courtesan Tying her Obi*,
1790s. Freer Gallery of Art, Smithsonian
Institution, Washington, DC

ABOVE RIGHT Fig. 8
Kawanabe KYŌSAI, *Japanese Beauty of the
Eleventh Century*, 1884–5. From Josiah
Conder, *Paintings and Studies by Kawanabe
Kyōsai* (1911)

drawing, there is no evidence as yet that this technique was used by Ukiyo-e artists. *Shita-e* preparatory drawings by them do occasionally survive, however, one of the earliest and most impressive being a study by Katsukawa Shun'ei (1762–1819) from the 1790s, *Courtesan Tying her Obi* (fig. 6), for a finished painting in the Freer Gallery of Art (fig. 7). What the preparatory drawing provided was the layout of the basic outlines of the composition which could then be traced on to the silk or paper support of the finished painting. Notice, though, how considerable attention is paid even at this early stage to the details of the face and hairstyle, which are much more completely worked out than any other part of the drawing. For an Ukiyo-e painter the painting of a face was of critical importance, the particular configuration of facial features – which look so simple, and yet are so difficult to balance with grace – being in effect the hallmark of his style. Kyōsai's painstaking stages of painting the face on his *Japanese Beauty of the*

Fig. 9
Andō HIROSHIGE, *Princess Usuyuki and the Boatman*, from *Ogura nazorae hyakunin isshu* (preparatory drawing), *c.* 1846.
British Museum

Eleventh Century (1884–5; fig. 8) are described in detail by Josiah Conder as follows:

> The original outlines of the head and features had been rendered faint by the first wash of flesh colour carried over them, and these were now restored in the following manner: – the lips were outlined with a mixture of vermilion and *taisha* [iron red], the lines being softened off at the ends with a wet brush. This was repeated with a light tint of pure vermilion, and over this again with *shōenji* [organic crimson from China], these red lines being all softened off with a wet brush and partaking more of the character of tiny washes. The *shōenji* outline shading was carried further to the lower lip in order to give it fuller colour than the upper. A purple brown, made of ink, vermilion and *shōenji*, was then used for repeating the outlines of the head, the nose, the eyelids, ear, chin, and neck, which was done with a very fine brush. Ink alone, not too black, was used for the darker lines round the eyes and nostril, and to the eye-brows. The white eye-balls were then washed with *gofun* [shell white], softened off with water to give roundness. With a very fine brush, and with the thickest black ink, the outlines and central black dot of the pupils of the eyes were put in; also the edge of the top eye-lid, this [*sic*] eye-lashes, the nostril, and the edge of the upper lip received the finest possible lines of deep black. The same ink, made a little lighter, was used for putting in the hairs of the eye-brows. The masses of hair which had been blocked in with opaque grey were next shaded with washes of *chū-sumi* [medium ink], using two brushes. This black shading was repeated several times to get sufficient depth and roundness, after which, using somewhat lighter ink and a spread brush, the edge of the hair over the brow was washed in and softened off. Then with a very fine long pointed brush, called *kegaki fude*, taking up the thickest ink from the ink-stone, the single hairs were drawn over the coils of hair, carefully following the curves of their contours, and keeping the lines perfectly parallel, whilst striking them in with a firm vigorous touch. The same brush, charged with rather lighter ink, was used for the thin separate hairs and short growth over the forehead, and these were drawn in two directions, as of hair dividing in the centre. Returning to the thickest black ink, obtained from the ink-stone after a few hard rubs with the ink-stick, the hanging tassels of the hair at the side of the face were drawn in single parallel lines, some broader than others and giving the appearance of hair clotted with grease. This completed the painting of the head of the figure, which was in this case finished before the other parts of the painting.[9]

By comparison the execution by an Ukiyo-e artist of a preparatory drawing (again the word *shita-e* is used in Japanese) for a woodblock print was a relatively straightforward process. The British Museum's collection contains a preparatory drawing by Andō Hiroshige (1797–1858) for a woodblock print of *Princess Usuyuki and the Boatman* from the series *Ogura nazorae hyakunin isshu* ('The Hundred Poets Likened to the Ogura Selection'), published *c.* 1846 (fig. 9), and this can be compared with the finished woodblock print (fig. 10). There is a bold, free quality apparent in the lines of the drawing which suggest that it is a 'first stage' preparatory sketch in which the artist is mapping out his basic ideas for the design. This first stage drawing would then be tidied up into a neat 'block copy' (*hanshita*) which was finally stuck to the face of the printing block and destroyed during the process of carving by

Fig. 10
Andō HIROSHIGE, *Princess Usuyuki and the Boatman*, from *Ogura nazorae hyakunin isshu*, *c.* 1846. British Museum

a master block carver (*horishi*), according to the collaborative process of Ukiyo-e printmaking by the quartet of publisher, artist, block carver and printer.[10]

Hanshita sometimes have rudimentary colour indications written in by the artist, together with occasional samples of drapery patterns required, but many of the detailed decisions about how the blocks were cut and printed were clearly left up to the master block cutters and printers, presumably guided to a certain extent by the publisher. The contribution of the artist ended once he had supplied the preliminary sketch and this permitted him to be extremely prolific. By the nineteenth century Ukiyo-e printmaking had taken on the character of an industrial production line, with individual artists responsible for total *oeuvres* of prints and book illustrations numbering in the tens of thousands of designs. In comparison, the number of paintings executed during the career of an Ukiyo-e artist would be several hundred at the most and often considerably fewer.

Shin Yoshiwara pleasure quarter

The hub of the 'floating world' – and the *locus* of many of the scenes depicted in the paintings in this catalogue – was Shin Yoshiwara (New Yoshiwara), the single government-licensed pleasure quarter relocated in open fields on the northern outskirts of Edo following the great fire of 1657.[11] The layout of this square fenced and moated enclosure, with a single entrance through the Ōmon (Great Gate) on the centre of the north side, consisted of Naka-no-chō, the central boulevard lined with assignation teahouses (*ageya*), from both sides of which one turned into the 'five streets' where the houses of pleasure were located. In its heyday in the early eighteenth century more than 3,000 women worked as prostitutes in Yoshiwara, but statistics of 1787 suggest that by that year numbers had fallen to 2,500 (including *kamuro*, the courtesans' child attendants). In addition to the prostitutes Yoshiwara had to support an even larger host of brothel owners, madams, geishas (entertainers), cooks and other servants. Yoshiwara was, in effect, a separate city within a city.

The social demarcation between samurai and townsman classes of the outside world was not supposed to apply in the pleasure quarter: in theory it was the wealth and decorum of the customer which counted. Somewhat ironically, however, Yoshiwara developed an elaborate etiquette and practice that could be every bit as stifling as the feudal world outside. This led in the eighteenth century to the emergence of dozens of unlicensed (that is, illicit) pleasure quarters (*okabasho*) throughout the city which provided more down-to-earth services of prostitution at prices which most townsmen could afford.

By the end of the Hōreki era (1750–64) the two highest grades of Yoshiwara courtesan, *tayū* and *kōshi*, had priced themselves out of existence, and the system of ranking was bumped up so that the *chūsan* and *yobidashi* grades were now at the top. The houses of pleasure where such high-ranking women lived were known as *ōmagaki*, after the lattice window at the entrance where the bars went all the way up to the ceiling. *Chūsan* and *yobidashi* grades were not expected to have to sit in this latticed 'display window' (*harimise*, no. 56) to attract customers, and processed instead with a retinue to the assignation teahouse to greet the wealthy client who had summoned them (no. 63). A customer could not expect to become intimate with a grand courtesan until his third visit, and on each occasion there would be dining and partying with attendant comedians (*hōkan* or *taikomochi*) and geishas in both the teahouse and the house of pleasure itself. The basic price for engaging one of the highest-ranking courtesans was 3 gold *bu* (4 *bu* = 1 gold *ryō*), but based on figures given in a manuscript, *Nama-giki sōshi*, thought to date from after the early 1780s, Nakano Mitsutoshi has calculated that the total cost once the entertainment expenses were added would be 5 gold *ryō* and 1 *bu*, which he suggests would be about 400,000 *yen* (about £1,600, including tips) at 1980 prices.[12] It may seem that this catalogue is preoccupied with describing details of the costumes worn by the women in the paintings; but costumes have much to tell about profession and status in Edo society, as well as often being decorated with patterns indicative of the season. The grander courtesans generally required a complete new wardrobe four times a year, and patrons were expected to foot the bill for this as well as other accessories, not to mention the considerable expenses incurred periodically in launching the *shinzō* apprentices who served individual courtesans. Not all entertainments in the quarter were so exorbitant, however. At the bottom of the Yoshiwara hierarchy were the *kirimise* located at the far end of Naka-no-chō near the moat, where a customer got a fixed time for a fixed price with considerably fewer frills. These are generally not shown in Ukiyo-e.

Given the chronic impoverishment of the bottom levels of the peasantry in Tokugawa Japan, there was never a shortage in the supply of young women entering the prostitution industry, and the peasant girls who, in Kabuki drama, are so often sold to a travelling scout from a brothel in order to rescue their aged parents from destitution evoked pity and admiration for their filial conduct from audiences, rather than any condemnation. For the youngest girls of about eight to thirteen years of age the best they could hope for was to be apprenticed as child servants (*kamuro*) to one of the high-ranking courtesans. *Kamuro* are often shown dressed in matching kimonos accompanying a courtesan in Ukiyo-e paintings and prints, and undoubtedly they were considerably spoiled and indulged by all in Yoshiwara. After extensive training in the required etiquette and a range of cultural accomplishments such as the Tea Ceremony, calligraphy and poetry composition between the ages of about thirteen and sixteen, teenagers were launched as apprentice courtesans (*shinzō*) wearing distinctive kimonos with long, hanging sleeves (*furisode*). From then on, all being well, they would advance through the ranks of *heya-mochi* ('having one's own room') and *zashiki-mochi* ('having one's own suite') to become fully fledged courtesans. After the standard indenture of ten years in Yoshiwara the future was uncertain for even the highest-ranking women. The most 'desirable' outcome might be ransom by a sympathetic and wealthy patron to be installed as his concubine or in one's own business. Failing this, there was the possibility of employment as a mature servant or madam in Yoshiwara itself. But all too often women were forced to leave Yoshiwara only to join those working in the unlicensed quarters in the city, where conditions could be pitiful.

Since Ukiyo-e paintings and prints were in the business of advertising the

Fig. 11
Katsukawa SHUN'EI, *Courtesan Seated Reading a Letter*, c. 1790s. Art Gallery of New South Wales, Sydney

pleasures of the 'floating world', in general their tone is idealising and unproblematic: little is shown of the seamier side of the prostitution industry that is known all too well to have existed from diaries, popular literature and other written sources. Nevertheless, certain individuals did occasionally adopt a tone more genuinely sympathetic with the courtesan's plight, and one such artist was Shun'ei, whose paintings consistently show a wider emotional range than is generally found in Ukiyo-e. A hanging scroll by him now in the collection of the Art Gallery of New South Wales, Sydney, *Courtesan Seated Reading a Letter* (fig. 11), clearly shows the poor woman in some considerable anguish over the letter's contents. Shun'ei affectingly expresses her despair in the crumpled pose and expression of utter dismay on her sunken head. In a Chinese-style inscription above, full of word-play around Buddhist notions of this world of illusion, the celebrated man of letters Ōta Nampo (1749–1823) reflects on the sad lot of the prostitute: 'Courtesans of the Five Streets of the Quarter/Ten years adrift on an ocean of troubles/Released at twenty-seven with misguided dreams/Ah! This bitter mirage of the brothels.'[13]

In search of the courtesan Segawa

The high-ranking courtesans of Yoshiwara were given names by their houses which were passed on from incumbent to incumbent (*myōseki*), and perhaps the most celebrated of all was the name (or 'title') Segawa ('shallow river') of the Matsubaya ('pine needle') house located in Edo-chō Itchōme, the first street on the right off central Naka-no-chō. In his memoir, *Zokuji kosui*, Ōta Nampo tells us of the fates of successive Segawas during the 1770s and 80s.[14] After the fifth generation Segawa (Segawa V) was ransomed by the blind money-lender Toriyama Kenkō in 1776, the title was in abeyance until the launch of Segawa VI on the first day of the fourth month (that is, the first day of summer), 1782. She was ransomed in the autumn of 1783 by a deputy manager (*tedai*) of the Echigoya Department Store for the reputed sum of 1,500 *ryō*. Segawa VII (see p. 20), who had formerly served as a *kamuro* named Konomo to the courtesan Utahime of the same house, acceded to the name on the first day of summer 1784. She reigned for almost four years until ransomed by Bunkyō, son of the lord of Matsumae, for 500 *ryō* in the third month of 1788 – just in time for Segawa VIII to appear the next month. Bearing in mind the tentative rate of exchange with modern currency suggested on p. 16, the selling of women was clearly a major part of the profitable business of the leading Yoshiwara establishments.

Needless to say, major events in the life of the quarter such as these were immediately woven into the plots of *sharebon*, the comic novelettes invariably set in Yoshiwara, and *kibyōshi*, their illustrated counterparts. The careers of successive Segawas can be traced, too, in a series of evermore lavish Ukiyo-e colour prints and paintings of the period, as well as in written accounts by that doyen of Yoshiwara, the author and artist Santō Kyōden (art name Kitao Masanobu, 1761–1816), the son of a pawnbroker from near the Fukagawa lumber yards who rose to be chief spokesman *cum* publicity agent for the quarter, as well as arbiter of its complex ritual.

The colour-printed book *Seirō bijin-awase sugata kagami* ('Comparison of Beauties of the Green Houses: A Mirror of their Lovely Forms') with illustra-

Fig. 12
Kitao SHIGEMASA and Katsukawa SHUNSHŌ,
Courtesans of the Matsubaya House, from *Seirō*
bijin-awase sugata kagami, 1776.
British Museum

tion jointly by Kitao Shigemasa (1739–1820) and Katsukawa Shunshō, published at the New Year 1776, opens with an illustration of what must be the soon-to-be-ransomed Segawa V quoting from a poetry anthology as her sister courtesan, Somenosuke, is about to write her first calligraphy of the New Year (fig. 12). The book includes forty-three double-page spreads showing the élite courtesans passing the seasons engaged in every cultured pastime imaginable, with not a hint of the presence of a customer or even the slightest allusion to their true vocation. The illustrations are followed by pages of *haiku* poems by the women on themes taken from nature.

Even grander is the colour-printed folding album *Yoshiwara keisei shin bijin-awase jihitsu kagami* ('Yoshiwara Courtesans: A Comparison of New Beauties with Samples of their Calligraphy'), designed by the young Masanobu/Kyōden and published in the New Year of 1784, which contained seven illustrations in the unprecedented double-*ōban* size, some having been issued as individual sheets in 1783. Here Segawa, who must be the sixth as this is one of the sheets issued in 1783, standing on the right, is shown a box of New Year decorated letter papers by Matsubito (seated, left), while two *kamuro* read a book next to the brazier behind (fig. 13). As in the previous book, according to the prevailing Ukiyo-e convention no attempt is made to distinguish the particular physiognomies of individual women (though this was certainly done in the case of male Kabuki actors) – all are presented as uniformly gorgeous, with the particular cast of features that was the hallmark of the artist concerned. The Chinese ode with Segawa's signature and seals printed above is supposed to imitate the actual elegant flow of her handwriting, and again advertises the high level of her cultivation.

The Yoshiwara quarter was completely destroyed by fire in the middle of the fourth month, 1784, barely two weeks after the accession of Segawa VII. A now extremely rare two-page printed broadsheet, *Sato no wakamuro* ('Elegant Rooms in the Quarter'), written by Kyōden is thought to describe the appearance of the newly reconstructed suites of rooms of thirty-seven of the leading Yoshiwara courtesans, '. . . like the palace in the moon right before your eyes . . .'.[15] This is what he says about Segawa's apartments, which incorporated a tearoom with exquisite architectural features:

> The parlour at the front on the west corner. Main room of 12 mats; an alcove of 1 *ken* [1.82 m]; walls of coloured sand; [to the side of this up on the wall] a cupboard of 3 *shaku* [90 cm] with a landscape in bright colours on the doors; under this a set of Tea Ceremony shelves (*sumi-dana*) of 2 *shaku* [60 cm]; ceiling with wooden boards like the bottom of a boat; curved rafters all coated in glossy black lacquer; gold roundels of brighty coloured flowers of the seasons surrounded by *maki-e* lacquer. To get to the next room you follow the corridor down and round: 12 mats; built-in cupboard on the far wall; under this a chest decorated with scattered crests of triple oak-leaves inside a 'snow-lozenge' shape [Segawa's standard crest]; an entrance in tea style of 3 *shaku* [90 cm]; [through to] a six-mat room, with an extra mat to the side for tea utensils; the hearth in Enshū style; the alcove of 3 *shaku* [90 cm] in grotto style to match; next a room for washing tea utensils fully papered [with scattered paintings, calligraphy, etc.], reed blinds, hanging 'jewel incense' decorations. All three rooms in elegant taste.[16]

Having described in detail their apartments, Kyōden went on to make public

Fig. 13
Kitao MASANOBU (Santō KYŌDEN), *The Courtesans Segawa and Matsubito*, from *Yoshiwara keisei shin bijin-awase jihitsu kagami*, 1783–4. British Museum

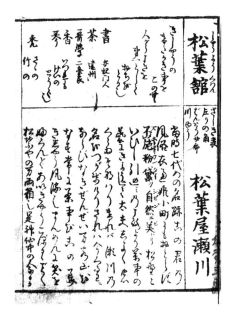

Figs 14a, 14b
Santō KYŌDEN (Kitao MASANOBU), *Concerning the Courtesan Segawa VII*, from *Keisei kei*, 1788. Tokyo Metropolitan Central Library (Kaga Bunko)

what he claimed was intimate personal knowlege about each of the courtesans in a printed guide of 1788, *Keisei kei* ('Guide to Courtesans'), which was infinitely superior to the standard twice-yearly *Yoshiwara saiken* guidebooks that gave little more than names and prices.[17] As he states in the foreword: 'I often enjoy the company of the courtesans listed in this book and so know well their temperaments, their likes and dislikes. I have recorded in detail, too, their accomplishments and even their childhood names so as to assist those pleasure seekers of shallow experience.'[18] The very first page is the entry concerning Segawa (fig. 14a). Above her name on the right is the information, as before, that her parlour is on the left corner at the front (ironically, Yoshiwara had once more been destroyed by fire less than two months before the book was published, and Segawa was actually camping out in temporary quarters (*karitaku*) in the rival unlicensed quarter at Nakazu); and that she was attended by the *shinzō* Kawayū. At the top of the page is the general observation that 'She likes a noble temperament; is applauded for rating goodness in a person most highly', a list of her accomplishments and the schools she follows in each, and the names of her *kamuro*: 'Calligraphy – pupil of Yasuchika; Tea Ceremony – Enshū school; Classical poetry – Nijō lineage; Incense, Koto – well versed in each. *Kamuro* – Sasano, Takeno.' The main entry below says:

> Presently the seventh generation to use the name, in terms of her manner and appearance this courtesan could rival [beauties from history such as] Princess Sotōri and Ono no Komachi. She has a natural beauty which does not rely on powder and paint. Since the time of her apprenticeship, when she was called Matsuno, she has taken a lively interest in all the accomplishments, and, well equipped for the highest rank of *tayū*, she was allowed to take the name Segawa. Now she is enjoying unprecedented popularity in the quarter, with thousands of suitors. Is fond of the Tea Ceremony and elegant in disposition. Her beaming smile seems to spill over with charm and she is the jewel [literally '10,000 *ryō* money box'] of the Pine Needle House. Is she a goddess come down to earth?

Turning the page (fig. 14b), the reader is provided with useful tips for identifying Segawa in the quarter: in the top right-hand corner is her 'standard crest' (*jōmon*) of the triple oak-leaves inside the 'snow-lozenge' shape; the note that she does not have an 'alternate crest' (*kaemon*); her 'secret crest' (*naisho no mon-dokoro*) of six small circles arranged like a blossom; her personal umbrella and large box-lantern with the triple oak-leaf crest; notes that she washes her hair on the twenty-seventh of each month and has a beancurd dinner on the thirtieth; her personal seal; and, finally, down the left-hand side of the page a line of calligraphy with her signature and seals which reads *tōrō bankaku shun*, the punning meaning of which, behind the apparent classical Chinese, is 'A thousand customers visit the brothel in spring'.

In the foreword Kyōden says that he copied these samples of calligraphy directly from works by the women themselves, so it should come as no surprise to find the same inscription in Segawa's actual hand on a hanging-scroll portrait of her (fig. 15) by the Ukiyo-e artist Isoda Koryūsai (worked *c.* 1766–88).[19] Without doubt this elegant painting shows Segawa VII, dressed

Fig. 15
Isoda KORYŪSAI, *The Courtesan Segawa VII*,
c. 1784–8. Japan Ukiyo-e Museum,
Matsumoto

in a snow-white kimono and *uchikake* (surcoat), stepping out with her *kamuro* Sasano and Takeno to meet a client. But what in actual fact does the portrait tell us about the 'real' Segawa? Not unlike the manner in which Kyōden's account in *Keisei kei* promises to give us intimate titbits of gossip, only to feed us with generalised clichés and appreciations of her beauty, so in the painting all Koryūsai can do is make a slight modification in his habitual conventions in portraying courtesans, by allowing her to stare directly out in self-introduction, rather than showing her in the normal, more passive three-quarter profile. To give some three-dimensionality to the face the bridge of the nose is registered with an extra layer of shell white. Otherwise all we can do is appreciate details of her tasteful outfit (dressed in a white kimono for the Hassaku Festival on the first day of the eighth month) and accessories, and the elegance of her calligraphy, as well, of course, as the beauty of Koryūsai's sophisticated painting style. And should we expect any more, bearing in mind that she had lived in the quarter since childhood and been drilled in every facet of fulfilling the needs of her clients for cultivated and compliant companionship? One can imagine that the painting might have been commissioned by Lord Bunkyō, who subsequently ransomed Segawa VII in the third month of 1788.

Courtesan as court lady

A very common pictorial device in Ukiyo-e prints and paintings – reflecting a common pattern of thought in Edo society as a whole – was that of *mitate-e*, variously translated, but not completely summed up, by such English words as 'parody', 'travesty', 'burlesque', 'analogue'. The basic form of such 'parody pictures' was already apparent in certain genre paintings before Ukiyo-e had ever appeared, and consisted of an ancient tale or incident, acted out or otherwise alluded to in some way by characters wearing contemporary dress. Thus the famous 'Hikone' genre screen depicts contemporary equivalents to the Four Accomplishments appreciated in ancient China – playing the *chin* (a transverse lute), playing *go* (a board game), calligraphy and painting.[20] The range of subjects suitable for reworking in this way was expanded and codified in a series of printed books and albums by Okumura Masanobu during the early decades of the seventeenth century and was often drawn from Chinese and Japanese classical literature or lore, generally already reworked in Japanese Nō plays, popular ballad singing, or Kabuki during the intervening centuries. The tone adopted varied from outright burlesque, such as pictures in which a courtesan changes clothes with Daruma, the monk patriarch of Zen Buddhism, to the simple parallels in which courtesans are likened to famous court women of Japan's classical past.

Mitate-e have recently been likened to the literary technique used in Bashō's *haiku* poetry known as *haigō*, in which the poet combines disparate imagery into a resonant poetic whole,[21] and it should also be recalled that in the plots of Kabuki plays, to avoid censorship by the military government of the reporting of contemporary events, many plots are relocated in the distant Kamakura period and the characters given new, but similar-sounding names. Popular literature of the eighteenth century, too, made extensive use of such techniques in order to evade the censor by encasing satires of

Fig. 16
Katsukawa SHUNSHŌ, *Snow*, from *Snow, Moon and Flowers*, 1780s. MOA Art Museum, Atami

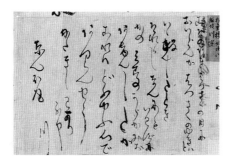

Fig. 17
KAWAYŪ, *Letter to Ōta Nampo*, 1780s. Nakano Mitsutoshi Collection, Fukuoka

contemporary politics or social mores in often impenetrable double and treble layers of parody and allusion. Such games in art and literature came to be appreciated for their own sake. As *mitate-e* themes became more established, an artist could show his originality by giving the treatment some slight new twist and introducing an unusual setting to depictions of beautiful women that always ran the risk of becoming stereotyped.

Katsukawa Shunshō's portrayal of the courtesan Hinazuru in the guise of the Bodhisattva Kannon has already been mentioned (fig. 2), and another set of three dazzling hanging scrolls by this artist shows women dressed in the fashions of the mid-1780s alluding to famous episodes in the lives of court women poets and authors of the classical Heian period (794–1185), linked by the well-established poetic theme of 'Snow, Moon and Flowers' (*setsugekka*). The scroll for *Snow* (fig. 16) shows a woman rolling up a blind to look out on to a snowy garden, while a dog plays by her feet. As Naitō Masato has pointed out, this composition contains twin allusions:[22] the first to the episode in the *Pillow Book of Sei Shōnagon* (late tenth to early eleventh centuries) in which Lady Sei quickly recognises a hint given by the Empress when she quotes a classical Chinese poem, and raises the blind so that all can admire the snow-covered scene outside; and the second to the scene in the 'New Herbs' chapter of the novel *Tale of Genji* by Lady Murasaki (early eleventh century), when the Third Princess's cat runs out beneath the blinds on to the verandah and she is seen by Kashiwagi, who immediately falls in love with her.

The cult of the Yoshiwara courtesan in pictures and novels of the eighteenth century undoubtedly exploited such parallels with the past in stressing the cultivation of the high-ranking women, portraying them in settings and engaged in cultivated pastimes that, it was suggested, somehow put them on a par with Lady Sei and Lady Murasaki. All this also served to stress the exclusivity of Yoshiwara in its increasingly intense competition with the dozens of unlicensed brothel districts in Edo and to justify, to a degree, its high prices.

Courtesans apparently even entered into such role-playing games themselves, as attested by a note sent by Kawayū, *shinzō* in the service of the great Segawa, to Ōta Nampo some time in the 1780s (fig. 17):

Dear Mr Nampo

On the day of the Hassaku Festival last autumn, when the courtesan asked 'And what of the Hassaku snow?', I said nothing and raised the Chinese paper blind. Now what was I thinking of? I simply haven't a clue.

KAWA[23]

As Koryūsai's painting of Segawa (fig. 15) shows, Yoshiwara courtesans wore pure white kimonos for the autumn Hassaku Festival, and this was the unseasonal 'snow' Segawa and Kawayū were expecting to see when they looked out into the quarter. And the game of raising the blind to look out on the 'snow' was intended by them to parody the episode from Lady Sei's diary just described. Clearly *mitate* were not just for pictures but were acted out as well, though it is amusing to think of courtesan and attendant going through such a carefully rehearsed charade for such an eminent man of letters and then having the gall to write at a later date to make sure he understood the joke!

Fig. 18
Hosoda EISHI, *Courtesan and Morning Glory*,
1795. From Tanaka Masuzō (ed.), *Ukiyo-e
gashū*, vol. 1 (1913)

Feudal lords as patrons of Ukiyo-e paintings

Judging from the few instances in which the circumstances surrounding the production of Ukiyo-e paintings are known, it seems that they were often specially commissioned, on occasion by high-ranking personages, and were relatively expensive.

One type of commission came from the Ukiyo-e publishers, with whom the artists must have had a kind of client status. In the spring of 1811, for instance, to mark the profitable completion of the novel *Chinsetsu yumihari-zuki* ('Strange Tales of the Bow Moon'), with text by Takizawa Bakin (1767–1848) and illustrations by Katsushika Hokusai (1760–1849), the publisher Hirabayashi Shōgorō commissioned Hokusai to do a painting *Tametomo and the Demons of Onigashima Island* (no. 96), illustrating an episode in the story, and had Bakin inscribe the scroll on the last day of the same year. Another scroll from the previous year showing *The Seven Gods of Good Fortune* (Chiossone Museum, Genoa), in which each god was painted by a different Ukiyo-e artist, was orchestrated by Santō Kyōden at the behest of the publisher Nishimuraya Eijudō.[24]

In the late eighteenth century there was a vogue among certain minor-ranking *daimyō* (feudal lords), bored perhaps with the stifling etiquette of their official lives, for getting involved in the popular culture of Yoshiwara, Kabuki and Ukiyo-e, and popular literature of the time contains a fair amount of gossip about certain members of the feudal aristocracy ransoming courtesans, patronising Kabuki actors and putting on amateur Kabuki performances in their mansions. Some lords commissioned, and even studied with, Ukiyo-e artists. Sakai Hōitsu (1761–1828), second son of the Lord of Himeji, for instance, studied Ukiyo-e painting with Utagawa Toyoharu (1735–1814) during the 1780s before switching to the Rimpa style for which he is widely known, and several paintings by him in pure Ukiyo-e style survive.[25] The artist and scholar Shiba Kōkan (1747–1818), who also worked in the Ukiyo-e style in his early years, records that on the twelfth day of the ninth month of 1781 he was summoned to paint, together with the calligrapher Mitsui Shinna and his son, in the presence of Date Shigemura, Lord of Sendai. It is highly likely that the pair of paintings *Japanese Man* and *Japanese Beauty* were done on that occasion.[26]

Lord Matsura Seizan (1760–1841) of Hirado was well known as a collector of antiques, as we learn from the pages of his own voluminous diaries, the 280-volume *Kasshi yawa* ('Night Talk from the Year of the Rat'), owning in addition to the famous pair of genre screens from the Kan'ei era, now commonly known as the 'Matsura' screens (which he purchased in Kyoto),[27] a hanging scroll by the Kyoto Ukiyo-e artist Nishikawa Sukenobu (1671–1751);[28] a scroll by Shunshō, *Courtesan and Swallow in Yoshiwara Naka-no-chō*;[29] the astonishing set of scrolls by Shunshō of *Pastimes of Women in the Twelve Months* that are his master-work (one wonders if Seizan actually commissioned these); and probably many more works that can no longer be traced. He is known to have actually commissioned a scroll, *Courtesan and Morning Glory* (fig. 18), in 1795 from Hosoda Eishi (1756–1829).[30]

Our most detailed knowledge concerning the commissioning of an Ukiyo-e painting, however, comes from the case of the painting *Geisha from the Nishigashi District* by Kitao Shigemasa (fig. 19), which forms a pair with a

Fig. 19
Kitao SHIGEMASA (KARAN), *Geisha from the Nishigashi District*, 1781. From a photograph in the author's possession

second hanging scroll on which the circumstances of how it came to be produced are described in considerable detail.[31] This long text was written by Lord Mizoguchi Naoyasu (1736–97) of the small fief of Shibata in an extremely complex and antiquated script known as *man'yō-gana*, so archaic as to constitute a kind of code; but through this code comes a very personal and rather touching story and for once an Ukiyo-e painting 'speaks':

> Since childhood I had never been fond of vulgar music such as *shamisen* and courtesans' songs. But a few years ago, in 1778, I happened to hear by chance what they call *gidayu-bushi* [chanting for the puppet theatre] and found it extremely interesting. After that I heard a caller [to the mansion] perform a piece of Tokiwazu chanting delightfully, and again found myself inspired by it. From then on, whenever the occasion arose, quite a few women who had made

their names with suave sounds from the Inlet of Osaka or voluptuous voices from Kyoto byways came and strummed and sang their various styles to the best of their ability. Among them were some of rare accomplishment who seemed to have pretty faces; but in fact they had covered indifferent features with powder and paint, and their beauty was simply the product of artifice. Then again there were many conceited ones who just followed the fashions of the times in the shades of their robes and sashes. They struck me as shallow-hearted and were importunate. I don't say this because I dislike them; I just think women should be proper and loving.

This spring, however, someone told me there was a performer of rare sensibility at Nishigashi in Nihombashi. As luck would have it, I was intending to have some entertainment at a banquet in celebration of the Doll's Festival [3rd day of the 3rd month] and so invited her. But what with the this and that of it being her first visit, the hour grew late. I decided it would not do to have her perform after the festivities for the day had come to an end and asked them not to send her. When I pressed them for someone else who could come in her place, they all had reasons why they could not come. Then I asked again for the Nishigashi woman, but the reply came that she had already been invited away on a boating party, and the matter ended there. At a later date I invited her again, but she said she had a cold and did not come. At any rate, as the days passed by in this manner I myself was laid low by fatigue from the end of the fourth month and ceased to concern myself with such affairs. However, my medical treatment proved effective and on the twenty-eighth day of the fifth month, thinking to celebrate my recovery, summoned together the various people normally in attendance on me to exchange cups of wine. Here, of course, was the perfect occasion for that music from Nishigashi, and I sent for her forthwith. Let me first describe the attire of the woman who presently arrived. As contemporary fashion it was certainly not unsuccessful, and considered in terms of old-fashioned styles it was in no way vulgar. The way she had done her hair and makeup was also alluring yet proper: in short, there was a quality of depth to her bearing that would not have been out of place in the old days. She performed several songs of the current fashion and then joined the banquet. Though the sake cup was passed around and around, she had little to say; and yet she did not seem melancholy. Nor did she gossip in private with the women who accompanied her. She was a delight to the drowsy eyes of those relaxing after too much wine, and all regretted the cock's crow which announced the dawn. Here truly was a beauty worthy of a king's ransom! Though she painted and decorated herself in this way for people, the strict rules of her teacher placed chastity above all else: one brief appearance by her could make one forget an eternity. At any rate, from the end of the summer into the beginning of autumn I invited her on many occasions, but still could find no peace. During a period of about one month, six days out of every ten she would come to call; but even this would not suffice my restless heart. Often I would go off to Katsushika, and she would be invited away by the younger crowd at Sugamo or on the waterfront at Mitsumata. When she did not come I yearned for some trace of her. I longed to see her so badly, I was at my wit's end. What was more, it rained for days on end, and even going out became impossible. Thinking to console my heart, I ordered the painter Karan [=Shigemasa] to copy from life her lovely form just as it was, and hung the painting on the wall of my chamber as the companion of my heart. It has always been the way in such cases of unrequited affection: no matter whether it leads to fulfilment or not, it is my belief that it is the truth of the heart that is the real truth. Smiling to myself, I write this at the dictates of an idle brush.

Eighth month, autumn of Temmei 1 (1781)
'Hermit at the Window'

Shigemasa has captured the qualities of restrained elegance and simple grace that so appealed to the lovesick Lord of Shibata. The geisha wears a simple striped cotton summer kimono, with a quite plain green *obi* decorated with stylised chrysanthemums and waves. Lying behind her on the floor, the three-stringed *shamisen* and its black lacquer box immediately indicate her profession as a singer/entertainer, while serving the compositional function of suggesting a rudimentary ground plane.

The Lord of Shibata commanded Shigemasa to 'copy from life her lovely form just as it was', but in fact the pose is essentially the same as used by Shigemasa in other paintings and prints – turning the head back to look over one shoulder and placing one hand in the top of the sash.[32] The other hand is pulled back into the sleeve, leaving a curious bunching of the cloth of the red under-kimono of the sleeve-opening. When it comes to a careful scrutiny of the facial features, however, there are certain elements of the drawing of the Nishigashi geisha which make it seem like a more individualised portrait – the slightly turned-up nose and the horizontal rather than angled eyes. These differences may seem very slight in themselves but are nevertheless significant in the context of the generally highly conventionalised set of facial features perfected by each Ukiyo-e painter. The Lord was clearly satisfied enough with the likeness to make it the 'companion of his heart', in the absence of the real woman.

The Lord of Shibata refers to Shigemasa not by that art name but by his name for composing *haiku* poetry, Karan. This suggests the likely route by which the commission was given, since both men were fellow pupils of *haiku* poetry under the master Tani Sogai (?1734–1823). It was certainly not necessary for the Lord of Shibata to 'shop around' for a suitable painter to execute the portrait.

'A scroll by Shunshō costs 1,000 gold pieces'

How much did Ukiyo-e paintings cost? At present there is, alas, no simple answer to this question, though the issue can be broached indirectly. It is known that in the early nineteenth century colour woodblock prints cost about 20 *mon* per sheet and that the authorities tried to reduce this to 16 *mon* (about the same price as a cup of buckwheat noodles in a restaurant) to curb the luxury of prints during the Tempō Reforms in 1842.[33] Prices for paintings seem to have been of a different magnitude.

Hiroshige's diary of his visit to Kai Province in 1841 mentions that he 'received 5 *ryō* as deposit against final fee' for painting a large theatre curtain for a town committee at Kōfu, though he tantalisingly does not record the full fee.[34] It is also known that more than 100 hanging scrolls of landscape paintings he did in sets of two and three for the Tendō fief, probably in 1850–1, were given to creditors as a substitute for amounts of between 60 and 300 *ryō* in each case; though Hiroshige must have been paid much less to make the whole scheme worth while.[35]

The postscript written by one Kichi Chinjin to the *sharebon* (comic novel) *Tōsei onna fūzoku tsū* ('A Guide to Contemporary Women's Fashions'), published in 1775 with illustrations by Shunshō, opens with the phrase 'A scroll by Shunshō costs 1,000 gold pieces' ('Shunshō ippuku atai senkin').[36] This text presents several problems, not least the fact that at present no paintings by Shunshō are known that predate *c.* 1779–80.[37] Clearly many paintings by him must have been lost, which suggests a tremendous attrition rate of Ukiyo-e paintings in general. Second is the problem of how to interpret the phrase. With an irreverence typical of the writers of comic fiction, it parodies the famous line 'One moment of a spring evening is worth a thousand gold pieces' by the Song poet Su Shi (1036–1101), from his *Poem on a Spring Night* (*Chun ye shi*). So while we should be wary of suggesting that a Shunshō painting literally cost a thousand gold coins, it is clear that the pun would not have any meaning if his works were not widely known to be expensive. Shunshō was the most accomplished Ukiyo-e painter of the later eighteenth century, working sometimes at the command of feudal lords such as Matsura Seizan. What can be stated for sure is that hanging scrolls by him were commodities of a high order.

No primitives, no decadents

This catalogue has been arranged basically chronologically, though following school lineages where this seemed appropriate. Many comments will be found along the way about changing aesthetics of beauty, but it is hoped that there is no sense that the early paintings are 'primitive' or the later ones 'decadent', following the misguided way in which the history of Ukiyo-e prints used to be written. Early prints were simpler, in the sense that they were black and white woodblocks with hand colouring, but there was little about their aesthetic or their execution that was 'primitive'. Similarly, later artists certainly moved away from the idealised canons of beauty practised by masters of the later eighteenth century, not because they all suddenly became in some way artistically incompetent but because those ideal canons of beauty were outmoded and a hindrance to further artistic growth. In all generations there are adventurous and timid artists, and Ukiyo-e had its fair share of both.

The fact that there is no clearly demonstrable technical 'progress' in Ukiyo-e painting – Moronobu's handscrolls are as technically sophisticated in their own way as Hokusai's hanging scrolls – should encourage us to look beyond a simplistic shackling of the history of Ukiyo-e to the political ups and downs of the Tokugawa Bakufu. It cannot be denied that art reflects changes in society, but those changes are rarely easily characterised and never moving in one direction. Ukiyo-e did not 'die' at the end of the Edo period (1600–1868), nor, indeed, at the end of the Meiji era (1868–1912). Even if artistic forms changed and elements of Ukiyo-e passed into 'Japanese-style painting' (Nihonga), the 'Creative Print' movement (Sōsaku hanga), the 'New Print' movement (Shin hanga) and beyond, popular culture and its images live on.

NOTES

For full details of abbreviated items see Bibliography.

1 i.e., Kyoto, Osaka and Edo.

2 *NU*, vol. 4 (1982), no. 28.

3 Translated and quoted by Richard Lane in *Images from the Floating World*, Oxford, Oxford University Press, 1978, p. 11.

4 The evolution and characteristics of *Kambun bijin* are described in detail in Kobayashi Tadashi, *Edo no bijinga*, Tokyo, Gakken, 1982, pp. 124–71.

5 Asano Shūgo, 'Hishikawa Moronobu no mago musume Osan', *Denki*, 7 (Sept. 1984), pp. 25–6.

6 Elisabeth West Fitzhugh, 'A Pigment Census of Ukiyo-e Paintings in the Freer Gallery of Art', *Ars Orientalis*, 11 (1979), pp. 27–38.

7 Josiah Conder, *Paintings and Studies by Kawanabe Kyōsai*, Tokyo, Maruzen, 1911, pp. 27–76 ('Painting Methods').

8 Ibid., pp. 35–6.

9 Ibid., pp. 58–9.

10 The process of collaborative printmaking is described in detail in T. Tokuno, *Japanese Wood-cutting and Wood-cut Printing* (from the *Report of the U.S. National Museum for 1892*), Washington, DC, Government Printing Office, 1894; reprinted in Peter Morse, 'Tokuno's Description of Japanese Printmaking', in Matthi Forrer (ed.), *Essays on Japanese Art Presented to Jack Hillier*, London, Robert Sawers Publishing, 1982, pp. 125–34. See also Tys Volker, *Ukiyo-e Quartet: Publisher, Designer, Engraver and Printer*, Leiden, 1949.

11 The most complete account of the Yoshiwara pleasure quarter in English still remains J. E. De Becker, *The Nightless City, or the History of the Yoshiwara Yūkaku*, Yokohama, Max Nössler & Co., 1905; repr. Tokyo, Charles E. Tuttle, 1971. Detailed information concerning courtesans is given, too, in Cecilia Segawa Seigle, 'The Impact of Yoshiwara Courtesans on An'ei–Temmei Edo', *The Japan Foundation Newsletter*, vol. XIV, no. 2 (July 1986), pp. 12–16. Nakano Mitsutoshi, 'Edo no yūri' in Jimbo Kazuya *et al.*, *Zusetsu Nihon no koten 18: Kyōden, Ikku, Shunsui*, Tokyo, Shūeisha, 1980, pp. 121–39, provides an excellent survey of all the Edo pleasure quarters from which much of the information given below is derived.

12 Nakano, ibid., pp. 129–30.

13 *Yūkun gochō kaku/kukai jūnen ryū/ nijūshichi meimu/aa shinkirō. Shokusanjin.*

14 Ōta Nampo, 'Zokuji kosui', in *Nihon zuihitsu taisei*, Tokyo, Nihon Zuihitsu Taisei Kankōkai, 1929, series III, vol. 2, pp. 555–6.

15 No copies of the original two-page broadsheet are presently known, but excerpts from it are transcribed in Kubota Seon, 'Shintaku fusei sato no wakamuro', in *Kisho chinseki*, 3 (June 1920), pp. 2–5. Segawa Siegle, ibid., p. 14, mentions that some scholars argue that this undated work describes the courtesan's apartments after the rebuilding following the fire of November 1787 rather than 1784. She herself argues for a date of 1784, however.

16 Kubota, ibid., p. 3.

17 Santō Kyōden, *Keisei kei*, Edo, Tsutaya Jūsaburō, 1788; facsimile reproduction issued by Tokyo, Beisandō, 1925; a modern printed version of the text appears in *Sharebon taikei*, vol. 6, Tokyo, Rokugōkan, 1931.

18 A slightly different translation appears in Iwasaki Haruko, 'The World of *Gesaku*: Playful Writers of Late Eighteenth Century Japan', Ph.D. thesis, Harvard University, May 1984, pp. 299–301.

19 See the commentary on this painting by Kobayashi Tadashi in Matsumoto 1985, text vol. no. 101, pp. 43–4.

20 *NU*, vol. 1 (1982), no. 37.

21 Zhu Jie, 'Mitate to haigō', *Kamisama to Nihonjin no aida*, Tokyo, Fukutake Books, 1991, pp. 11–45.

22 Naitō Masato, 'Mitate-e kaidoku no omoshirosa, muzukashisa', *Idemitsu Bijutsukan zōhin zuroku: Nikuhitsu ukiyo-e*, Tokyo, Idemitsu Bijutsukan, 1988 (unnumbered insert to catalogue).

23 Nakano Mitsutoshi, 'Nampo kōdoku: sono 8', in Iwanami Shoten (eds), *Ōta Nampo zenshū geppō 9 (dai-13 kan)*, April 1987, pp. 7–8.

24 *UT*, vol. 10 (1987), no. 28.

25 A hanging scroll, *Promenading Courtesan* by Hōitsu in the Museum of Fine Arts, Boston (11.7837), painted *c.* 1787 and signed with the unusual 'Fūsō Toryū' signature, is so close to Toyoharu's style that it was ascribed to Toyoharu by the painter Kawanabe Kyōsai (1831–89), when he acquired the scroll in 1883. See Ōno Tomoko, 'Sakai Hōitsu no gafū tenkai to sono tokushoku', *Bijutsushi*, 126 (March 1989), pp. 137–8.

26 See Naruse Fujio's comments in Ōta Kinen Bijutsukan (eds), *Shiba Kōkan ten*, Tokyo, Ōta Kinen Bijutsukan, 1984, no. 15, p. 140.

27 Yamato Bunkakan 1984, p. 4.

28 Nagoya 1984, no. 50.

29 Itabashi 1989, no. 49.

30 Nagoya 1984, no. 50. The present whereabouts of the painting is not known but it is illustrated in Tanaka 1911, vol. 1 (pls not numbered), from which the present figure has been taken.

31 The present whereabouts of this painting is not known, but it was reproduced in several pre-World War II publications and described as being in the collection of Shibui Kiyoshi; see, for instance, Kyoto Hakubutsukan, *Nikuhitsu ukiyo-e taikan*, 1933, no. 52, for a black and white and Hoshino 1927 (pls not numbered) for a rudimentary colour photograph. The present figure is taken from an old collotype photograph of the painting and its companion scroll with the long inscription kindly supplied by Jack Hillier. The inscription was first transcribed (somewhat inaccurately) into printed characters by Fukui Kyūzō in his *Sho daimyō no gakujutsu to bungei no kenkyū*, 2 vols, Tokyo, Kōseikaku, 1937 (repr. Hara Shobō, 1976), pp. 587–8. It was then translated from *manyōgana* into standard printed Japanese in Shibui Kiyoshi, 'Ukiyo-e no onna-tachi', *Geijutsu shinchō*, vol. 28, no. 2 (February 1972), pp. 135–6. The translation given below has been prepared from Shibui's text, with slight corrections made on the basis of the original inscription as shown in the photograph.

32 What is essentially a mirror image of the present composition, though with a very different costume, is found in *Geisha*, another painting by Shigemasa; see Matsumoto 1985, no. 113.

33 Akai Tatsurō, 'The Common People and Painting', in Nakane Chie and Ōishi Shinzaburō (eds), *Tokugawa Japan: The Social and Economic Antecedents of Modern Japan*, Tokyo, University of Tokyo Press, 1990, pp. 182–6.

34 Edward Strange, *The Colour Prints of Hiroshige*, London, Cassell & Co., 1925, p. 80.

35 Ichikawa Nobunari, 'Tendō Hiroshige – sakuhin bunseki o chūshin ni', *Ukiyo-e geijutsu*, 101 (July 1991), pp. 21–35. See particularly the section on p. 26.

36 The text is given in modern printed characters in *Sharebon taikei*, 12 vols, Tokyo, Rokugōkan, 1930–2, vol. 2, p. 32.

37 As pointed out by Naitō Masato, 'Katsukawa Shunshō no nikuhitsu bijinga ni tsuite', *Bijutsushi*, 125, vol. XXXVIII, no. 1 (March 1989), pp. 57–81. See particularly note 13, p. 81.

THE STUDY, COLLECTING AND FORGING OF UKIYO-E PAINTINGS

Ukiyo-e artists discover their past

The beginnings of the historical study of Ukiyo-e paintings can be traced back, as can be expected, to around the time of the emergence of the study of Ukiyo-e as a whole. *Ukiyo-e kōshō*, an early manuscript of the compilation of Ukiyo-e artists' biographies which later grew into the better-known *Ukiyo-e ruikō*, was copied from a (now lost) original by Ōta Nampo that can be dated on internal evidence between 1795 and 1800.[1] Nampo was a life-long recorder of minutiae of the Edo urban scene in voluminous diaries and miscellaneous 'jottings' (*zuihitsu*), and was on friendly terms, too, with many of the leading Ukiyo-e artists, with whom he collaborated in the genre of illustrated comic fiction (*kibyōshi*) during the 1780s. Thus this pioneering attempt to record the biographies of Ukiyo-e artists past and present doubtless stemmed primarily from simple motivations of curiosity and scholarship. But it should also be seen in the context of the Kansei Reforms (1787–93) of Senior Councillor Matsudaira Sadanobu which, under the banner slogan 'arms and letters' (*bunbu*), sought to revitalise the dwindling military skills and neo-Confucian ethos of the warrior class. Writers of this samurai class who had constituted the core of the movement of comic popular literature during the culturally buoyant An'ei (1772–81) and Temmei (1781–9) eras were brought to account and forced to renounce such frivolous activities. Nampo himself seems to have been pressured into ceasing to write comic 'crazy verse' (*kyōka*) at the end of the summer of 1787.[2] Just as the passing of the 'golden age' of the Italian Renaissance prompted Giorgio Vasari to write his *Lives* (1550) of famous painters, so perhaps a consciousness that the free-wheeling exuberance of the 'floating world' had been dampened encouraged Nampo to take stock in his *Ukiyo-e kōshō*.

The historical study of Ukiyo-e was also taken up by Nampo's younger contemporary Santō Kyōden (art name Kitao Masanobu, 1761–1816), leading writer and illustrator of comic fiction during the 1780s, who in 1791 had actually been punished with fifty days in handcuffs for several of his *kibyōshi* that satirised the political reforms. Thereafter Kyōden modified his habitually acerbic tone and devoted himself to more edifying novels in the *gōkan* ('combined volume') genre and, increasingly, to scholarship. As well as revising and enlarging Nampo's biographies of Ukiyo-e artists with his *Tsuikō* ('Additional Thoughts') of 1802, Kyōden began the encyclopaedic study of manners and customs of the Edo period in printed works such as *Kinsei kiseki kō* ('Thoughts on Unusual Relics of the Recent Past', 5 vols, 1804) and *Kottō shū* ('A Collection of Curiosities', 3 vols, 1814–15). Of particular interest is his use in these books of illustrations after genre paintings of the seventeenth century to explain the fashions of bygone eras, as in a page on which a painting of *Kamuro and Dog* (fig. 20) is copied to explain the fashions of pre-Kan'ei times (1624–44), particularly the so-called 'Nagoya *obi*', the multicoloured cord sash with tassels on the end that the girl is wearing (fig. 21). This is perhaps the first instance of Ukiyo-e paintings being considered historically, even if it is primarily for their pictorial content – what might be called their documentary value – rather than in an artistic or stylistic context. One can sense the novelty and thrill of this nascent historical consciousness when Kyōden writes in the commentary, 'It is just as though the old fashions of 200 years ago are before your very eyes'.

RIGHT Fig. 20
Anon., *Kamuro and Dog*, early 17th century.
Chiba City Art Museum (Preparation
Section)

FAR RIGHT Fig. 21
Santō KYŌDEN, *Kamuro and Dog*, from *Kottō
shū*, 1814–15. British Museum

The same impulse no doubt guided Kyōden when he painted the hand-scroll *Edo fūzoku zukan* ('Illustrated Handscroll of Customs of Edo') in 1808, in which he illustrates ten male and sixteen female 'floating world types' dressed in the fashions of 'fourteen to fifteen years ago' (that is, 1794–5), 'for people to look at 100 years hence, if it survives'.[3] Kyōden also supplied written commentaries which were attached to paintings by earlier artists, such as the *Kyō Shijō-gawara fūzoku zukan* ('Illustrated Handscroll of Customs at the Dry Riverbed at Shijō, Kyoto') in the collection of the New York Public Library, which Kyōden dated to the late Kan'ei (1624–44) or Shōhō (1644–8) eras.[4] There is, too, the well-known example of fellow authors Nampo, Shirakatsube Magao and Sakuragawa Jihinari writing commentaries which were incorporated by the then owner, one 'Matsuzakaya Shujin', into the new handscroll mounting of the famous set of paintings by Hishikawa Moronobu *Hokurō oyobi engeki zu* ('Illustrations of the Northern Quarter [that is, Yoshiwara] and [Kabuki] Theatres') some time in the Bunka (1804–18) or early Bunsei (1818–30) eras.[5]

Ukiyo-e paintings in archaistic styles

It is no coincidence that about this time consciously archaistic styles began to appear in Ukiyo-e paintings, and the prime agent in this vogue was Kyōden's fellow pupil Kitao Masayoshi (Kuwagata Keisai, 1764–1824). Originally an out-and-out Ukiyo-e artist – albeit making bold experiments wth his 'bird's-eye' panoramic views – and the most prolific illustrator of *kibyōshi* ever, the character of Masayoshi's art changed substantially after he was employed as a painter in attendance to the Tsuyama fief in 1794. A number of commissions from Matsudaira Sadanobu, now retired from politics, for genre handscrolls much broader in the scope of their subjects than normal Ukiyo-e – the *Tōto hanjō zukan* ('Illustrated Handscroll of Prosperity in the

Fig. 22
Kitao MASAYOSHI (Kuwagata KEISAI), *Beauty with a Shuttlecock and Battledore*, Bunka (1804–18)–early Bunsei (1818–30) eras. Idemitsu Museum of Arts, Tokyo

Eastern Capital', 1803), *Kinsei shokunin-zukushi ekotoba* ('Annotated Illustrations of All the Trades of the Recent Past', 1804) and *Yoshiwara jūni-ji ekotoba* ('Annotated Illustrations of Twelve Hours in the Yoshiwara Quarter', with text by Kyōden, known only by a copy dated 1861) – encouraged a wider scrutiny of the contemporary world and, concomitantly, seem to have freed Masayoshi to make explorations of past styles as well. A number of scrolls survive from his latest period in the Bunka (1804–18) and early Bunsei (1818–30) eras when he used the 'Tsuguzane' (Shōshin) signature, which are reworkings of seventeenth-century genre scenes, such as *Merrymaking under the Cherry Blossom* (Ōta 1985, no. 82) and Moronobu-style women such as *Beauty with a Shuttlecock and Battledore* (fig. 22) in a pseudo-archaistic manner. Thereafter, copying works of the past became an option explored by other Ukiyo-e artists, as in the cases of the *surimono* (de luxe, privately issued) prints by Totoya Hokkei (1780–1850) after Moronobu,[6] and the study of the style of Hanabusa Itchō by Utagawa Kunisada (1786–1864) from the late 1820s onwards.

Patronage and exhibition of Ukiyo-e paintings in the late Edo period

As has already been discussed above ('Feudal lords as patrons of Ukiyo-e paintings', pp. 23–6), what little is known of the patronage of Ukiyo-e paintings suggests that they were sometimes specially commissioned by wealthy clients such as Ukiyo-e publishers, and even by feudal lords. Artists of many schools, including occasionally Ukiyo-e painters, were summoned to paint in the presence of high-ranking persons.[7] Otherwise, we still do not know a great deal about the context in which Ukiyo-e paintings were used in the late Edo period.

From 1792 onwards regular twice-yearly (spring and autumn) public exhibitions of paintings and calligraphies by contemporary artists were organised in Kyoto by the scholar/painter Minagawa Kien (1734–1807), the *Shin shoga tengan* ('Exhibition of New Calligraphies and Paintings').[8] These were filled with the works of local painters of the Maruyama-Shijō and *bunjin* (scholar/painter) styles, with occasional submissions from Edo *bunjin* painters, particularly from Tani Bunchō and his pupils. Looking at some of the surviving catalogues of these exhibitions one can see that they did not apparently contain any Ukiyo-e paintings.[9] It was on the seventeenth day of the first month of 1792, too, that a group of seven painters interested in promoting new styles from China – Tani Bunchō and three pupils including Suzuki Fuyō, the *bunjin* painter Haruki Nanko, and the Nagasaki school artists Kaburagi Baikei and Sō Shizan – met in the Yorozuya (Mampachirō) restaurant at Yanagibashi to do paintings on the spot, one of the earliest examples of the craze in Edo for *shogakai* (calligraphy and painting meetings). *Shogakai* came to be regular features of the cultural scene, planned and advertised in advance, at which leading calligraphers and painters performed in front of a paying audience, who were able to obtain modest works from the masters there and then in return for a small 'gratuity' (*o-rei*).[10]

The first exhibition in Edo of contemporary calligraphies and paintings appears to have been one organised by Sawara Kikuu, proprietor of the Kitanoya antique store, Sumiyoshi-chō, in the fifth month of 1804.[11] The commemorative catalogue of this event, *Shūhōen shin shoga tengan*

Fig. 23
Utagawa KUNISADA, *Actors at a Calligraphy and Painting Meeting at Mampachirō Restaurant*, c. 1831. Fitzwilliam Museum, Cambridge

mokuroku,[12] lists sixty-nine works, but among the illustrious painters of heterodox schools included – Sakai Hōitsu, Tani Bunchō, Kita Busei, Uragami Shunkin, Watanabe Nangaku, and so on – there is only one, Kuwagata Keisai (the aforementioned Kitao Masayoshi), who could be classified as Ukiyo-e, and it is pertinent to the discussion of archaism above (p. 30) to note that he exhibited not an Ukiyo-e painting but one entitled 'Picture in the Old Style of the Tosa School' (*Tosa koyō zu*).

Hokusai engaged in public displays of painting on several occasions, executing gargantuan bust portraits of *Daruma* at Gokoku-ji Temple, Edo, in the fourth month, 1804, and again at the Nishikake-sho, Nagoya, in 1817.[13] Very occasionally one comes across Ukiyo-e paintings done in an unexpectedly painstaking technique and with a high degree of finish, but nevertheless bearing a signature including the phrase '. . . painted at an event' (. . . *sekiga*).[14] In general, however, one assumes that the works executed impromptu at parties must have been small fan paintings, contributions to handscrolls and folding albums and the like (nos 102, 109, 111, etc.) in fairly abbreviated wash styles. The true extent to which Ukiyo-e artists joined in the *shogakai* boom that reached its artistic peak in the Tempō era (1830–44), dominated as such events were by 'professional' *bunjin* artists, has yet to be investigated, but fragmentary evidence suggests that certain artists – in particular pupils of Hokusai such as Hokuba and Shigenobu – were regular participants.[15] Kabuki actors had, of course, long been called upon to paint autographed trifles on scrolls, fans, hand-towels and so on to present to patrons and distribute among their supporters. A pair of *surimono* prints by Kunisada probably datable to *c.* 1831[16] show a group of leading actors at Mampachirō restaurant painting on fans and hanging paintings and writing poems on *tanzaku* cards for female guests (fig. 23).

The collecting of Ukiyo-e paintings in the Meiji era (1868–1912)

A few Ukiyo-e paintings left Japan through the Dutch trading entrepôt of Nagasaki, before the opening of the country to regular intercourse with the United States of America and European nations after 1854. Notable among these are two groups of paintings in Western-influenced style on Western paper by Hokusai and/or his atelier: twenty-five obtained in Edo in 1826 by Johan Willem de Sturler, head of the Nagasaki Dutch Factory;[17] and fifteen brought out of Japan by Philipp Franz von Siebold, physician to the same mission.[18] Otherwise it was not generally until the 1870s onwards that foreigners visiting, or living and working in Japan began to amass sizeable collections of Japanese prints and paintings, which now form the basis of most of the large museum collections outside that country. One of the earliest of these must be the comprehensive collection of 1,063 paintings and 2,236 unmounted sketches formed by Dr William Anderson (1842–1900), during his sojourn as Director of the Naval Medical College in Tokyo from 1873 to 1880, which were sold upon his return to England to the British Museum. Of the 200 items in the present catalogue thirty-two are from the Anderson collection, including the beautiful pair of handscrolls by Chōshun, *Popular Amusements in Edo* (no. 37), and the highly important *Tametomo and the Demons* by Hokusai (no. 96). Nothing is presently known of the circumstances under which this collection was acquired in Japan. In 1875 Edoardo Chiossone (1832–98) was invited to Tokyo to advise the Printing Bureau of the Japanese Ministry of Finance on the production of Western-style banknotes. Chiossone was to remain in Japan until his death in 1898 and his collection of some 15,000 items was bequeathed to the city of Genoa, where it is now housed in the museum which bears his name opened in 1971. Forty-six important Ukiyo-e paintings from this collection have recently been introduced.[19]

But it was to the United States of America that the largest number of Ukiyo-e paintings were taken. Ernest Francisco Fenollosa (1853–1908) arrived in Japan in 1878 as Professor of Philosophy at the University of Tokyo, but he quickly became drawn to the study of Japanese art, to which he would devote the rest of his life.[20] Active in lobbying the Meiji government to preserve the best of the traditional arts that were at the time neglected as a result of the pervading enthusiasm for all things Western, he was authorised to undertake extensive surveys of temple treasures and used the opportunity to make acquisitions of important 'specimens of Japanese pictorial art' for his own collection. The chance survival of one of Fenollosa's early collecting notebooks from 1880 reveals the eclecticism of his tastes, the various opinions he solicited concerning individual works from a circle of acquaintances composed in part of artists of the Kanō school, and the role of the government-run Kiritsu Kōshō Kaisha in offering him works of art to obtain much-needed foreign currency.[21] From 1882 onwards Fenollosa was joined in his activities by the wealthy Boston physician William Sturgis Bigelow (1850–1926), who during more than seven years spent in Japan amassed a huge and comprehensive collection of works of art including perhaps 40,000 Ukiyo-e prints and close to 400 Ukiyo-e paintings, all of which were donated to the Museum of Fine Arts, Boston. The Bigelow collection was complemented in 1889 by Fenollosa's own collection of over 700 paintings, including 50–100 Ukiyo-e examples, which had been purchased for the Boston Museum by Bigelow's friend Charles Goddard Weld (1857–1911). Notwithstanding the de-accession of 192 examples of Ukiyo-e painting from the Bigelow collection which were auctioned at the Tokyo Bijutsu Kurabu in 1933,[22] the Boston collection still must be the largest and most select group of Ukiyo-e paintings outside Japan, though its full parameters have yet to be revealed.[23]

As Yamaguchi Seiichi has pointed out, Bigelow can be said to have organised the first scholarly exhibition of Ukiyo-e, when examples of the Ukiyo-e and Soga schools from his collection were shown at the fifth meeting of the Kangakai, the Club for Art Appreciation, held in May 1884.[24] Initially, Fenollosa did not match his friend's enthusiasm for the art of the 'modern vulgar schools' (that is, Ukiyo-e), criticising the chapter on painting in Louis Gonse's pioneering study *L'Art japonais* of 1883 as a 'Hokusai-crowned pagoda of generalisations'[25] and stating 'In his paintings Hokusai falls very low indeed'.[26] A tour of America and Europe in 1886 seems to have changed his opinion, however, and early issues of the art journal *Kokka* founded in October 1889 contained his essays on the history of Ukiyo-e.[27] Already by this time Fenollosa had been engaged to establish a Department of Japanese art at the Boston Museum, and the first in a series of 'Special Exhibitions of the Pictorial Art of Japan and China' was *Hokusai, and his School*, which included some 158 paintings and drawings by Hokusai and his pupils. In the catalogue to this exhibition Fenollosa now asserts 'In fact, the true history of the course of changes in Hokusai's style must be founded primarily on a study of his paintings rather than of his prints'.[28]

Fenollosa was on leave of absence from the Boston Museum during the autumn of 1895 during the divorce scandal which eventually led to his resignation. It must have been about this time that he was writing the text of his seminal catalogue for an Ukiyo-e exhibition held at the Fine Arts Building, New York, in January 1896, *The Masters of Ukioye: Japanese Paintings and Color Prints*, in which he organised 447 items – some belonging to private collectors, but most to the dealer W. H. Ketcham – into an aesthetic ranking with Kiyonaga at the summit which was to become canonical in later Ukiyo-e studies. Many of the items in this exhibition were subsequently purchased by Charles Freer of Detroit and formed the basis of the highly important collection of some 350 or so Ukiyo-e paintings now in the Freer Gallery of Art, Washington, DC.[29]

The source of Ketcham's paintings in Japan is not clear but may well have been Kobayashi Bunshichi (1864–1923), the premier Ukiyo-e dealer in Tokyo at the time, who had been acquainted with Fenollosa since at least 1888.[30] Kobayashi opened his business at Asakusa Komagata-chō in about 1887[31] and quickly came to prominence both in his own right – opening short-lived branches in Yokohama, San Francisco and Boston and making personal trips to sell to Freer in Detroit – and also as a supplier to Hayashi Tadamasa (1853–1906), the major dealer in Ukiyo-e in Europe, through Hayashi's wife, Satoko, in Tokyo.[32] It is well known that between 1890 and 1901 consignments were sent to Hayashi in Paris totalling 156,487 prints, 10 handscrolls, 20 boxes of woodblocks, 90 preparatory drawings, 9,708 volumes of illustrated books, 846 painted screens and hanging scrolls.[33] In addition, Kobayashi's legendary private collection, said to have been the largest in Japan, numbered some 100,000 prints and included many paintings – 500 by Hokusai and his pupils alone, it is said.[34] All these were destroyed without trace in fires following the great Kantō earthquake of September 1923, within months of Kobayashi's death in March that year. Kobayashi held

Ukiyo-e exhibitions on six occasions – in 1892, 1894, 1897, 1898, 1900 and 1910 – and beginning with the first which contained 119 examples these always included a high percentage of Ukiyo-e paintings.[35] Indeed, in all his own writings on Ukiyo-e he championed paintings over prints.[36]

Following Fenollosa's return to Japan in July 1896 his professional relations with Kobayashi became very close. Fenollosa was sent by Kobayashi as his agent with a consignment of paintings to New York in the winter of 1896–7,[37] and the two collaborated on exhibitions of Ukiyo-e paintings and prints at Ikao Onsen, Ueno, in 1898[38] and Hokusai paintings at the Nihon Bijutsu Kyōkai, Ueno, in 1900.[39] On both occasions Fenollosa's catalogues were translated into Japanese, as too was Fenollosa's *An Outline of the History of Ukiyo-e*, published by Kobayashi in 1901.[40] Fenollosa was also acting during the early years of the century as an adviser to Charles Freer on purchases for his collection. Kobayashi's firm Hōsūkaku issued scholarly works on Ukiyo-e by his patron Iijima Kyōshin (Hanjūrō, 1841–1901), including his important early biography of Hokusai.[41]

Generally speaking it was foreigners who took the lead in appreciating Ukiyo-e, but by the late Meiji era important collections were being formed in Japan itself as well, particularly after the series of major auctions held in Tokyo between 1907 and 1912 of works belonging to the estate of Hayashi Tadamasa following his death in 1906.[42] The main collectors of Ukiyo-e paintings were in the Kansai region, notably the dealer Matsugi Zen'emon, who opened his business in Kyoto in 1879,[43] and Takeoka Toyota of Kobe. Takeoka's collection was frequently shown in the Kansai region, culminating in an exhibition at the Kyoto Imperial Museum in 1923 of 100 of his paintings, of which seventy are illustrated in the catalogue *Ukiyo-e shūei*.[44] In Tokyo major exhibitions of Ukiyo-e paintings were held in three consecutive years at the Tokyo Imperial Museum from 1911 to 1913, including many fine examples in the Takamine Toshio collection, which was subsequently acquired by the Imperial Museum.[45]

In 1910 a group of 100 Ukiyo-e paintings from the collection of Kuwabara Yōjirō (Fukuba Tōru) were sent to London as part of the Japan–British exhibition held at Shepherd's Bush. They then toured Stockholm and Paris. Some copies of the catalogue[46] have what appear to be prices written in, suggesting it was a sales exhibition. However, most of the paintings seem to have returned to Japan and were photographed together with others from this major early collection at the Tokyo National Institute for Research into Cultural Properties in September 1933. In his short preface Kuwabara champions Ukiyo-e paintings and warns, 'Very few of these old paintings are exported, and frequently those sent abroad are counterfeits'.

In 1911 the novelist Arthur Morrison published his two-volume *Painters of Japan*, which contains a generally accurate chapter on Ukiyo-e painting illustrated with some of the works in the current exhibition: in 1913 Morrison's entire collection was purchased for the British Museum by Sir William Gwynne-Evans, Bt, and of the 200 items in the present catalogue ninety-one derive from Morrison's collection. Though Morrison never went to Japan, in the preface to his book he acknowledges the assistance of many Japanese experts by name and also makes special mention of Mr Harold Parlett, H.M. Consul in Dairen, who had given assistance 'over many years of his long residence in Japan, in the acquisition of many of my best pictures'.[47]

Early forgeries of Ukiyo-e paintings

The forging of Ukiyo-e paintings was undoubtedly carried out on a fairly large scale during the Meiji period and probably even before. It can be imagined that as soon as the vogue for archaistic styles outlined above (p. 30) took hold unscrupulous individuals may have begun to produce forgeries of older works to cater to this antiquarian taste. Four of the paintings from the Anderson collection (left Japan 1880) and eight from the Morrison collection (acquired 1913) have, after all, been described as forgeries in the present catalogue. If a scholar has misgivings about the authenticity of an Edo period painting, his first instinct is to dismiss it as a 'Meiji forgery'. And yet not a single fact has been published concerning the forging of Ukiyo-e paintings during this period, and very little conjecture. William Sturgis Bigelow (p. 33) had no doubt that such underhand practices went on in Japan. In a letter to John Cabot Lodge of 1883 he warned:

> Painting here is like painting in Europe, in regard to (1) Schools, (2) pictures by masters – 'old masters' – & by a) the best pupils or descendants & b) the 2d and 3d rate men. Among the latter come, as with us, the great mass of 'school pictures' which make up the rank and file, and 9/10 in quantity of the whole mass. Then there is not a trick of a Paris picture dealer that a Jap dealer does not know – copies – forgeries – imitations of style and signatures – school pictures of the 4th class sold as the work of the head of the school – names washed out & altered – & so on. With some men's names the forging is carried to an amazing extent. Fenollosa says as a result of his 5 years of it that of 200 Okios [Maruyama Ōkyo, 1733–95], 199 are fake, as a rule.[48]

To illustrate the kinds of problems encountered in considering Meiji-era forgeries two versions can be compared of a famous composition by Hokusai, *Collecting Shellfish at Low Tide* (*Shiohi-gari zu*) – one in the collection of the Osaka Municipal Museum of Fine Arts, registered as an Important Cultural Property,[49] which should be considered genuine (figs 24 and 24a, which will be referred to below as A), and the other, which should be considered a Meiji-period copy, in the collection of the Freer Gallery of Art, Washington, DC[50] (figs 25 and 25a, which will be referred to as B). The sizes of the two paintings are very close (A is 54.3 × 86.2 cm; B is 56.5 × 78.8 cm). The following are some observations on the copy, which are, admittedly, coloured to an extent by the 'foregone conclusion' outlined above:

1. Hokusai is not known otherwise to have made two such close versions of any of his compositions.
2. The colours of B – including pale yellow, pink and turquoise blue – are not found in Hokusai paintings of the Bunka era (1804–18), which is the period when he used this combination of signature and seal.
3. There are many differences in the composition of B: Mt Fuji is larger; the clouds more stylised; the line of the bay curves round at the right; there is a second small boat pulled up on the beach behind the man with the basket on his head; there is a different configuration of small figures on the sandbank in the middle ground; the three boys on the left have

Figs 24, 24a
Katsushika HOKUSAI, *Collecting Shellfish at Low Tide*, Bunka era (1804–18). Osaka Municipal Museum of Fine Arts

Figs 25, 25a
After Hokusai, *Collecting Shellfish at Low Tide*, ?late 19th century. Freer Gallery of Art, Smithsonian Institution, Washington, DC

caught a flat fish (which is not visible in A), etc. Of course, none of these differences *per se* prove that one version is genuine and the other a copy.

4. Smaller differences in the execution of certain details do, however, suggest that B is of inferior quality: the basket hat on the end of the pole is too 'flat' to stay on anyone's head; the sack and rolled mat inside the boat are more cursory in B; the many baskets in B are coarsely painted and do not have the customary v-shaped weave seen in A and many other genuine Hokusai paintings; there are more regular dots and a gradated white band around the edge of the sandbank in B, but none of the spontaneous 'flicking' of white pigment from the brush on to the silk seen in A.

5. A conclusive comparison of the *kimō dasoku* ('hair on the tortoise and legs on the snake') seals is made difficult by the fact that the top two characters in B (fig. 25a) have not been impressed distinctly. However, the three upward 'prongs' of *mō*, the bottom right-hand character in the seal on B, appear to go straight upwards rather than curving slightly to the left, as in A (fig. 24a) and other impressions of the genuine seal.

An investigation of the provenance of each work is significant: A, the genuine version, is known definitely to have been in the collection of Takeoka Toyota and, if an article by Kaneko Fusui is to be believed, was sold to him by Kobayashi Bunshichi;[51] B, the copy, was sold to Charles Freer in 1903 by Kobayashi Bunshichi.[52] The 'best' conclusion is that Kobayashi assumed that both versions were genuine (unlikely, considering he had the biggest collection of Hokusai paintings in private hands at the time); the 'worst' is that he sold B to Freer knowing that it was a copy, or even that he had it made. Freer himself questioned Kobayashi's integrity on several occasions in his letters, the most explicit mention being in one to Frederic Gookin of 31 October 1900:

> I am sorry that I was absent from the country during Mr. Kobayashi's visit, as I would have been glad to have seen him in Detroit. I met him in Japan some years ago, at which time I was shown his prints and paintings then on sale, and have during the last two years bought a number of paintings formerly owned by him, and which Ketcham at one time had in charge. As hinted in your letter, his reputation is none too good, and still my experience with his things has, as a rule, been very satisfactory. He has in his employ most skillful copyists of old prints and paintings, many of which are so skillfully done that *I cannot tell the real from the imitation* [my italics].[53]

Clearly it would be wrong to brand Kobayashi a forger from this one example, based in part as it is on hearsay evidence. Nevertheless, if knowledge concerning Meiji-era faking is to progress at all, his activities certainly warrant closer scrutiny.

The 'Shumpōan' forgery incident of 1934

The late 1920s witnessed a flowering of scholarship heralded by the publication in 1926 of *Shoki nikuhutsu ukiyo-e*[54] ('Early Ukiyo-e Paintings') by the leading Western-style painter Kishida Ryūsei. A sudden frosty chill was cast over this early spring, however, by the events of the Shumpōan forgery incident of 1934, the only case in which the events surrounding the forging of Ukiyo-e paintings are known in detail, and it is worth relating the main facts here.[55]

In May 1934 the Kawabe Company staged an auction at the Tōkyō Bijutsu Kurabu (Tokyo Art Club) of a group of nineteen Ukiyo-e paintings which it was claimed had been discovered in the old storehouse of the family of a feudal lord, the Shumpōan ('Spring Peak Hut'), somewhere in northern Japan. It was during the viewing session that the story broke in the newspapers that the whole group, which included three hanging scrolls with 'Sharaku' signatures, were elaborate forgeries made by Yata Senkurō of Okayama and his three sons Michio, Osamu and Kanemitsu. Kanemitsu, though only sixteen at the time, had been sickly as a child, and had become adept at copying magazine illustrations while confined to bed. He used a pantograph to enlarge some of these illustrations.

About seven years earlier, in 1927, Michio had sold the first forgery, *Beauty of the Kan'ei Era*, to the dealer Shimizu Naoji (Gensendō) for 50 *yen*, and since that time Shimizu had been commissioning a steady stream of pictures. Several Yata forgeries were noticed by the scholar/dealer Kaneko Fusui when they began appearing in Ukiyo-e exhibitions, and he, too, soon became intimately involved in the business to the extent of providing subject-matter for the forgeries and purchasing the final results directly from the Yata family. Old man Yata was often seen scouring the antique shops at Nishikubo-chō in Shiba for tattered hanging scrolls whose mountings could be reused for the forgeries.

Shimizu and Kaneko conspired to sell a group of the paintings to a triumvirate of rival Ukiyo-e enthusiasts comprising the dealer Chikamatsu Hachirō, the Nō actor Sanō Heiroku and Komatsu Teihachi. The paintings were shown to Chikamatsu at the residence of Shibutani Yoshitomo in Shinjuku. This was a clever touch – the Shibutani had been retainers of the Matsudaira lords of Fukui, and Shumpōan smacked of the name of Lord Matsudaira Shungaku. Chikamatsu and his associates decided to auction the group of nineteen paintings immediately in the expectation of handsome profit. The Shumpōan group might have aroused little suspicion in the early 1930s when many old family collections were being sold off, but to their credit most of the major auction houses refused to handle paintings of such obscure provenance. Finally an arrangement was made whereby the Kawabe Company, of which Shimizu was a member, agreed to auction the paintings if a scholar would authenticate them first. A meeting was arranged at the Ikao restaurant, Ueno, with the veteran Ukiyo-e scholar Sasakawa Rimpū at which he agreed to provide an introductory essay for the Shumpōan catalogue. It was reported in the newspaper that Sasakawa was paid 800 *yen* for this essay, although Michio claimed the true figure was 5,000 *yen*. Either sum was large enough to implicate him in the conspiracy, but the scholar maintained his faith in the authenticity of the paintings throughout the court proceedings.

The affair had its humorous, even bizarre episodes. It is said that the Ministry of Education wanted to send a photographer so that the paintings could be designated Important Art Objects. Later, during the preliminary court hearings, the authorities had Kanemitsu execute some paintings for the prison museum. Indeed, public sympathy for the 'young genius' was

ABOVE Fig. 26
Cover of *Shumpōan kahō shū*, 1934.
British Museum

running high, and soon after the trial the wealthy art collector Nezu Kaiichirō installed Kanemitsu in his Hakone villa and had him turn out more paintings for what became a sell-out exhibition of 'Copies of Ukiyo-e Paintings' (*Nikuhitsu ukiyo-e mosha ten*) held at the Shirogi Department Store in May 1935.

Amazingly, both a lavishly illustrated auction catalogue – brazenly including details of faces and signatures and seals – and a de luxe volume on the paintings were produced (fig. 26).[56] In an article in *Kikan ukiyo-e* journal in 1967 a mysterious 'Mr T.' introduced the Shumpōan auction catalogue to readers and showed what the original sources might have been for each of the forgeries.[57] The simplest type of forgery is a line-for-line copy of an original painting. Copies of this type probably account for the largest percentage of spurious Ukiyo-e paintings now in circulation. Lot 9 in the catalogue, a set of four paintings purporting to be by Eishi, *Beauties of the Four Season* (fig. 27), mounted with two panels of calligraphy on a six-fold screen, were very accurate copies (with a pastiche created for winter) of a set of three Eishi paintings formerly in the Bigelow collection (now San Francisco Museum of Asian Art, fig. 28)[58] which had been auctioned by the very same Kawabe company in December 1933, barely five months before the Shumpōan auction. How could the forgers suppose that this would escape

the attention of dealers and collectors? Comparing photographs, the main feature which betrays the inferior quality of the Shumpōan forgeries is a certain limpness of some of the internal drapery lines: where the lines of the original seem to whip back on themselves tautly, the Shumpōan copy will make a much more meandering and slack turn-about. Probably colour combinations would appear slightly 'off key', too, if the copies were examined directly.

Ukiyo-e painters were often individually responsible for thousands of designs in woodblock prints, so providing an almost limitless source of motifs for the would-be forger. Many of the Shumpōan paintings turn out to be almost direct copies of prints: the 'Sharaku' pair of hanging scrolls of the actors *Ichikawa Danjūrō and Segawa Kikunojō* (lot 7); the 'Okumura Masanobu' *Beauty under an Umbrella*, with added snow and a different kimono pattern (lot 16); the two 'Eisen' landscapes (lot 21). Slightly more complex are the paintings derived from an amalgamation of prints by two different artists: the other 'Sharaku' painting, a double bust portrait of *Actors Reflected in a Mirror* taken from the Sharaku print of *Sanogawa Ichimatsu and Ichikawa Tomizaemon* (lot 8), has headgear and a lantern courtesy of Utamaro's famous print of lovers *Koharu and Jihei*, from the series *Jitsu kurabe iro no minakami*. Even more daft is the 'Shunchō' six-fold screen *Moonlit Banquet* (lot 10) in

LEFT Fig. 27
After Eishi, *Beauties of the Four Seasons*, c. early 1930s.
From *Shumpōan kahō shū* (1934)

RIGHT Fig. 28
Hosoda EISHI, *Beauties of Three Seasons*, late Kansei (1789–1801) –Bunka (1804–18) eras. Asian Art Museum of San Francisco, The Avery Brundage Collection, B60 D80–82

which figures taken from various Kiyonaga prints are set against a background derived from one of Hiroshige's three last great triptych prints, *Moonlight at Kanazawa*.[59] It came out during the trial that the screen had been intended as a 'Kiyonaga' but the figures turned out so badly that the forgers thought they had better make it by his follower Shunchō instead. Another forged screen not included in the auction catalogue, showing figures in a room opening on to a snowy landscape, is here introduced for the first time

Fig. 29
After Kiyonaga, *Snow Viewing, c.* early 1930s. Metropolitan Police Headquarters, Tokyo

(fig. 29). It is on regular display in the Museum at the Metropolitan Police Headquarters in Tokyo (preserved there since the Shumpōan trial), where a label explains that the perpetrators were convicted of forging a signature. Readers may like to work out for themselves how figures were combined from three famous prints by Kiyonaga (figs 30–2).

Not all the forgeries in the Shumpōan catalogue can be accounted for by the methods already described. In particular, the 'Matabei' works (lots 1–5) and the 'Hokusai' two-fold screen *Waterbirds* (lot 14) seem set apart from the others by the quality of their conception. A source for the large black cormorant in the 'Hokusai' is given by 'Mr T.' in his article, a famous genuine painting of a *Cormorant on a Rock* by Hokusai now in the Okayama Art Museum,[60] but at the time of the forgery incident it was the only one of the group Noguchi Yonesaburō said he was unsure about (that is, he thought it might possibly be genuine).

When sentences were passed in 1936 it was clearly hoped this would put an end to the matter once and for all. Kaneko Fusui and Yata Osamu were sentenced to two years and eighteen months in gaol, respectively; Yata Michio and Shimizu Naoji were given suspended sentences of one year; and Shibutani and Yata Senkurō were acquitted. The subsequent research of Shirasaki Hideo and others has made it clear, however, that the ghost of Shumpōan cannot yet be laid to rest.

Kaneko Fusui later claimed that three Shumpōan paintings said to have been executed by Yata Michio – 'Hokusai' (lot 14), 'Toyoharu' (lot 18), 'Eisen' (lot 21) – were actually the work of one Bunrin, as was a 'Matabei' painting in the Hasegawa Minokichi collection which had been exhibited at Tokyo Mitsukoshi Department Store around the time of the Shumpōan auction.[61] Shirasaki believes that the 'Matabei' forgeries in the Shumpōan group were also supplied by Bunrin (whose family name, he says, was Akaza and who lived in Ōmori), which might explain their relatively higher quality.[62] So the nineteen paintings in the auction catalogue are just the tip of the iceberg.

ABOVE Fig. 30
Torii KIYONAGA, *A Snowy Garden* (right sheet of a diptych), *c.* 1786. Art Institute of Chicago, Clarence Buckingham Collection, 1925.2673

ABOVE RIGHT Fig. 31
Torii KIYONAGA, *Snow Viewing at Matsuchiyama*, *c.* 1785. Art Institute of Chicago, Clarence Buckingham Collection, 1925.2654/2655

Shimizu alone, by his own testimony, purchased more than forty items from the Yata family, some of which were sold abroad. The activities of another forger, Akaza Bunrin, must also be taken into account, and it is impossible to conjecture to what extent his operations overlapped those of the Yata. Shirasaki's continuing researches have yielded a list of what he considers the most likely subjects for Yata forgeries, as well as a list of paintings already published which he attributes to them.[63] 'Mr T.' illustrates a six-fold screen of *Figures in Front of a Curtain* purporting to be of the Kan'ei era, which he claims is also a Shumpōan product.[64]

Shumpōan is significant as the only case study in the forging of Ukiyo-e paintings yet documented to a useful degree, but since the forgers were quickly tripped up by their own ineptitude, it should not be taken as a complete blueprint for forging in general, nor as an indication of the level of accomplishment of other forgers. Shirasaki talks about 'creative pastiches' being made in Matabei style which owe no debt to particular original works. In order to detect such works much more subtle judgements will have to be made based on notions of period style, complemented by an assessment of the levels of quality of which particular artists are considered capable.

The revival of Ukiyo-e painting studies

The scandal of the Shumpōan forgery incident cast a long shadow over Ukiyo-e painting studies, characterised by Richard Lane as a 'taboo' whereby scholars simply ceased to pass judgement of the authenticity of

Fig. 32
Torii KIYONAGA, *Ninth Month*, from the
series *Twelve Months in the Southern Quarter*,
c. 1784. Art Institute of Chicago, Clarence
Buckingham Collection, 1925.2611

paintings.[65] This state of affairs lasted until at least the 1960s, when a newer generation of scholars not directly linked to the affair, headed by Narazaki Muneshige, began once more to publish Ukiyo-e paintings. The major landmark in recent Japanese scholarship is undoubtedly the series *Nikuhitsu ukiyo-e* ('Ukiyo-e Painting'), published from 1980 to 1982 in ten volumes under Narazaki's editorship, but including contributions from leading specialists such as Kobayashi Tadashi, Tanaka Tatsuya, Asano Shūgō, Nagata Seiji and many others, thereby to some degree alleviating the problem of relying too heavily on one individual's fallible judgement. Connoisseurship by committee (or at least by consensus) has produced in this case a core of paintings of generally accepted authenticity – well reproduced in colour with details of signatures and seals – that has restored a much needed confidence to Ukiyo-e painting studies. The 1980s have also seen the opening of several specialist Ukiyo-e painting museums – the Azabu Museum of Arts and Crafts,[66] the Nasu Royal Museum[67] and the New Ōtani Museum of Art;[68] as well as major exhibitions of Ukiyo-e paintings in the collections of other Ukiyo-e Museums – the Ōta Memorial Museum of Art[69] and the Japan Ukiyo-e Museum;[70] and of Ukiyo-e paintings in other art museums – the Tokyo National Museum,[71] the Idemitsu Museum of Arts,[72] the Itabashi Ward Museum[73] and the recently discovered Imanishi collection at the Kumamoto Prefectural Museum.[74] In the West Jack Hillier has written catalogues of the collections of Ralph Harari[75] and Richard Gale,[76] both of which contain a large proportion of Ukiyo-e paintings, and in 1973 Harold Stern published a catalogue[77] and organised an international symposium around the important collection of Ukiyo-e paintings in the Freer Gallery of Art.

Issues of authenticity of paintings have not traditionally been discussed in publications by Japanese scholars, but, as Richard Lane already pointed out in his review article of 1968, this is precisely the Gordian knot which must be cut. One is still haunted by the no fewer than six versions of the composition *Two Geishas on a Snowy Night* by Kubo Shumman which Lane cites.[78] It seems to the present writer that the next step forward in Ukiyo-e painting studies should be the compilation of *catalogues raisonnés* of paintings by individual masters – the basic research tools for any art historian, after all – since this would force us to confront issues of authenticity and assemble, at least provisionally, a core of 'best versions' of each composition together with related copies.[79] Simultaneously, a critical study of provenance and what little that can be ascertained of the activities of forgers might begin to clean out the Augean stables that Ukiyo-e painting studies remain.

Above all things I would not wish that my argument produced the impression that I feel sure of myself. This is by no means the case. Not only I, but also my teachers – for whom I have the greatest regard – have been taken in – though in truth, it seemed impossible to understand later on, how this had come about (Max Friedlaender, *On Art and Connoisseurship*, London, Bruno Cassirer, 1942, p. 263).

NOTES

For full details of abbreviated items see Bibliography.

1 See Nakano Mitsutoshi's comments on the Jingū Bunko Library's manuscript *Ukiyo-e kōshō*, in Hamada Giichirō (gen. ed.), *Ōta Nampo zenshū*, 20 vols, Tokyo, Iwanami Shoten, 1985–90, vol. 18, pp. 690–1.

2 Haruko Iwasaki, 'The World of Gesaku: Playful Writers of Late Eighteenth Century Japan', Ph.D. Thesis, Harvard University, 1984, p. 358.

3 Takahashi Seiichirō and Narazaki Muneshige (eds), *Kinsei fūzoku zukan*, 3 vols, Tokyo, Mainichi Shumbunsha, 1974, vol. 3, pp. 49–51, 214–21. The passage quoted was written by Kyōden at the end of the scroll and is transcribed by Endō Takeshi on p. 50.

4 Murase Miyeko, *Tales of Japan: The New York Public Library Collection*, Tokyo, Suntory Museum of Art, 1987, no. 54. The execution of this work seems too 'new' to be a mid-seventeenth-century painting: is this perhaps a faithful copy made by Kyōden of an early genre painting?

5 Fully reproduced and described by Narazaki Muneshige in *Kinsei fūzoku zukan*, vol. 3, 1974, pp. 53–112, text vol. pp. 24–7. Narazaki suggests that the Nampo inscription may be by Nampo II (Kameya Bumpō) but nevertheless dates the inscriptions to the late Bunka (1804–18) or early Bunsei (1818–30) eras, while Nampo I was still alive.

6 See, for instance, Roger Keyes, *The Art of Surimono*, 2 vols, London, Sotheby, 1985, vol. 1, no. 136, p. 168.

7 See the example of Shiba Kōkan given on p. 23 above.

8 Kobayashi Tadashi, 'Edo jidai no shogakai', in Haga Tōru (ed.), *Edo to wa nani ka I: Tokugawa no heiwa gendai no esupuri (bessatsu)*, Tokyo, Shibundō, 1985, pp. 166–77.

9 The most complete annotated listing of Edo-period exhibition catalogues to have come to my attention so far is Nakano Mitsutoshi, 'Zōsho-moku sono jūichi: shoga tengan mokuroku', *Bunken tankyū*, 15 (20 Feb. 1985), pp. 42–53. I am grateful to Professor Nakano for allowing me to study these.

10 Kobayashi, ibid., pp. 166–70.

11 This event and its catalogue are described by Robert Campbell, 'Tada kaori nomi ni shite kage naki ga gotoku – bungei-shi no Shin Umeyashiki', *Edo shijin senshū geppō*, 5, Tokyo, Iwanami Shoten, Dec. 1990, pp. 4–8.

12 Photographs of the copy of this catalogue belonging to the Kariya City Library were kindly shown to me by Robert Campbell.

13 Described by Richard Lane, 'Teacher without School: the Artist as Showman', ch. XII of *Hokusai: Life and Work*, London, Barrie and Jenkins, 1989, pp. 110–19.

14 For instance, the painting by Shunshō, *Shakkyō Dancer*, illustrated in Shibui 1983, vol. 1, Hōreki–Kansei-ki, no. 21.

15 Robert Campbell discusses *shogakai* of the Tempō era (1830–44) in an article, 'Tempō-ki zengo no shogakai', *Kinsei Bungei*, 47 (Nov. 1987), pp. 47–72. Hokuba is listed among the twenty-two members of the leading Kimo-iri group of *shogakai* 'professionals' in *Shogakai kimo-iri nabe*, published in 1838; a portrait of Shigenobu appears among twenty-three members of the rival Kimo-iri Nozoki group in an illustration to *Ika ke-naoshi* of the same year (ibid., pp. 68–9).

16 One of the prints is signed with the *gō* 'Tōjuen' only otherwise recorded on a triptych of actor prints datable to 1831. See Yoshida Segi, 'Kunisada nishiki-e sō mokuroku,' *Kikan ukiyo-e*, 68 (Jan. 1977), p. 44.

17 Now in the Bibliothèque Nationale, Paris. See *UT*, vol. 8 (1989), nos 41–65.

18 Now in the National Museum of Ethnology, Leiden. See Nihon Ukiyo-e Kyōkai (eds), *Shiiboruto korekushon o chūshin to shita ukiyo-e ten*, exh. cat., 1976, nos 133–47. The Siebold collection also contains several unsigned hanging scrolls in Hokusai style and a version by Eishi of his popular handscroll *The Seven Gods of Good Luck Visit Yoshiwara*.

19 *UT*, vol. 10 (1987), nos 1–46. See also Mainichi Shimbunsha (eds), *Kiyossōne to kinsei nihonga sato-gaeri ten*, exh. cat., Tokyo, 1990.

20 My information on the history of the Boston collections is drawn principally from Jan Fontein, 'Notes on the History of the Collections', in *Asiatic Art in the Museum of Fine Arts Boston*, Boston, Museum of Fine Arts, 1982, pp. 6–15.

21 Excerpts from the notebook are introduced in Akiyama Terukazu, 'Fenorosa shukō Nihon kaiga shūshūhin kaisetsu-tsuke sōmokuroku', in *Zaigai Nihon no shihō bessatsu: Kaisetsu shiryō hen*, Tokyo, Mainichi Shimbunsha, n.d. (c. 1981), pp. 30–5. See also the comments by Yamaguchi Seiichi, 'Bosuton no Nihon bijutsu – ryūshutsu meihin no rirekisho', *Geijutsu shinchō* (March 1983), p. 104.

22 Tokyo, Bijutsu Kurabu 1933.

23 Thirteen superb examples of Ukiyo-e painting from the Boston Museum are to be found in Tokyo National Museum 1983, nos 64–77.

24 Yamaguchi Seiichi, 'Kobayashi Bunshichi jiseki', *Saitama Daigaku kiyō sōgō hen*, vol. 6 (Feb. 1988), p. 17.

25 Ernest F. Fenollosa, *Review of the Chapter on Painting in Gonse's 'L'Art Japonais'*, Boston, J. R. Osgood, 1885, p. 21.

26 Ibid., p. 46.

27 *Kokka*, nos 1, 2, 4, 6, 8.

28 Ernest F. Fenollosa, *Special Exhibition of the Pictorial Art of Japan and China No. 1: Hokusai, and his School*, Boston, Museum of Fine Arts, 1893, p. xviii.

29 117 Ukiyo-e paintings from the Freer Gallery collection are introduced in Stern 1973 and a wider selection of 174 items in *US*, vol. 16 (1981). The latter volume actually lists (but does not illustrate) 348 'Important Ukiyo-e Paintings' on pp. 221–3.

30 This is the date suggested by Yamaguchi, ibid., pp. 18–19.

31 Yamaguchi, ibid., p. 4.

32 Higuchi Hiroshi, *Ukiyo-e no ryūtsū shūshū kenkyū happyō no rekishi*, supplement to Harigaya Shōkichi et al. (eds), *Ukiyo-e bunken mokuroku*, Tokyo, Mitō Shooku, 1972, p. 31. This work provides a detailed history of the trade in, collection and study of Ukiyo-e from a Japanese perspective.

33 These figures were originally reported in Shibui Kiyoshi, 'Ukiyo-e no yushutsu', *Mita bungaku* (1939), pp. 90–7, and are also given in Yamaguchi, ibid., p. 16.

34 Yamaguchi, ibid., pp. 10–11.

35 Yamaguchi, ibid., pp. 22–3; the covers of the catalogues are illustrated on pp. 30–1.

36 Kobayashi Bunshichi, 'Ukiyo-e no kanshō ni tsuite', *Shoga kottō zasshi*, 106 (Apr. 1917), and 'Ukiyo-e no nikuhitsu to hanga', *Bijutsu kōron*, vol. 2, no. 2 (Feb. 1921). Both quoted in full in Yamaguchi, ibid., pp. 40–5.

37 Lawrence W. Chisolm, *Fenollosa: The Far East and American Culture*, New Haven, Yale University Press, 1963, p. 132.

38 Fenollosa 1898 and Kobayashi 1898.

39 Fenollosa 1901.

40 Ernest F. Fenollosa, *An Outline of the History of Ukiyo-e*, Tokyo, Kobayashi Bunshichi, 1901.

41 Iijima Hanjūrō, *Katsushika Hokusai den*, Tokyo, Hōsūkaku, 1893.

42 Higuchi, ibid., p. 41.

43 Higuchi, ibid., p. 16. In 1926 some of Matsugi's paintings were sold to Kanda Raizō (ibid., p. 75) and others were dispersed. The Kanda collection was subsequently acquired by Ōtani Yonetarō and is now housed in the New Ōtani Art Museum, Tokyo (Tokyo 1991).

44 Kyoto 1923.

45 Tanaka 1911–13.

46 Kuwabara 1911.

47 Morrison 1911, p. viii.

48 William Sturgis Bigelow to John Cabot Lodge, 30 Sept. 1883. Akiko Murakata, 'Selected Letters of Dr William Sturgis Bigelow', 2 vols, typescript, doctoral dissertation, George Washington University, 1971, vol. 2, pp. 64–9.

49 Illustrated in a large-size colour reproduction in *NU*, vol. 7 (1982), no. 20.

50 Illustrated in large-size, colour reproduction in *US*, vol. 16 (1981), no. 53. In his commentary Narazaki Muneshige writes 'it is definitely a genuine work'.

51 Kaneko Fusui, 'Honmono to nisemono sono 2: Hokusai no futatsu no gibutsu', *Kikan ukiyo-e*, 2 (1962), p. 11. In this article Kaneko compares the genuine version A with a forged version of the composition on a six-fold screen. He was apparently unaware of the existence of the Freer B version. The provenance of version A, such as it has been possible to ascertain it, seems to be: Kobayashi Bunshichi–Takeoka Toyota–Hosomi–Nakajima Shōichirō–Osaka Municipal Museum of Fine Arts.

52 Folder-sheet 03.2, Freer Gallery of Art.

53 Charles Lang Freer to Frederic Gookin, 31 October 1900. Freer Gallery of Art, Letterbook vol. 6, p. 455.

54 Kishida Ryūsei, *Shoki nikuhitsu ukiyo-e*, Tokyo, Iwanami Shoten, 1926.

55 My account is derived from the following three sources: Yata Michio, 'Shumpōan gisaku jiken', *Geijutsu shinchō*, vol. VIII, no. 12 (1957), pp. 194–208; Shirasaki Hideo, 'Shumpōan jiken', in *Shingan*, Tokyo, Kōdansha, 1965, pp. 8–46; 'Mr. T.', 'Shumpōan nisemono zuroku: shōkai to bunseki', *Kikan ukiyo-e*, 30 (1967), pp. 57–67.

56 Tokyo Bijutsu Kurabu, *Shumpōan jūshū ukiyo-e tenkan nyūsatsu mokuroku*, auction cat., 14 May 1934; and *Shumpōan kahō shū*, n.p., n.d.

57 'Mr. T.', ibid.

58 *NU*, vol. 6 (1981) nos. 39–41. Two of the four forged paintings recently resurfaced at an auction in New York, this time remounted as hanging scrolls. They were withdrawn from sale when the auctioneers realised their mistake. There are two further versions of these compositions by Eishi in the Freer Gallery of Art and the Museum of Fine Arts, Boston, which appear to be genuine.

59 This, too, was recently sold at a Paris auction for a not inconsiderable sum.

60 Ōta (Hokusai) 1985, no. 556.

61 Shirasaki, ibid., pp. 24–5.

62 Shirasaki, ibid., pp. 24–7.

63 Shirasaki, ibid., pp. 41–6.

64 'Mr. T.', ibid., p. 66.

65 Lane 1968, p. 207.

66 Tokyo, Azabu Bijutsukan 1984; Tokyo, Azabu Bijutsukan 1986; Sendai 1988; Tokyo, Azabu Museum of Arts and Crafts 1989.

67 Nasu Royal Museum of Art, *Ukiyo-e nikuhitsu meisaku shū*, n.d.

68 Tokyo 1991.

69 Tokyo, Ōta Kinen Bijutsukan 1985.

70 Matsumoto 1985.

71 Tokyo Kokuritsu Hakubutsukan 1984.

72 Tokyo, Idemitsu Bijutsukan 1988.

73 Tokyo, Itabashi Kuritsu Bijutsukan 1989.

74 Kumamoto 1989, 1990, 1991. A useful list of museums in Japan which have collections of Ukiyo-e, including paintings, is given in Narazaki Muneshige (ed.), *Nihon no bijutsu 248: Nikuhitsu ukiyo-e I*, Tokyo, Shibundō, 1987, p. 98.

75 Hillier (Harari) 1970.

76 Hillier (Gale) 1970.

77 Stern 1973.

78 Lane, ibid., p. 192, to which can be added a seventh version with a spurious 'Utamaro' signature in the Freer Gallery of Art, 98.60.

79 Naitō Masato has recently listed all the known paintings by Shunshō. Naitō 1989.

THE PAINTINGS

Japanese eras

Keichō	1596–1615
Genna	1615–24
Kan'ei	1624–44
Shōhō	1644–8
Keian	1648–52
Jōō	1652–5
Meireki	1655–8
Manji	1658–61
Kambun	1661–73
Empō	1673–81
Tenna	1681–4
Jōkyō	1684–8
Genroku	1688–1704
Hōei	1704–11
Shōtoku	1711–16
Kyōhō	1716–36
Gembun	1736–41
Kampō	1741–4
Enkyō	1744–8
Kan'en	1748–51
Hōreki	1751–64
Meiwa	1764–72
An'ei	1772–81
Temmei	1781–9
Kansei	1789–1801
Kyōwa	1801–4
Bunka	1804–18
Bunsei	1818–30
Tempō	1830–44
Kōka	1844–8
Kaei	1848–54
Ansei	1854–60
Man'en	1860–1
Bunkyū	1861–4
Genji	1864–5
Keiō	1865–8
Meiji	1868–1912
Taishō	1912–26
Shōwa	1926–89
Heisei	1989–

Note on biographies

Much of the biographical information supplied is derived from Narazaki Muneshige (gen. ed.), *Genshoku ukiyo-e daihyakka jiten*, vol. 2, Tokyo, Taishūkan, 1982, by Asano Shūgō *et al*. This has been supplemented from Narazaki Muneshige (ed.), *Nikuhitsu ukiyo-e I (Nihon no bijutsu 248)*, Tokyo, Shibundō, 1987, by Asano Shūgō; essays contained in the series Narazaki Muneshige (gen. ed.), *Nikuhitsu ukiyo-e*, 10 vols, Tokyo, Shūeisha, 1981–3; Laurance P. Roberts, *A Dictionary of Japanese Artists*, Tokyo/New York, Weatherhill, 1976; Roger Keyes, *The Art of Surimono*, 2 vols, London, Sotheby, 1985; Kawakita Michiaki (ed.), *Kindai Nihon bijutsu jiten*, Tokyo, Kodansha, 1989.

The biographies of individuals during the Edo period are complicated by their use of many different names, depending on status and the purpose for which the name was used. It is important to record all known names of artists, since these are often used in signatures and seals on paintings and prints and in the colophons of books. The following is a list of the various categories of name in the order in which they are presented in each biographical entry:

1. Clan name (*kabane*). Affiliation with a large aristocratic clan, for example, Minamoto.
2. Family name. Surnames were generally the privilege of the aristocracy and samurai class. They were not normally held by commoners until after 1870.
3. Art surname (*gasei*). Generally the name of a sub-school, for example, Utagawa.
4. *Na*. True personal name of an adult male.
5. *Imina*. Literally 'avoided name' of a venerated dead person.
6. *Azana*. Scholar's formal name.
7. Childhood name (*yōmei*). Used before a male child reached maturity.
8. Common name (*tsūshō*). Simple personal names often derived from official or military titles, for example, names ending in -uemon or -saemon.
9. *Gō*, or *betsugō*. Pen name or art name, periodically changed by individuals.
10. *Kyōka-gō*. Name used for composing *kyōka* (crazy verse).
11. *Haigō*. Name used for composing *haiku* (*haikai*) poetry.
12. *Gesaku-gō*. Name used for composing popular literature.
13. *Ingō*. Name used for designing erotica.

Note on signatures and seals

In signatures on Ukiyo-e paintings the name of the artist is frequently followed by one of the characters *ga, hitsu, sha, zu* – all of which have the basic meaning 'painted by . . .'. If a fine distinction between their meanings were to be drawn, it would be:

ga	'drawn by'
hitsu	'from the brush of'
sha	'copied by' or 'captured by'
zu	'pictured by'

In addition, certain characters are commonly found following names in the text of seals:

no in	'seal of'
gain	'painting seal of'
-uji	'family'
-uji in	'seal of the . . . family'

Utagawa KUNITOSHI, *Killing the Nue* (detail), early Meiji era (no. 167).

I (1361)

I (1362)

ANON.

I Fan Dancers

c. Kan'ei era

Two panels from a (?)folding screen; ink and
  colour on paper, each 53.3 × 30.8 cm (approx.)
PROVENANCE: Arthur Morrison
LITERATURE: Morrison 1911, vol. 2, pl. VIII; *UT*, vol. 1
  (1987), col. no. 6, BW no. 1
1913.5–1.0364/0365 (Japanese Paintings 1361/1362).
  Given by Sir W. Gwynne-Evans, Bt

Though now mounted on separate panels,
these paintings probably originally formed
two panels of a pair of small six-fold
screens showing women in various
movements of a fan dance. One woman,
with open fan held delicately at the end of
an outstretched arm, seems to move
forward in some gently rhythmical line
dance; the other has tucked a semi-folded
fan into the nape of her kimono, drawn her
hands into her sleeves, and is about to
stamp her foot with gusto.

Four pairs of six-fold screens with similar

single figures of fan dancers on each panel
are known in other collections (New Ōtani
Art Museum, Boston Museum, Kyoto City
Museum, Suntory Museum; illustrated in
Kobayashi 1982, BW nos 1–30). They are
thought to date from the Kan'ei era (1624–
44), and come midway in the shift in
interest from screens in the genre painting
tradition showing large groups of figures in
brothel interiors to hanging scrolls of single
standing figures of courtesans (the so-called
'beauties of the Kambun era (1661–73)'; see
nos 3, 4) that are the earliest Ukiyo-e
paintings proper. Though their
compositions are virtually identical with
figures in the pairs of screens mentioned
above, the British Museum pair do not
share the gold-leaf backgrounds of all other
known versions. The confident, flowing
line quality and certain archaic details of
the costume make it likely that they are
among the oldest examples of paintings of
the fan-dancer 'type'.

2 (1397)

2 (1396)

ANON.

2 Scenes in a House of Pleasure

c. Kambun era
(?)Two album leaves; ink, colour and gold on
  paper, 40.6 × 30.9 cm (1396), 40.0 × 30.8 cm
  (1397)
PROVENANCE: William Anderson
LITERATURE: *UT*, vol. 1 (1987), col. no. 7, BW no. 2
  1881.12–10.02054/02055 (Japanese Paintings
  1396/1397)

Ukiyo-e painting developed out of certain
strands of genre painting of the first half of
the seventeenth century and in particular
screens showing scenes inside houses of
pleasure, such as the famous pair
bequeathed by the mother of Lord
Tokugawa Yoshinao of Kii to the Sōō
Temple upon her death in 1642 (*NU*, vol. 1
(1982), no. 34). In such screens, often
painted on a gold-leaf ground, extensive
and luxurious apartments and gardens are
populated with a host of courtesans and
their generally samurai patrons. The

present pair of small paintings represent
the final stage of this lineage, their
compositions in effect scenes extracted from
parts of earlier screens and the gold-leaf
backgrounds imitated with just a sprinkling
of cut gold leaf. The fashions of the women
are dominated by the tie-dyed fabrics and
narrow *obi* characteristic of the Kambun era
(1661–73), and although the painting style
has become abbreviated and impoverished
in comparison with the great genre screens,
even at this late date the facial expressions
have considerable animation and charm.

Both compositions show large parlour
rooms opening on to gardens with scenes
of courtesans chatting, reading, playing the
shamisen, challenging customers to games of
sugoroku (a kind of backgammon) and
plying them with food and drink. In the
yard a group of henchmen sit resting on
travelling cases, waiting for their masters to
tire of their pleasures. One can imagine
that such small paintings might be pasted

in groups on to sliding doors or collected
together and mounted in an album, and
clearly they would have served as
important precursors to early Ukiyo-e
painted handscrolls and print series of
scenes in the Yoshiwara pleasure quarter,
such as *Yoshiwara no tei* (late 1670s) by
Moronobu.

3 detail (*opposite*)

3

3

4

MORITOSHI (dates unknown)

3 Courtesan in a White Kimono

c. Kambun era
SIGNATURE: Moritoshi hitsu (in gold)
SEAL: Moritoshi
Hanging scroll; ink, colour and gold on paper,
    85.2 × 31.2 cm
PROVENANCE: Ralph Harari
LITERATURE: Hillier 1970, vol. 1, no. 9; *UT*, vol. 1
    (1987), no. 21; Smith 1990, no. 190
1982.7–1.015 (Japanese Painting ADD 700)

A courtesan wears a white short-sleeved
kimono decorated with an all-over tie-dyed
pattern of white circles, and a bright blue
obi with a design of interlocking plant
tendrils in gold. Walking probably in the
street of the pleasure quarter, she has her
left hand placed on her hip inside her
kimono so as to spread out the sleeve in
display. With her right hand she pulls up
the skirt at the front, and the simple
flowing outlines of the drapery suggest the
curves of her body beneath. The ends of
her hair have been swept up and knotted
to form the loop of the *hyōgo-mage* style.

Hanging scrolls of this sort, depicting
single figures of courtesans set against a
plain background, sometimes with a poem
written by the woman herself in elegant
calligraphy above, were painted in large
numbers during the third quarter of the
seventeenth century and are now known as
'Kambun beauties' after the Kambun era
(1661–73). Most are thought to have been
produced in Kyoto, showing courtesans of
the Shimabara pleasure quarter, before the

focus of Ukiyo-e shifted to the new eastern
capital, Edo (Tokyo).

It is uncommon for a 'Kambun beauty'
painting to be signed, though nothing is
known of the artist, Moritoshi. It may be
surmised that he belonged to the group of
so-called 'town-painters' (*machi-eshi*) who
though trained in the Kano school
sponsored by the military aristocracy,
dropped out of its formal academic system
to paint for a wider audience of the
burgeoning 'townsman' (merchant) class.
Unusual, too, is the degree of character
revealed in the painting of the face, in what
is frequently a stereotypical genre,
suggesting that this may be a portrait of a
particular high-ranking Kyoto courtesan.

ANON.

4 Seated Courtesan

Kambun–Jōkyō eras
Hanging scroll; ink and colour on paper,
    37.1 × 22.2 cm
PROVENANCE: Arthur Morrison
1913.5–1.0366 (Japanese Painting 1364). Given by
    Sir W. Gwynne-Evans, Bt

A courtesan is seated with one knee raised,
wearing a white kimono decorated with
large tie-dyed stars in red and white,
intertwined with leaf tendrils in black. Her
hair is parted in the middle and then
dressed at the back in a form of the
'Shimada' style in which the long tresses
are bent back towards the rear of the head
and tied in place using paper tapes. This
fashion did not become widespread among
women until the 1680s, after which it
remained the dominant style (with many
variations) for the rest of the Edo period.
Thus, although this work shows many
stylistic features generally associated with
paintings of beauties of the Kambun era
(1661–73; see no. 3) – the single figure
isolated against a plain background and set
back from the picture plane; the cool,
somewhat impassive expression; the
extensive use of tie-dyed dots in the
costume – the hairstyle may imply a
somewhat later date of execution. This
would indicate that an archaic 'Kambun
beauty' style lingered on in the work of
certain artists even after Moronobu's
revolutionary manner of painting women
had taken Edo by storm (nos 6–9).

5

ANON.

5 The Battle of Yashima

Kambun–Empō eras
Six-fold screen; ink and colour on paper,
124.0 × 365.8 cm
PROVENANCE: Arthur Morrison
1927.10–13.09 (Japanese Painting ADD 49).
   Presented by Arthur Morrison

Though Ukiyo-e would always be dominated by the twin themes of beautiful women and Kabuki actors – the two major leisure-time preoccupations of Edo townsmen – there were other, smaller genres of subject-matter which maintained their popularity. One of these was prints and paintings of warrior and battle subjects, doubtless deriving from the battle screens by artists of more orthodox schools which decorated the mansions of the warrior aristocracy. Particularly common were scenes from battles in the civil wars between the Taira and Minamoto clans in the late twelfth century which served as a reminder of the heroic origins of samurai rule. The present screen shows the battle fought at Yashima in Sanuki Province in 1185, in which the Minamoto general Yoshitsune drove the army of Taira no Munemori back into their boats, forcing them finally to relinquish the Inland Sea.

Battle pieces were frequently performed to *jōruri* chanting in the popular puppet theatres in the late seventeenth century, and another screen of warrior subjects in a similar style in the Idemitsu Museum of Arts (see Idemitsu 1988, no. 14) is made up of paintings originally hung as signboards in front of such theatres. The caricature style of the figures, with their bulging eyes and grimacing features, is also found in the illustrations of cheap printed novels of the period known as 'Kimpira books' (*Kimpira-bon*), after the name of their muscular hero. This bombastic style of drawing would be later adapted during the Genroku era (1688–1704) for images of Kabuki actors.

5 detail

6

Hishikawa Moronobu d. 1694

Common name Kichibei; *gō* Yūchiku. Born
into a family of fabric decorators and
embroiderers at Hota in Awa Province,
Moronobu is regarded as the founder of the
Ukiyo-e school, in as much as he is the first
artist of Ukiyo-e to be known by a large
corpus of signed works. His first signed
work is the illustrated book *Buke hyakunin
isshu*, published in 1672, but earlier books
with illustrations in a wide variety of
genres have also been ascribed to him. The
subject-matter of the more than fifty books
in his mature style is wide-ranging,
including historical subjects from China
and Japan, genre scenes, landscapes, birds
and flowers, and warriors. But increasingly
his books and paintings (in screen,
handscroll and hanging-scroll formats)
came to be dominated by scenes of
pleasure in and around the
neighbourhoods of Edo along the Sumida
River, where the merchant and artisan
classes lived – in particular featuring the
Yoshiwara pleasure quarter and Kabuki

theatres where 'floating world' culture was
developing its own distinctive character. In
addition, Moronobu designed many series
of prints bound in album form showing
scenes in Edo and also erotica. These can
be regarded as the precursors of the single-
sheet Ukiyo-e print.

A large number of paintings in various
formats survive in Moronobu style and
bearing his signature, and apart from the
numerous forgeries which still wait to be
weeded out, there is much debate as to
which works of the period are by the
master and which by the numerous pupils
in the atelier he assembled around him.
Works by pupils such as Morofusa (his son)
and Moroshige tend to be in the style of
the Genroku era (1688–1704), suggesting
that up to that time these individuals may
have been busy assisting Moronobu to
meet the burgeoning demand for works in
the new Ukiyo-e style. Central to a
consideration of Moronobu's developing
style is a group of seven fragments of

handscrolls, the *Hokurō oyobi engeki zukan*
('Illustrated Handscroll of the Northern
Quarter [Yoshiwara] and Theatres'),
mounted together with annotations by
Shirakatsube Magao, Ōta Nampo and
Sakuragawa Jihinari in the early nineteenth
century (Tokyo National Museum). Each
fragment bears a signature and a date
between Kambun 12 (1672) and Genroku 2
(1689), and though the signatures
themselves may be doubted, the paintings
undoubtedly reflect the general course of
development of Moronobu's figure style as
corroborated by his illustrated books. Other
important works by Moronobu and his
atelier are listed by Kobayashi Tadashi in
NU, vol. 2 (1982), pp. 129–30, and Asano
Shūgō in Narazaki 1987, vol. 1, pp. 26–7.
Moronobu established the parameters of
subject-matter and treatment which would
continue to dominate Ukiyo-e for at least
the first half of the eighteenth century.

HISHIKAWA MORONOBU

6 Amusements in Spring and Autumn

Tenna–Jōkyō eras
SIGNATURE: Nihon-e Hishikawa Moronobu zu
 ('Japanese picture by Hishikawa Moronobu')
SEALS: Hishikawa, Moronobu
Handscroll; ink and slight colour on silk,
 29.0 × 213.5 cm
PROVENANCE: Arthur Morrison
LITERATURE: *UT*, vol. 1 (1987), nos 23–5
1913.5–1.0371 (Japanese Painting 1370). Given by
 Sir W. Gwynne-Evans, Bt

Popular amusements of each season are a
common theme in Moronobu's books and
paintings, and here scenes of pleasure in
spring are paired with those of autumn.
The scroll does appear to have been cut in
the middle, however, and is rather shorter
than one would normally expect, so a
section devoted to summer may be
missing. In the first section a party of three
samurai women accompanied by two
servants and a small child enter from the
right to view the cherry blossom, while
across the river two elderly gentlemen are
being entertained by a blind masseur and

two young men. In the second section a
boat has been moored under a willow to
allow a party including two trainee Kabuki
actors to toast the full moon, and a circle
dance is in progress as part of O-Bon, held
each year in the seventh month to pay
respect to dead ancestors.

Many of these motifs – the three samurai
women viewing cherry blossom, for
instance – are repeated frequently in
identical configurations in the works of
Moronobu and his pupils and followers,
but here they are distributed along the
scroll with particular confidence. Also, the
contrasts of washes and accents of dark
ink, reminiscent of the techniques used by
Edo–Kanō artists, are handled with
considerable skill, suggesting that this may
well be a work from the hand of the master
himself (see discussion of Moronobu's
studio on p. 56). Another work by
Moronobu in this deft, abbreviated figure
style is known – a *Fuwa-Nagoya Vendetta*
handscroll (ink and slight colours on paper)
in the Ōta Memorial Museum of Art, Tokyo
(see Ōta 1985, no. 1).

6

7

7

HISHIKAWA MORONOBU

7 The Bodhisattva Jizō

Tenna–Jōkyō eras

SIGNATURE: Bōkoku Hishikawa Moronobu zu ('Picture by Hishikawa Moronobu of Awa Province')

SEALS: Hishikawa, (?)Nihon

Hanging scroll; ink, colour and gold on paper, 90.8 × 38.3 cm

PROVENANCE: Arthur Morrison

LITERATURE: Morrison 1911, vol. 2, text p. 28; UT, vol. 1 (1987), no. 22

1913.5–1.0372 (Japanese Painting 1371). Given by Sir W. Gwynne-Evans, Bt

The Bodhisattva Jizō (Sanskrit: Ksitigarbha) is an agent of Amida Buddha, a benevolent saviour who comes to greet the faithful at the time of their death and escort them to the Pure Land Paradise of Amida in the west. As the inscription above by Shōrei Shamon Keitsū (probably a monk) says:

What we desire in this transient world –
He fulfils all our needs.
After rebirth in the Pure Land,
We will receive beneficence without limit.

Here Moronobu uses exactly the same sensitive, flowing line as in his paintings of beautiful women, to show the Bodhisattva descending on lotus pedestals and a trail of cloud, wearing white monk's robes, a gold brocade stole (*kesa*) and carrying his attributes of a ringed staff (*shakujō*) and 'treasure jewel' (*hōju*). The plump face has a compassionate, introspective expression, without a hint of the worldliness one might expect from an Ukiyo-e artist.

Indeed, it is very unusual for an Ukiyo-e painter to have executed a Buddhist work, and the fact that Moronobu has included the name of his native region 'Bōkoku' (Awa Province) in his signature suggests that this might have been a special commission for some temple in Edo, or even perhaps in his home province.

8

HISHIKAWA MORONOBU

8 Scenes in a Theatre Teahouse

1685
SIGNATURE: Jōkyō ni kinoto ushi fuyu Hishikawa
    Moronobu hitsu ('Painted by Hishikawa
    Moronobu in the winter of 1685')
SEAL: Moronobu
Handscroll; ink and colour on silk,
    31.5 × 147.0 cm
PROVENANCE: William Anderson
LITERATURE: Anderson 1886, no. 1710; Narazaki
    1975, pp. 9–12; UT, vol. 1 (1987), no. 38; Smith
    1990, no. 191; Tokyo 1990, no. 7
1881.12–10.01710 (Japanese Painting 1375)

The theatre teahouses (*shibai-jaya*) were
often luxurious establishments located near
the Kabuki theatres in Sakai-chō and
Fukiya-chō where actors could meet their
patrons, and young trainee female
impersonators (*onnagata*) provided services
of homosexual prostitution. This
handscroll, which may have been cut from
the end of a longer work including onstage
scenes as well, depicts the pleasures to be
had there, just as other handscrolls by
Moronobu treat the boudoirs of the grand
courtesans of the Yoshiwara pleasure

quarter. In a parlour room on the right a
wealthy customer is having his shoulder
rubbed by a blind masseur and is
entertained with sake and music by two
young actors (identified by the purple
kerchief, *murasaki-bōshi*, they were required
to wear by law); while in the bed chamber
to the left an *onnagata* relaxes with his client
beneath a mosquito net. The scroll
concludes with a view of the entrance gate
to the establishment, where a
distinguished-looking samurai is arriving
with servants bearing expensive gifts for
the actor who has caught his fancy.

A set of seven similar fragments by
Moronobu and his atelier, dated between
1672 and 1689, showing scenes in the
pleasure quarters and Kabuki theatres is in
the collection of the Tokyo National
Museum (*NU*, vol. 2 (1982), nos 5–8, BW no.
66). The authenticity of the signatures and
seals on these as well as their attribution to
Moronobu and/or his pupils are much
debated, but certainly they form the basis
for a consideration of the development of
the Hishikawa style.

8

9 (ADD 26)

9 (ADD 26)　　　　9 (ADD 25)

9 (ADD 25)

HISHIKAWA MORONOBU

9 Scenes of Craftsmen

(?)c. 1680
SIGNATURE: Hishikawa Moronobu zu
SEALS: Hishikawa, Moronobu
Pair of handscrolls; ink and colour on silk,
    27.5 × 833.0 cm (ADD 25), 27.5 × 843.0 cm
    (ADD 26)
PROVENANCE: K. Murakami
LITERATURE: TNM 1987, no. 22; UT, vol. 1 (1987),
    nos 26–37; Tokyo 1990, no. 8
1923.11–14.02 (1–2) (Japanese Paintings ADD 25,
    26)

'Scenes of craftsmen' (*shokunin-zukushi*) had
been a common subject for genre painters
of the Kanō school at the beginning of the
Edo period, as the country reverted to
peaceful commerce after the long civil wars.
Moronobu is one of a very few Ukiyo-e
artists to have taken up this theme in
paintings and illustrated books such as
Wakoku shoshoku e-zukushi ('Pictures of All
the Trades of Japan'), reflecting his general
interest in life and customs in Edo (*Edo
fūzoku*). The present handscrolls treat a total
of fifty-two trades (twenty-four in the first
scroll, twenty-eight in the second), and

illustrated here are a doll-maker and paper-
maker. Many of the trades depicted served
the samurai class exclusively – armourers,
arrow-makers, horse-breakers, and the like
– and, indeed, many of the customers are
clearly of samurai rank, with retainers
shown waiting outside the shop. This may
indicate that the works were painted for a
samurai patron.

The present scrolls provide a good
example of the kind of problems
encountered in the connoisseurship of
Moronobu paintings. The compositions are
clearly by the master and the signatures
appear authentic, but there are certain
small deformations in the figure style and
details careless in their execution that lead
one to suspect that they were actually
painted by a workshop pupil. Nishiyama
Matsunosuke, in his detailed commentary
on the scrolls (UT, vol. 1 (1987), pp. 225–8)
suggests that they might predate 1682,
since they contain an advertising slogan,
 No. 1 in the Realm' (*tenka ichi*) on the sign
at the brush-maker's shop, the general use
of which was prohibited in that year.

10

10

HISHIKAWA SCHOOL

10 Scene on the Sumida River

(?)Late 17th century
SIGNATURE: Jōkyō ni kinoto ushi Hishikawa
  Moronobu hitsu ('Painted by Hishikawa
  Moronobu in 1685' (?spurious)
SEAL: Moronobu (?spurious)
Hanging scroll; ink and colour on silk,
  32.0 × 66.5 cm
PROVENANCE: William Anderson
LITERATURE: Anderson 1886, no. 1703
1881.12–10.01703 (Japanese Painting 1374)

The large barge is that of a *daimyō*
household, and the figure seated leaning
on the railing of the raised deck attended
by page boys may well be the lord himself.
Family crests are emblazoned on a large
awning which protects the double row of
standing oarsmen from the sun. A
swimming party of warriors and youths are
sporting from a small skiff: samurai were
expected to keep in training, and there
were annual swimming competitions held
on the Sumida attended by the Shōgun.

The signature is feeble and is probably a
later interpolation, added to a section cut
from a much longer handscroll of customs
and pastimes around the river in summer.
The painting does appear to have some age
to it – the small figures have considerable
vigour, and the washes and waves are
executed with care. However, the figures
are too small to permit a definite attribution
to Moronobu himself, and the work may at
best be regarded as a Hishikawa workshop
piece.

| |

| |

HISHIKAWA MOROHIRA
worked *c.* Genroku (1688–1704)–
Hōei (1704–11) eras

┃ ┃   Erotic Scenes

Genroku–Hōei eras
SIGNATURE: Nihon-e Hishikawa Morohira
  ('Japanese picture by Hishikawa Morohira')
SEAL: Hishikawa
Handscroll; ink, colour and gold on silk,
  32.6 × 254.0 cm
PROVENANCE: Fukui Rikichirō
OA+0140 (Japanese Painting ADD 533)

From the earliest anonymous Ukiyo-e
woodblock prints that followed the great
Edo fire of 1657 (some uniform enough in
style to be attributed by Richard Lane to a
'Kambun Master') onwards, printed and
painted erotica formed a vital part of the
new artistic movement, springing from a
long tradition of such painted handscrolls
by generally anonymous artists working in
the medieval Yamato-e style. Moronobu
and his contemporary Sugimura Jihei
(worked late Empō (1673–81)–Genroku
(1688–1704) eras) both designed many erotic
series, issued as printed albums, which

celebrate the pleasures of lovemaking in a
bold and unashamedly sensual manner. No
erotic paintings by Moronobu have yet
come to light, but they undoubtedly
existed.

Erotic works are invariably in the discreet
formats of the handscroll, album or
illustrated book, often, as here, showing a
sequence of twelve scenes. Though the
lovers gradually undress, nudity is not
featured for its own sake, and more
attention is paid to the artistic possibilities
of juxtaposing limbs with the gorgeousness
of the costumes and accessories, as well as,
of course, to illustrating the lovers' mutual
pleasure.

Hishikawa Morohira is assumed to be a
direct pupil of Moronobu, though his figure
style also shows the influence of Miyagawa
Chōshun (clearly apparent here). The
assurance of line, delicacy of flesh tones
and skill at composition apparent in this
rare work give a good indication of the
splendour of Moronobu's now-lost erotic
masterpieces.

ANON. (Hishikawa school)

12   Noblewoman Alighting from a Palanquin

(?)Late 17th–early 18th centuries
Hanging scroll; ink, colour and gold on silk,
   33.0 × 52.9 cm
PROVENANCE: Arthur Morrison
LITERATURE: *UT*, vol. 1 (1987), BW no. 4
1913.5–1.0375 (Japanese Painting 1383). Given by
   Sir W. Gwynne-Evans, Bt

A noblewoman from a samurai household
has alighted from a palanquin set down
beneath a grove of pine and flowering
cherry trees and is being greeted with bows
by a crouching retainer and maidservants.
A senior lady-in-waiting of advanced years
indicates the way the mistress should
proceed.

Such single-scene hanging scrolls are not
common in Moronobu's *oeuvre* – an
incident like this would generally form just
a part of one of his much larger screen or
handscroll compositions – but seem to have
proliferated among the generation of his
immediate pupils. A scroll very similar to
this in theme and execution in the Ōta
Memorial Museum (Ōta 1985, no. 11), for
instance, bears the signature Furuyama
Moroshige. Moroshige was the most
prolific of Moronobu's pupils, already
running an independent workshop by

12

Genroku 2 (1689) (Narazaki 1987, vol. 1,
p. 34). Works of this somewhat limited
calibre are frequently encountered (see nos
13, 14), and one wonders if, once a more
thorough investigation of the Hishikawa
school has been carried out, they will come
to be evaluated as nineteenth-century
copies or pastiches in Hishikawa style.

13

ANON. (Hishikawa school)

13 Noblewomen Viewing Cherry Blossom

(?)Late 17th–early 18th centuries
Hanging scroll; ink, colour and gold on silk,
37.0 × 53.0 cm
PROVENANCE: Arthur Morrison
1913.5–1.0373 (Japanese Painting 1372). Given by
Sir W. Gwynne-Evans, Bt

In a curtained enclosure beneath flowering cherry trees and with a folding screen behind them a party of women from a high-ranking samurai household are seated on mats enjoying a picnic and listening to one of their number playing on the *koto* (thirteen-stringed transverse harp). They are watched from outside the curtain by three women wearing flat travelling hats.

Though the style is not quite identical with the previous painting (the trees are more heavily outlined, for instance), in general the same comments concerning authenticity apply.

14

ANON. (Hishikawa style)

14 Courtesan Seated Beneath a Willow

(?)19th century
Hanging scroll; ink, colour and gold on silk,
34.2 × 51.8 cm
PROVENANCE: Arthur Morrison
1913.5–1.0367 (Japanese Painting 1381). Given by
Sir W. Gwynne-Evans, Bt

A courtesan is seated on a bench beneath a willow, enjoying cooling breezes from the river. In one corner of her mouth she bites the end of a letter which had been carried in the long lacquer box on the end of the bench. Biting letters or cloths was a sign of emotional anguish, and presumably a lover has written to terminate their liaison.

At least three other versions of this composition exist, one with the signature 'Furuyama Moromasa' (Narazaki 1970, BW nos 13–15). Though the style is reminiscent of Moronobu's followers, none are particularly convincing as 300-year-old works. This painting, in particular, gives every indication of being a nineteenth-century pastiche: the drapery lines are hard and unyielding, the patterns on the drapery flat, and the willow branches rudimentary.

15

ANON.

15 Standing Courtesan

c. Genroku era
Hanging scroll (mounted on a panel); ink and
  colour on paper, 68.5 × 28.6 cm
PROVENANCE: Yamanaka & Co.
1931.4–27.04 (Japanese Painting ADD 82)

A courtesan, wearing a pale blue kimono
with white clematis on the long hanging
sleeves and around the hem, stands
clasping her hands in such a manner that
the sleeves fall stiffly parallel in front of
her. The dressing of her hair in the
'Shimada' fashion (see no. 4) and the
obvious stylistic influence of Moronobu
allow us to date the work to the Genroku
era (1688–1704). The painting is a modest
anonymous piece – the pose somewhat
rigid and the lines having none of the
flowing grace seen in the work of
Moronobu or his pupils – and yet it is
interesting to see just how pervasive was
the Hishikawa style at the time.

16

ANON.

16 The Actors Nakamura Shichisaburō I *(right)* and Hayakawa Hasse I *(left)*

c. 1700–6
(?)Album leaf; ink, colour and gold on paper,
  22.3 × 32.3 cm
PROVENANCE: Arthur Morrison
  1913.5–1.0368 (Japanese Painting 1382). Given by
  Sir W. Gwynne-Evans, Bt

Shichisaburō I (right), identified by the crest of two linked squares on his kimono, appears in the role of a swashbuckling young samurai, with two exaggeratedly long swords thrust through his *obi*. He exchanges amorous glances with Hasse I (left) in a female role, his paulownia crest

emblazoned on the sleeve of a red kimono, a single sword through his rope sash (*nawa obi*) and holding a pair of sandals behind his back.

Hasse I came to Edo to join Shichisaburō I in the play *Yorimasa mannen-goyomi* ('Everlasting Calendar of Minamoto Yorimasa'), presented as the opening-of-the-season (*kaomise*) performance at the Yamamura theatre in the eleventh month of Genroku 13 (1700), with Shichisaburō I in the title role as Yorimasa and Hasse I as Lady Ayame no Mae. The duo immediately found favour with the Edo public, continuing to act together until Hasse I moved to the Ichimura theatre in Hōei 3

(1706). Thus it is highly likely that the painting dates from between these years. The sandals hidden behind Hasse I's back may provide the clue necessary for a Kabuki historian to identify the actual roles depicted.

The size of the figures suggests that the painting was originally an album leaf or segment of a handscroll. The handling of the outlines does not have the boldness or variation in thickness one associates with artists of the Torii school who dominated depictions of actors at the time, and it is not possible at present to attribute the work to a particular master.

17

17

ANON. (Hanabusa school)

17 The Tale of Nagoya Sanzaburō

Genroku–Kyōhō eras
SEALS: (unread – collector's seals?)
Handscroll; ink and colour on paper,
  28.0 × 1280.0 cm
PROVENANCE: William Anderson
LITERATURE: *UT*, vol. 1 (1987), nos 48–56
1881.12–10.02046 (Japanese Painting 1838)

The tale of the rivalry between Nagoya
Sanzaburō and Fuwa Banzaemon for the
love of Katsuragi, a courtesan of the
Shimabara quarter in Kyoto (*Nagoya
Sanzaburō monogatari*), is one of the oldest
themes in popular theatre in the Edo
period and is known to have been
performed in versions for the puppet
theatre as early as the Kambun era
(1661–73). It appears to have enjoyed a
particular boom around the Genroku era
(1688–1704) and has gone on to become a
staple of Kabuki right up to the present
day. In the eighteen scenes of the British
Museum scroll the story is told of the
rivalry in love, a duel, Banzaemon's
murder of Sanzaburō's father, the revenge
of Sanzaburō and his henchman Umezu

Kamon, and the final happy union of
Sanzaburō and Katsuragi.

As Hattori Yukio has pointed out
(*UT*, vol. 1 (1987), pp. 230–2), the British
Museum scroll is very similar to, and may,
indeed, have been copied from, a version
in the collection of the Toyama Kinenkan,
Saitama Prefecture, by Hanabusa Itchō
(1652–1724) or a close follower. Though
trained in the orthodox Kanō style, Itchō
broke out of the rigid confines of the
subjects and styles constantly repeated by
masters of this school to paint the world of
popular customs in the pleasure quarters
and simple genre scenes linked to *haiku*
poetry. Because of this interest in the world
of the pleasure quarters Itchō is sometimes
classed as an Ukiyo-e painter, but
stylistically he in fact falls halfway between
Kanō and Ukiyo-e. As this scroll – which
must have been faithfully copied by a pupil
in the Itchō lineage – demonstrates, the
Hanabusa figure style has a lightness,
vivacity and freedom not generally found
in the more polished and poised world of
Ukiyo-e contemporaries such as Miyagawa
Chōshun (nos 36–9).

18

18

Furuyama Moromasa
worked *c.* Kampō (1741–4)–
Enkyō (1744–8) eras

Common name Shinshichirō (or Shinkurō);
gō Getsugetsudō, Bunshi. According to
traditional accounts Moromasa is said to be
the son of Furuyama Moroshige
(Moronobu's senior pupil) and to have
worked from the Hōei era (1704–11) using
first the name Hishikawa Masanori. But as
Asano Shūgō has pointed out (Narazaki
1987, vol. 1, p. 34), all his extant works,
including a dozen or so paintings and four
woodblock prints, would appear on stylistic
grounds to date from the Kampō (1741–4)
and Enkyō (1744–8) eras. Apart from
accomplished paintings of beauties in an
idiosyncratic style (influenced to an extent
by contemporaries such as Okumura
Masanobu), there is a long handscroll of
mitate subjects in the Azabu Museum of
Arts and Crafts (Sendai 1988, no. 15).

FURUYAMA MOROMASA

18 Courtesan and Attendant

Kampō–Enkyō eras
SIGNATURE: Furuyama Moromasa ga
SEAL: Moromasa no in
Hanging scroll; ink, colour and gold on paper,
96.0 × 26.5 cm
PROVENANCE: Ernest Hart
LITERATURE: *UT*, vol. 1 (1987), BW no. 7
1901.5–16.027 (Japanese Painting 1378)

A courtesan, accompanied by her *kamuro*,
stands on a verandah, pulling up her skirts
slightly at the front, perhaps preparing to
put on the clogs now lying on the ground.
She wears a purple *uchikake* with a design
of flowering *kōhone* plants beside a stream,
over a red kimono with a pattern of plovers
and waves. The large face, tilted forward
and outlined in red (as always in
Moromasa's paintings), has the
characteristic long nose, downturned
mouth and hair combed directly back from
the forehead that are the hallmarks of his
idiosyncratic style. The composition of a
courtesan and attendant(s) standing or
seated on the corner of the verandah of a
house of pleasure is common in
Moromasa's small *oeuvre*; compare, for
instance, Ōta 1985, no. 14, and Ithaca 1966,
no. 16.

19   19

FURUYAMA MOROMASA

19 Courtesan and Retinue Walking in
the Rain

Kampō–Enkyō eras
SEAL: Moromasa no in
(?)Album leaf; ink and colour on paper,
  27.0 × 37.7 cm
PROVENANCE: Arthur Morrison (inscribed on verso
  'with best wishes from all at Salcombe House,
  Loughton')
1989.2–14.01 (Japanese Painting ADD 885)

One of the rituals of the Yoshiwara
pleasure quarter was the procession of a
courtesan to meet a patron at one of the
assignation teahouses (*ageya*) which lined
the main street of the quarter, Naka-no-chō
(see also no. 63). Here a manservant
carrying a long-poled umbrella attempts to
protect the courtesan as she walks, tilting

her head to avoid the shower, towards the
teahouse hung with reed blinds,
accompanied by two *kamuro*. The pattern of
chrysanthemums and butterflies on her
robes and the flowering bushclover on
those of her attendants suggest that this is
autumn, a season prone to sudden
showers.

Though this is possibly a section from a
handscroll, the position of the seal suggests
that it is more likely a sheet from a large
album, possibly showing scenes in the
Yoshiwara at different times of the year. As
in the previous painting (no. 18), the
figures have Moromasa's habitual red
outline, yet with a sweetness and intimacy
not found in his larger works. There is
considerable worm damage to the top left-
hand corner of the painting.

Tamura Suiō

worked *c.* Genroku (1688–1704)–
Shōtoku (1711–16) eras

Na Sesshin; *gō* Museishi, Kankun,
Bōkanshi. Thought to have worked in Edo,
since a handscroll of *Scenes of Pleasure*
shows cherry viewing at Ueno and scenes
on the Sumida River. His style –
particularly in hanging scrolls on silk – is
exceedingly refined, the figures a mixture
of Moronobu with more traditional Tosa/
Sumiyoshi elegance and restraint, and
landscape elements in Edo–Kanō manner.
The twenty or so paintings published can
be broadly divided into two types: single
courtesans in rudimentary settings; or
horizontal compositions showing luxurious
apartments opening on to lyrical landscape
settings – generally with a single figure
arriving to meet several others waiting in
the building (including *mitate* of scenes
from *Genji monogatari* and *Ise monogatari*).

20

TAMURA SUIŌ

20 Beauty Seated on a Red Plum Tree

Genroku–Shōtoku eras
SIGNATURE: Suiō hitsu
SEAL: Sesshin
Hanging scroll; ink, colour and gold on paper,
   41.0 × 56.0 cm
PROVENANCE: Arthur Morrison
1946.2–9.042 (Japanese Painting ADD 225).
   Bequeathed by Arthur Morrison

A beauty wearing a pale blue kimono with
a motif of large chrysanthemums on the
sleeves and skirts is seated on the twisting
trunk of a flowering plum tree, enjoying
the beauty and fragrance of its blossoms
which herald spring. Her fine features are
framed beneath the high crown of a
'Shimada' hairstyle reminiscent of the
works of Moronobu, suggesting that the

painting may date from as early as the
Genroku era (1688–1704). The outlines of
the kimono are overlaid in gold, in addition
to *sumi*, and, as in so many works by Suiō,
a Chinese character (*shinobi*, 'secret (love)' –
a word often used in classical poetry) is
picked out in dotted tie-dyeing on the
sleeve.

Suiō's paintings are hybrid in style,
showing the influence of the traditional
Kanō and Tosa/Sumiyoshi schools as much
as of the new Ukiyo-e style of Moronobu.
Here the refined figure, which has a
coolness and detachment not generally
seen in Moronobu's work, contrasts with
the Kanō-style plum tree, executed with
spontaneous ink strokes and washes
to suggest the gnarled bark of the aged
tree.

20

Kaigetsudō Ando

worked *c.* Hōei (1704–11)–
Kyōhō (1716–36) eras

Family name Okazawa (or Okazaki);
common name Dewaya Genshichi; *gō*
Kan'unshi. Thought to have lived in Suwa-
chō, Asakusa. Banished to Izu Oshima for
his involvement in the Lady Ejima scandal
in 1714, but pardoned and returned to Edo
in 1722. Thought to be the same individual
as the poet Kaigetsudō Jōsen and
Kaigetsudō Shisui, whose *haiku* poems
appear in anthologies of Kyōhō 15 (1730)
and Kyōhō 17 (1732).

Ando (or perhaps read 'Yasunori'?) is
best known for his paintings of single
standing beauties against a plain
background, characterised by a bold
modulating outline to the drapery
contrasting with delicate features on a large
oval face. Ando himself is not known to
have designed any prints, but his style was
faithfully replicated in many paintings and
a small number of large black and white
woodblock prints in the *kakemono-e* format
(which imitated a hanging painting) by his
pupils. The close similarity in style, the use
of the 'Ando' seal on paintings by pupils,
and the use of an identical sobriquet *Nihon
giga* ('light-hearted painting in Japanese
style') suggest that these artists were
organised into a closely knit atelier. Anchi
(Yasutomo?), the only artist to share the
'An' character of his teacher's name, is
assumed to be the senior pupil. He used
the *gō* Chōyōdō and designed eight prints.
The other pupils and the number of their
prints is as follows: Dohan (Norishige?)
twelve prints; Doshin (Noritoki?) three
prints; Doshu (Noritane?) no prints; Doshū
(Norihide?) no prints. Paintings and prints
by Ando and his pupils are traditionally
dated to the first two decades of the
eighteenth century, and the atelier's
continued activity after Ando's banishment
remains undemonstrated. Ando's paintings
cover a much wider range of themes,
including warrior, genre and parody
subjects, than do those of his pupils.

21

21

KAIGETSUDŌ ANDO

21 Courtesan Entering a Mosquito Net

Hōei–Shōtoku eras
SIGNATURE: Nihon giga Kaigetsudō Ando kore [o]
zu [su] ('Light-hearted painting in Japanese
style, this picture was done by Kaigetsudō
Ando')
SEAL: (trimmed)
Hanging scroll (mounted as a panel); ink, colour
and gold on paper, 106.0 × 45.0 cm
PROVENANCE: Arthur Morrison
LITERATURE: Morrison 1911, vol. 2, pl. x; UT, vol. 1
(1987), no. 92; Tokyo 1990, no. 27
1913.5–1.0348 (Japanese Painting 1387). Given by
Sir W. Gwynne-Evans, Bt

Ando's compositions for paintings of
beautiful women were consistently more
inventive than the single standing figures
of beauties that came to dominate the
works of his pupils (nos 22, 23), and here a
courtesan pauses, turning to look back, as
she enters the hanging tent of a mosquito
net, where summer sleeping-mats have
already been laid. Her kimono has a design
of *tomoe* roundels built up in three-
dimensional swirls of gesso covered in gold
paint (to suggest gold-thread embroidery)
and boughs of wistaria, in which the leaves
are painted to suggest combined techniques
of *yūzen* dyeing, tie-dyed dots and more
gold embroidery. Such bold, all-over
designs in mixed techniques were typical
on kimonos of the Genroku era (1688–1704)
and shortly after. The woman carries a
summer fan (*uchiwa*) painted with a
seasonal design of vine leaves.

22

22

The figure is large and ample, but the outlines of the kimono are not as heavily modulated as they became in the paintings of Ando's pupils. The sensuousness of the thick skein of hair that hangs heavily over the courtesan's shoulder is echoed by the long, trailing curve of the transparent netting. A very similar painting to the present, but with the composition reversed and the woman looking down at a kitten, is illustrated in Kuwabara 1911, no. 39; and a third work on a similar theme, with the courtesan emerging from the mosquito net and reading a love-letter, is illustrated in Ōta 1985, no. 21.

The painting has been trimmed by several centimetres at the bottom, losing the seal beneath the signature.

KAIGETSUDŌ DOHAN
worked *c*. Hōei (1704–11)–Shōtoku (1711–16) eras

22 Courtesan Arranging her Hair

Hōei–Shōtoku eras

SIGNATURE: Nihon giga Kaigetsu matsuyō Dohan kore [o] zu [su] ('Light-hearted painting in Japanese style, this picture was done by the Kaigetsu pupil Dohan')

SEAL: (unread)

Hanging scroll (mounted as a panel); ink and colour on paper, 95.4 × 44.7 cm

PROVENANCE: Shōzō Katō

LITERATURE: *UT*, vol. 1 (1987), no. 94; Tokyo 1990, no. 28

1921.3–17.01 (Japanese Painting ADD 16)

Once the composition for a painting of a single standing beauty was established within the Kaigetsudō atelier, it was frequently reused by the various members of the group with different patterns substituted on the kimono. The use of such formulas and the relatively simple, bold manner of execution must have assisted greatly in mass-producing paintings to meet popular demand. The pose of the woman raising both hands to adjust her hairpins or comb is seen in a number of Kaigetsudō works, such as an Ando

painting in the Idemitsu Museum of Arts (Idemitsu 1988, no. 32), as well as prints by Dohan and Anchi, and here Dohan shows her passing a tortoiseshell hairpin through the loop of her 'Shimada' coiffure. Where the artist is able to make an individual contribution, however, is in the striking originality of the designs of the robes: one sleeve of the outer-kimono with its subtle black-on-black design of flower roundels has been shrugged off to reveal the brilliantly contrasting under-kimono of blue and white chrysanthemums against bands of red and white. The outlines of the black kimono are painted in pale grey reserve.

The painting appears to have been trimmed, somewhat over-emphasising the monumentality of the figure.

23

KAIGETSUDŌ DOSHIN
worked *c.* Hōei (1704–11)–Shōtoku (1711–16) eras

23 Standing Courtesan

Hōei–Shōtoku eras
SIGNATURE: Nihon giga Kaigetsu matsuyō Doshin
kore [o] zu [su] ('Light-hearted painting in
Japanese style, this picture was done by the
Kaigetsu pupil Doshin')
SEAL: Ando
Hanging scroll; ink and colour on paper,
121.0 × 46.7 cm
PROVENANCE: Jonathan Hutchinson; Oscar Raphael
LITERATURE: Binyon and Sexton 1923, p. 195;
UT, vol. 1 (1987), no. 93
1945.11–1.058 (Japanese Painting ADD 183).
Bequeathed by Oscar Raphael

A courtesan, her long hair looped
informally at its ends, wears a kimono
decorated with large orange
chrysanthemums against a background of
pale blue and white bands and stylised
brown clouds. The pose, standing tall with
hands drawn inside the kimono, stomach
pushed slightly forward, long hanging
sleeve drawn across the body in display,
and head tilted forward pensively, even
coyly, is, once again, found in several other
Kaigetsudō school works. There is a Doshin
print which matches the present work
almost line for line, except that the kimono
is decorated with large falcon feathers and
the hair is arranged differently. A Doshin
painting in the Suntory Museum of Art of
an *onnagata* actor is also similar, except that
the kimono pattern is of dwarf bamboo in
the snow and one sleeve hangs down at
the back (*NU*, vol. 2 (1982), pl. 43). In yet
another painting – this time by Dohan – the
hair is coiled up and the kimono has a
design of ivy-covered pine trees (Narazaki
1987, vol. 2, no. 9). As if any more
evidence were necessary, the use of the
'Ando' seal after the Doshin signature on
this painting confirms the tightly knit
character of the atelier.

23

Matsuno Chikanobu

worked *c.* Hōei (1704–11)–
Shōtoku (1711–16) eras

Gō Hakushōken. Nothing is known of
Chikanobu's biography, but more than a
dozen paintings of beauties have been
identified which all share strong stylistic
features: hair combed straight back from a
sweetly smiling face with a small upturned
mouth, a rhythmical modulating outline to
the drapery and the use of strong, high-
quality pigments. Chikanobu's *gō*
'Hakushōken' is written in two different
ways with characters that sound the same,
but it is not known how these different
signatures relate to the chronology of his
works. In the past Chikanobu has
sometimes been described as a minor
imitator of the Kaigetsudō style, but recent
writing ranks him – together with artists
such as Baiōken Eishun, Baiyūken
Katsunobu, Nishikawa Terunobu and
Uegaki Hōryū – equally as an independent
master working in parallel (and in
competition) to the Kaigetsudō atelier (see
Asano Shūgō's comments in Narazaki 1987,
vol. 1, p. 72).

MATSUNO CHIKANOBU

24 Standing Courtesan

Hōei–Shōtoku eras
SIGNATURE: Hakushōken Matsuno Chikanobu kore
[o] zu [su] ('This was drawn by Hakushōken
Matsuno Chikanobu')
SEAL: (?)Sen
Hanging scroll; ink and colour on paper,
75.0 × 30.0 cm
PROVENANCE: Arthur Morrison
LITERATURE: *Kokka*, 42 (1893), colour woodblock
facsimile facing p. 114; Morrison 1911, vol. 2,
p. 31; *UT*, vol. 1 (1987), no. 103; Smith 1990,
no. 192
1913.5–1.0283 (Japanese Painting 1405). Given by
Sir W. Gwynne-Evans, Bt

As so often in late seventeenth- and early
eighteenth-century paintings, the courtesan
wears kimonos in two layers, with one
sleeve of the over-kimono shrugged off and
hanging down to display the pattern of the
robe underneath. Here the pale blue and
white over-kimono, decorated with large
blue chrysanthemums (suggesting autumn)
contrasts strikingly with the scarlet under-
kimono with a design of dwarf bamboo in
the snow (representing winter). The whole
composition is enlivened by Chikanobu's
habitual use of dancing outlines –
particularly on the flouncing *obi* – which
accord well with the brilliant colouring in
high-quality pigments. The face has the
same sweetly smiling expression as is
found in all works by this master.

24

24

25

25

Baiōken Eishun

worked *c.* 1700–Kyōhō (1716–36) era

Family name Hasegawa; *gō* Baiōken, Shōsuiken, Baisuiken, Baihōken. Thought to be a native of Edo. Also used the name Takeda Harunobu. A pair of handscrolls of *Customs of the Twelve Months in Edo* (Art Institute of Chicago) can be dated to Hōreki 1 (1704), and Asano Shūgō has suggested that a triptych of paintings of actors may date even earlier, *c.* 1700–1 (Narazaki 1987, vol. 1, p. 71). This indicates that Eishun – like Matsuno Chikanobu – was an independent rival of the Kaigetsudō atelier, rather than a later follower or lesser imitator as had been formerly suggested. More than twenty paintings of beauties are known, many of very elongated proportions and with similar faces – a somewhat squarish jaw, with the features concentrated in the centre of the face. The use of an identical seal (unread) and the recent appearance of *Beauty Beside a Mosquito Net* (Kumamoto 1989, no. 10) which has the signature 'Nihonga Baiōken Harunobu hitsu' ('Japanese picture painted by Baiōken Harunobu') prove that Eishun is the same individual as a painter who

signed himself Takeda Harunobu and is known by half a dozen or so paintings of beauties in a related style. Asano (ibid.) suggests that Harunobu might be the name used in the later part of Eishun's career. Similarities in style and the forms of the signatures used by Baiyūken Katsunobu and Hakushōken (Matsuno) Chikanobu indicate that these three artists may have been grouped together into some form of association.

BAIŌKEN EISHUN

25 Reclining Courtesan

c. Hōei–early Kyōhō eras
SIGNATURE: Nihonga Baiōken Eishun zu ('Japanese painting drawn by Baiōken Eishun')
SEAL: (unread)
Hanging scroll; ink, colour and gold on paper, 37.7 × 51.6 cm
PROVENANCE: Michael Alishan
1990.3–14.01 (Japanese Painting ADD 937)

A courtesan, wearing a thin summer kimono, reclines in a languid pose against a padded arm-rest reading a book, while her *kamuro* kneels behind cooling her with a

round summer fan. A small celadon incense burner placed on a red lacquer tray on the floor sends up a wisp of fragrant smoke, and the intense, airless heat of late summer is almost palpable. The transparency of the pale blue gauze robe, shot through with a faint check of brown, blue and white lines, is handled with extreme delicacy, revealing the breasts, slender arms and pink underskirt beneath, and these pastel shades are offset with shocks of bright scarlet lining at the collar and sleeve-openings.

In addition to paintings of single standing beauties of a fairly standard type Eishun explores more unusual compositional possibilities of reclining figures in several of his works, for example, *Courtesan Seated Beside a Sleeping Client* (Azabu Museum of Arts and Crafts), *Courtesan Reclining Writing a Letter beside a Mosquito Net* (Kumamoto 1989, no. 10). The shape of the face in the British Museum painting, which is close in style to those works signed 'Takeda Harunobu', suggests that it might date towards the end of the artist's 'Eishun' period, perhaps the early Kyōhō era (1716–36).

26

Baiyūken Katsunobu

worked *c*. Hōei (1704–11)–
Shōtoku (1711–16) eras

Known by a dozen or so paintings of
beauties dating from the first two decades
of the eighteenth century and clearly
influenced by the dominant Kaigetsudō
idiom. A single seal is used which has been
deciphered as the character 'Shin' (or *kami*,
meaning 'god'). Because of the similarity in
their *gō* and stylistic affinities in the
painting of faces Baiyūken Katsunobu is
thought to have been associated in some
way with the artists Hakushōken (Matsuno)
Chikanobu (no. 24) and Baiōken Eishun
(no. 25). The artist Kondō Katsunobu
(no. 27), who produced prints and
paintings in the Torii school style around
the Kyōhō era (1716–36), is thought to be a
separate individual.

BAIYŪKEN KATSUNOBU

26   Courtesan Seated on a Bench

Hōei–Shōtuku eras
SIGNATURE: Nihon-e Baiyūken Katsunobu gō
('Japanese picture from the brush of Baiyūken
Katsunobu')
SEAL: (?)Shin
Hanging scroll; ink and colour on silk,
119.8 × 44.4 cm
PROVENANCE: J. J. O'Brien Sexton
LITERATURE: *UT*, vol. 1 (1987), no. 102
1942.4–11.07 (Japanese Painting ADD 149). Given
by Mrs O'Brien Sexton

A courtesan is seated on a bench, perhaps
to enjoy a cooling evening breeze in
summer, and is placing a tortoiseshell comb
in her hair. Her kimono is decorated with
calligraphy in white reserve against dyed
bands of green, brown, white and blue:
individual large Chinese characters
apparently picked at random from poems
(spring, wistaria, love, warbler, and so on)
are set amongst lines of calligraphy in the
cursive women's style. The folding-fan
crest prominent on her sleeve suggests she
may be a courtesan of the prestigious
Ōgiya ('fan') house.

The dozen or so known paintings by
Baiyūken Katsunobu of beauties, though
clearly influenced by the dominant
contemporary Kaigetsudō style (nos 21–3),
also have certain original elements: the tall
slender body with sloping shoulders is
matched by a long face of refined
appearance. As with the Kaigetsudō atelier,
too, certain compositions are repeatedly
reused, and there is a painting in the
Idemitsu collection showing a beauty in an
almost identical pose (Idemitsu 1988, no.
48). The differences in detail between the
two paintings – the face in the British

26

Museum example is more finely executed
and the signature is in the formal *kaisho*
(square script) style – may be explained in
part by the different medium (painting on
silk rather than paper), but as with so
many eighteenth-century painters now
known by only a handful of works it is
difficult to establish the exact parameters of
this individual's style.

Kondō Katsunobu
worked *c.* Kyōhō (1716–36) era

Known by one *akahon* (red-covered picture-book), eight single-sheet prints and eight paintings which can be dated stylistically to the Kyōhō era, and which show the prevailing influence of the Torii school, Okamura Masanobu and Nishimura Shigenaga. The influence of the Kaigetsudō style is not apparent and so this artist is probably a different individual from Baiyūken Katsunobu (no. 26). The name suggests some relationship, possibly as a pupil, with the artists Kondō Kiyoharu and Kondō Kiyonobu.

Attributed to
KONDŌ KATSUNOBU

27 Courtesan Wearing a Red and White Surcoat

c. Kyōhō era
Hanging scroll (trimmed); ink, colour and gold on paper, 55.9 × 25.7 cm
PROVENANCE: Arthur Morrison
1913.5–1.0363 (Japanese Painting 1393). Given by Sir W. Gwynne-Evans, Bt

Pulling her surcoat (*uchikake*) around her, a courtesan walks forward, turning back to look over her shoulder in a *contrapposto* commonly used by Ukiyo-e painters. Her kimono has a pattern of (?)peonies surrounded by yellow foliate tendrils, and the surcoat is red around the shoulders fading to white below, with scattered cherry flowers (some larger in red tie-dye). The work has in the past been attributed to Okumura Masanobu, but the tall, statuesque figure and long face and nose, small eyes with tiny dot pupils and rosebud mouth all point to the style of Kondō Katsunobu. A similar figure, wearing an *uchikake* decorated with chrysanthemums done in a similar technique to the cherry flowers of this painting, appears in a signed work by Katsunobu, accompanied by two *kamuro* (Kumamoto 1989, no. 11).

The painting has clearly been trimmed down considerably from the normal proportions of a hanging scroll, probably because of severe damage, and it is likely that Katsunobu's signature was lost at that time.

27

28

ANON. (after Okumura Masanobu)

28 Hotei with a Young Kabuki Actor

(?)Hōei–Shōtoku eras
(?)Album leaf (mounted as a hanging scroll); ink,
   colour and gold on paper, 22.7 × 36.6 cm
PROVENANCE: Arthur Morrison
1946.2–9.035 (Japanese Painting ADD 189).
   Bequeathed by Arthur Morrison

Hotei is one of the Seven Lucky Gods
(*Shichifukujin*), bald, pot-bellied and
smiling, and always shown with his
treasure sack fastened to the end of a staff.
In this informal rendition Hotei is shown
taking his ease lying back against the
treasure sack, following the libretto
(reading through spectacles) as a young
trainee Kabuki actor plays him some tune
of the moment on the *shamisen*.

The composition is a direct copy (but
with different patterns on the robes) of a
black and white print by Okumura

Masanobu (1686–1764) from an untitled
album of twelve such subjects dated to the
first decade of the eighteenth century
(AIC 1955, no. 24, p. 124; Shibui Kiyoshi,
'Masanobu no sumi-e', *Ukiyo-e no kenkyū*,
vol. VI, no. 3 (March 1929), nos I–XI). In
general one is suspicious of paintings
which imitate the compositions of
woodblock prints too closely (remembering
that traditional Japanese prints do not serve
the function of reproducing paintings – as
they often do in the West), but this scroll
does appear to have some age to it, and it
is suggested it may have been copied from
Masanobu's print fairly soon after its
publication. A painting after another
composition in this album, *Daikoku and a
Courtesan*, signed 'Riendō', an otherwise
unrecorded artist, is in the Ōta Memorial
Museum of Art, Tokyo (Ōta 1985, no. 59).

29

ANON. (Okumura school)

29 Parody of Fujiwara Teika's Cottage
   at Mt Ogura

c. Kyōhō era
Hanging scroll; ink, colour and gold on paper,
   42.2 × 58.3 cm
PROVENANCE: Arthur Morrison
LITERATURE: *UT*, vol. 1 (1987), BW no. 5
1913.5–1.0362 (Japanese Painting 1392). Given by
   Sir W. Gwynne-Evans, Bt

Legends concerning the love affair between
the poet Fujiwara no Teika (1162–1241) and
Princess Shokushi at Teika's cottage
Shigure no Chin ('Arbour of the Autumn
Showers') at Mt Ogura in Kyoto had
already formed the basis for the Nō play
Teika. In the seventeenth and early
eighteenth centuries these were adapted for
performance in more popular narrative
forms – in particular, Tosa *jōruri* versions in
which Princess Shokushi visits Teika's
cottage disguised as a young dandy
(*wakashu*).

   In this painting the place of Princess
Shokushi is taken by an eighteenth-century
courtesan, wearing a man's striped *haori*

jacket and with two swords stuck through
her sash, standing outside the gate of
Teika's cottage, sheltered from the autumn
shower by a maid with an umbrella. Inside
the hut a handsome youth, impersonating
Teika, plays the *shakuhachi* flute,
accompanied by a blind musician on the
koto. This technique of repopulating well-
known literary or historical episodes with
characters in contemporary dress – a
common convention in the theatre
throughout the Edo period – is known as
mitate. Though this term is translated for
convenience with the English word
'parody', the motives underlying *mitate-e*
('*mitate* pictures') are many and varied,
ranging from salacious fun-poking through
visual puns and riddles to a simple desire
to emulate or even appropriate the
emblems and values of the classical past.
The ability of an Edo audience to savour
the odd conjunctions and
transmogrifications of these pictures which
bring together such disparate worlds gives
evidence of an enviable flexibility of mind.

   Examples exist of *mitate* in paintings of
the seventeenth century, but it was the

Ukiyo-e artist Okumura Masanobu (1686–
1764) who vastly expanded and codified the
range of subjects suitable for reworking in
this way, in a series of printed albums
dating from the first two decades of the
eighteenth century. Though the figures in
the present painting are highly reminiscent
of Masanobu's style – and the work may
certainly be attributed to his circle – the
composition lacks the discipline of his
famous version of the subject in the Tokyo
National Museum (*NU*, vol. 3 (1982),
no. 29), in which the figure of the young-
dandy-impersonating-Princess-Shokushi-
impersonating-a-young-dandy is given
much more prominence. A further
unsigned version of the subject is in the
Freer Gallery of Art, Washington, DC
(Stern 1973, no. 39).

Yamazaki Joryū

worked *c.* Kyōhō (1716–36)–
Kampō (1741–4) eras

The daughter of a Bakufu retainer,
Yamazaki Bunzaemon, who lived first in
Shitaya Chōja-machi and then at the
approach to Zōjō-ji Temple in Shiba, Joryū
was a child prodigy, apparently self-taught,
who is said to have painted from the age of
six or seven. At present works have come
to light which give her age in the signature
as between twelve and thirty-three. Asano
Shūgō has pointed out that the actor's crest
which appears in a painting by Joryū of a
Beauty With an Umbrella (MOA Art
Museum) on which her age is given as
fourteen can be dated between the years
1723 and 1729, thus extending her period of
activity at least to the Kampō era (1741–4).
The paintings are almost all of Yoshiwara
courtesans, often with poems inscribed
above by Joryū herself.

YAMAZAKI JORYŪ

30 Courtesan Reading a Letter Beside
a Mosquito Net

c. 1723–9
SIGNATURE: Joryū jūyon-sai hitsu ('Painted by
    Joryū, aged fourteen')
SEAL: (?)Yamazaki-uji onna ('Woman of the
    Yamazaki family')
INSCRIPTION: Kimi matsu to/neya e mo iranu/maki
    no to ni/itaku na fuke so/aki no yo no tsuki
Hanging scroll; ink and colour on paper,
    75.5 × 31.0 cm
PROVENANCE: Ernest Hart
LITERATURE: *UT*, vol. 1 (1987), no. 104
1901.5-16.028 (Japanese Painting 1398)

On an evening in early autumn, with the
weather still warm enough to warrant a
mosquito net, a courtesan sits with the
gauze of the net trailing over her
shoulders, reading a letter from her lover,
unable to sleep as she waits for him to
arrive. Her kimono, with a design of
trailing purple clematis, is outlined with
ample, fluid strokes that echo the curves of
the mosquito net; yet above all it is her
bewitching, almost impish, face which
draws the viewer's attention.

   The poem inscribed on the painting,
probably by Joryū herself, derives from a
verse by Princess Shokushi (no. 1204 in the
Imperial *Shin kokin waka shū* anthology of
AD 1201, with a modified last line) and
articulates the woman's longing:

   Thinking to wait for my love
   I do not even enter the bedchamber,
   But stay at this door of precious wood.
   Moon of the autumn night that shines
      here
   Do not set so fast!

30

In Ukiyo-e prints and paintings parallels
are often drawn in this way with episodes
of courtly love from Japan's classical past,
suggesting an audience well educated in
literature and poetry.

TŌENSAI KAŌ
worked mid-18th century

31 Courtesan and Two Attendants Beneath Cherry Blossom

Gembun–Kan'en eras
SIGNATURE: Tōensai Kaō ga
SEAL: (?)Yasunobu
Hanging scroll; ink and colour on paper,
 90.0 × 26.9 cm
PROVENANCE: *Arthur Morrison*
LITERATURE: *UT*, vol. 1 (1987), no. 116
1913.5–1.0361 (Japanese Painting 1410). Given by
 Sir W. Gwynne-Evans, Bt

In spring the central street in Yoshiwara pleasure quarter, Naka-no-chō, was lined with flowering cherry trees, and here a courtesan pauses as she walks under the blossoms to turn and talk to her two *kamuro*, one of whom holds a (?)flute in a brocade bag. The courtesan's surcoat (*uchikake*) is decorated with an elaborate hand-painted design of swallows flying among willow branches above swirling water.

Kaō is known by only a handful of accomplished paintings of beauties whose small, plump features show the strong stylistic influence of Okumura Masanobu. On the basis of his use of the name Yasunobu in his seal he may be the same individual as Shibata Yasunobu, who is known by a single hand-coloured woodblock print. Other examples of his paintings are illustrated in Ōta, April 1985, no. 63, and Narazaki 1987, vol. 2, no. 121 (Tokyo National Museum Collection).

31

Nishikawa Sukenobu 1671–1750

Common name Uzaemon; *gō* Bunkadō, Jitokusai, Jitokusō. Lived at Kyoto Yanaginobanba Ayakōji kudaru. The most accomplished and influential Ukiyo-e painter in Kyoto during the first half of the eighteenth century, and more than 100 illustrated books designed by him spread his fame to Edo as well. He is recorded as having been in service to the aristocratic Saionji family, by whom he was granted the title 'Ukyō' ('right section of the Capital'), often incorporated into his signature.

Sukenobu is said to have studied with Kanō Einō (1631–97), third generation head of the Kyoto Kanō school, and Sukenobu's essay on painting included in volume 10 of *Ehon Yamato hiji* of 1742 was probably composed in emulation of Einō's famous history of painting, *Honchō gashi* (1678). It is possible that he also studied with Tosa Mitsusuke (1675–1710). Sukenobu was the principal illustrator of novels published by the leading Hachimonjiya publishing house in Kyoto from *c.* 1700 through the 1730s, but it was with his picture-book showing 100 courtesans from the Shimabara pleasure quarter, *Hyakunin jorō shina sadame* (1723), that Sukenobu's illustrations of scenes of women's customs and pastimes took on their classic form. His large corpus of paintings, too, generally shows single figures or groups of women in poses similar to those in the illustrated books.

Sukenobu's art established the point of departure for all later Ukiyo-e painters of women in the Kyoto–Osaka area, but his illustrated books were assiduously studied and borrowed from by artists in Edo as well, such as Okumura Masanobu, the Kawamata school painters Tsuneyuki and Tsunemasa, and particularly Suzuki Harunobu. As Akai Tatsurō has pointed out (*NU*, vol. 9 (1982), p. 130), Sukenobu's paintings were highly prized by contemporaries, Yanagisawa Kien in his *Hitorine* of *c.* 1726 going so far as to call him the 'supreme master' (*hijirite*) of Ukiyo-e, superior to Okumura Masanobu, Torii Kiyonobu, Hanekawa Chinchō and Kaigetsudō.

NISHIKAWA SUKENOBU

32 Courtesan Walking

Gembun–Enkyō eras
SIGNATURE: Nishikawa Ukyō Sukenobu hitsu ('Painted by Nishikawa Sukenobu of Ukyō rank')
SEALS: Nishikawa-uji, Sukenobu kore [o] zu [su] ('This was drawn by Sukenobu')
Hanging scroll; ink and colour on silk, 80.7 × 40.0 cm
PROVENANCE: Arthur Morrison
LITERATURE: Morrison 1911, vol. 2, pl. XIII; *UT*, vol. 1 (1987), no. 110
1913.5–1.0391 (Japanese Painting 1399). Given by Sir W. Gwynne Evans, Bt

A courtesan steps out wearing a grey *uchikake* with a pattern of (?)shells, over a scarlet kimono with 'hemp leaf' (*asa no ha*) design in white tie-dyed dots (lined in pale blue), tied with a jet-black *obi*. This colour combination – black, white, red and pale blue – is frequently seen in Sukenobu's paintings. The composition is reminiscent of the single standing figures of courtesans against a plain background as seen in the illustrated book *Ehon Asakayama* (1739).

A comparison with *Walking Courtesan* (no. 39) painted by Miyagawa Chōshun in Edo at roughly the same time is instructive. With typical Kyoto reticence Sukenobu sets his figure much smaller in the composition, and the costume is much less gaudy. Sukenobu's faces, too, are always of a distinctive type – more rounded, 'sweeter' in expression, with a slightly upturned nose, tiny breaks in the outline next to the eyes and chin, producing a softening effect, and a blush to the cheeks.

32

32

33

NISHIKAWA SUKENOBU

33 Saigyō and Eguchi

Gembun–Enkyō eras
SIGNATURE: Nishikawa Ukyō Sukenobu kore [o]
    egaku ('This was painted by Nishikawa Ukyō
    Sukenobu')
SEALS: Bunkadō, Sukenobu
Hanging scroll; ink and colour on paper,
    116.0 × 51.0 cm
PROVENANCE: Arthur Morrison
LITERATURE: *UT*, vol. 1 (1987), no. 111
1913.5–1.0392 (Japanese Painting 1400). Given by
    Sir W. Gwynne-Evans, Bt

The famous exchange of poems between
the itinerant monk Saigyō (1118–90) and a
courtesan at Eguchi, on the mouth of the
Yodo River near Osaka, is first recorded in
the anthology *Senjūshō*, attributed to Saigyō
himself. He was caught in a storm and
chided the courtesan, who was also named
Eguchi, for refusing him temporary lodging
for the night. She replied that since he was
a holy man she had thought he would not
wish to enjoy such transient pleasures. In
the fifteenth century the episode became
the basis for the Nō play *Eguchi*, in which
Eguchi reveals herself to be a manifestation
of the Bodhisattva Fugen. In the Edo
period the story was further adapted in
popular drama and narration and as an
appropriate vehicle for *mitate* depictions of
courtesans by Ukiyo-e artists.

33

Saigyō, wearing a travelling hat and
monk's black robes and carrying a walking-
stick, is shown with his head raised in a
gesture of petition, while the courtesan
(dressed in contemporary eighteenth-
century style) turns away from the door, as
if she has already decided to refuse him
lodging. Doubtless Sukenobu's patron was
amused by the incongruity of seeing a
smartly dressed Kyoto courtesan in such a
humble thatched cottage and delighted by
the contrast between her girlish features
and the artist's sensitive portrait of the
aged monk.

A version of *Saigyō and Eguchi* by
Miyagawa Chōshun in the Powers
Collection (see John Rosenfield, *Traditions of
Japanese Art*, Fogg Art Museum, Harvard
University, 1970, no. 143) must be almost
contemporary with this Sukenobu work;
both are among the earliest depictions of
the theme in Ukiyo-e painting.

34

NISHIKAWA SUKENOBU

34 Lovers Hiding on Musashi Moor

Gembun–Enkyō eras
SIGNATURE: Nishikawa Sukenobu kore [o] egaku
  ('This was painted by Nishikawa Sukenobu')
SEALS: Nishikawa-uji, Sukenobu kore [o] zu [su]
  ('This was drawn by Sukenobu')
Hanging scroll; ink and colour and gold on silk,
  91.5 × 40.0 cm
PROVENANCE: Arthur Morrison
LITERATURE: Morrison 1911, vol. 2, pl. XII
1913.5–1.0393 (Japanese Painting 1401). Given by
  Sir W. Gwynne-Evans, Bt

Ise monogatari, the Heian period set of tales
with poems centring on the exploits of a
courtier lover thought to be Ariwara no
Narihira (825–80), includes a story
commonly known as 'Musashi Moor'
(chapter 12). 'A certain man' (as he is
invariably styled) abducts a young woman
and carries her off to lonely Musashi Moor.
The man is captured by the guards of the
Governor of the province but has managed
to hide the young woman in the dense
susuki grasses of the moor. Soldiers are just
about to set fire to the grass when they
hear the woman reciting a poem of love for
her 'husband' and take her back with them.

As in the painting of *Saigyō and Eguchi*
(no. 33), Sukenobu sometimes followed the
practice of *mitate* in reworking ancient tales
in modern costume, but here he has chosen
to clothe the lovers in Heian court dress,
she wearing the 'twelve-layered' long
brocade robes (*jūni hitoe*) and he hunting
costume (*kariginu*) and stiff, black *eboshi* hat.
Sukenobu adopts a similarly historical
approach in his illustrated book *Ise
monogatari* of 1747, an abridged version of
the Heian classic which contains
illustrations of twelve chapters (but not
'Musashi Moor').

Sukenobu has devised a touching
composition in which the lovers press close
together amid the desolation of the moor,
he kneeling and alert for any approaching
danger, and she standing leaning on his
shoulder, one hand raised to her face in
dejection. Such sentimental courtly themes
would certainly have found favour with a
Kyoto audience, nostalgic for the long-
vanished age of Imperial rule.

34

36 (left)

35

35

NISHIKAWA SUKETADA (d. 1758)

35 Genre Scene after Iwasa Katsushige

Mid-18th century
SIGNATURE: Iwasa Katsushige no zu/Bunkadō
  Sukenobu chakunan Nishikawa Shigetada hitsu
  ('A picture by Iwasa Katsushige/painted by
  Nishikawa Suketada, eldest son of Bunkadō
  Sukenobu')
SEAL: Suketada
Hanging scroll; ink and colour on silk,
  125.4 × 57.5 cm
PROVENANCE: Shōzō Katō
LITERATURE: *UT*, vol. 1 (1987), BW no. 9
1927.10–13.08 (Japanese Painting ADD 48)

The seated woman who is reading and the
girl kneeling next to her gesticulating both
derive ultimately from the famous genre
screen of the Kan'ei era (1624–44), the so-
called 'Hikone' screen – though the figure
of the kneeling girl has been reversed. The
three musicians behind, playing (left to
right) *kokyū* (Chinese fiddle), *shakuhachi*
(bamboo flute) and *shamisen* will probably
prove to have been taken from some quite
separate genre work. The girl carrying the
shamisen is close, though not identical, to a
figure in a triptych of genre paintings
which belonged to Shimazu Iehisa, Lord of
Satsuma (d. 1638) (*NU*, vol. 1 (1982),
no. 41). Suketada says that he copied the
composition from a picture by Iwasa
Katsushige, son of Iwasa Matabei
(1578–1650). Either the Hikone screen was
attributed to Katsushige at that time, or
else Katsushige made a (now lost) copy of
it. It is interesting to see an Ukiyo-e artist
of the middle of the eighteenth century
already taking an interest in studying the
genre tradition of the previous century.

Suketada was a prolific book illustrator in
the 1750s, after the manner of his father,
Sukenobu. Two other paintings by him are
known, in a style almost indistinguishable
from Sukenobu (Narazaki 1987, vol. 1, no.
55; New Ōtani 1991, no. 43).

(ght)

Miyagawa Chōshun ?1682–1752

Common name Chōzaemon; *gō* Shunkyokudō. Native of Miyagawa village in Owari Province. Lived in Edo first in Ryōgoku Hirokoji, later in Shiba Shimbori-chō. His date of birth is calculated based on his age as given in a self-portrait (now lost). Pre-eminent painter of the first half of the eighteenth century and progenitor of the Miyagawa–Katsumiyagawa–Katsukawa–Katsushika line that would form the mainstream of Ukiyo-e painting until the end of the Edo period. Chōshun did not design any woodblock prints or illustrated books which would provide helpful dates of publication, and at present his many paintings – generally hanging scrolls of single courtesans or handscrolls of seasonal genre scenes – have been only tentatively grouped into early, middle and late periods depending on such factors as the degree of stylistic influence of Hishikawa Moronobu (d. 1694; nos 6–9) and the form of his signature and seals.

Ōta Nampo (1749–1823) recorded the existence of a votive painting showing women at their leisure, presented to the Kannon Temple at Ichiba in Sagami Province in the fourth month of 1706, but this does not survive. Early extant works show the strong thematic and stylistic influence of Hishikawa Moronobu; sometimes whole groups of figures are borrowed with little or no modification. An early handscroll of erotic scenes bears the signature 'Hishikawa Chōshun hitsu' and seals 'Chōshun no in' and 'Hishikawa-uji in' (Lane 1979, scroll no. xxxv), which demonstrates that even if Chōshun were too young to have studied directly with Moronobu he nevertheless saw himself as a faithful disciple in the Hishikawa line.

In 1749 Chōshun was invited with pupils to participate in repair work at the Tokugawa Mausoleum at Nikkō, under the supervision of Kanō Shunga. A dispute over payment for this work led to a violent attack by Chōshun's son, Chōsuke, in which Shunga and several others were killed. It is thought that Chōshun died in the eleventh month of 1752, about the same time that his leading pupil, Isshō, was permanently banished to Niijima, a remote island off the Izu peninsula. Chōshun's other talented pupil, Miyagawa Chōki, seems to have died some time before the incident took place, and leadership of the Miyagawa school, renamed the Katsumiyagawa school, subsequently passed to Shunsui.

UNSIGNED (attributed to Miyagawa Chōshun)

36 Scenes of Pleasure in Spring and Summer

Hōei–Shōtoku eras
Two sections of a handscroll (mounted on a two-fold screen); ink and colour on silk, each section 31.6 × 76.7 cm (approx.)
PROVENANCE: Arthur Morrison
LITERATURE: Morrison 1911, vol. 2, pl. IX
1913.5–1.0369 (Japanese Painting 1368). Given by Sir W. Gwynne-Evans, Bt

These two sections from a handscroll, now mounted on a low two-fold screen, are unsigned but may be attributed to Miyagawa Chōshun. They would appear to date from a period early in his career, however, when his figure style and choice of subjects were still heavily influenced by Hishikawa Moronobu – so heavily influenced, indeed, that the one former owner, Arthur Morrison, attributed them to Moronobu (Morrison 1911, vol. 2, pl. IX). Certain small motifs, such as the manner of painting tufts of grass on the left section, can be linked to the early painting by Chōshun in the Toyama Kinenkan (NU, vol. 3 (1982), no. 14), though the present painting does not match the limpid brushwork of the Toyama work.

On the right young couples are shown relaxing in a room opening on to a verandah and river scene. A woman reclining on the corner of the verandah offers a pipe to two women standing admiring the flowering cherry. On the left eleven figures are engaged in a lively circle dance (compare with the Moronobu painting, no. 6) with musical accompaniment provided by a group of young men. Such scenes of carefree pleasures in spring and summer were the staple of screens and handscrolls by Moronobu.

An almost identical composition with the right-hand section is reproduced as part of a handscroll of *Amusements of the Seasons* by Chōshun ('Collection of the Mitsukoshi Dry Goods co.') in *Kokka*, 184 (1905), p. 90. In *Kokka* magazine this work is reproduced by techniques of colour woodblock printing, however, and until the original painting comes to light once more it would be unwise to comment on their relative merits.

37 (1390)

37 (1391)

37 (1390)   37 (1391)

MIYAGAWA CHŌSHUN

37 Popular Amusements in Edo

c. Kyōhō era
SIGNATURE: Nihon-e Miyagawa Chōshun zu
   ('Japanese picture drawn by Miyagawa
   Chōshun')
SEAL: Chōshun no in
Pair of handscrolls; ink, colour and gold on
paper, each 40.1 × 510.0 cm (approx.)
PROVENANCE: William Anderson
LITERATURE: Anderson 1886, nos 1707, 1708;
   UT, vol. 1 (1987), nos 98–100; Smith 1990, no.
   193; Tokyo 1990, no. 9
1881.12–10.01707/01708 (Japanese Paintings
   1390/1391)

One of the glories of the British Museum's
Ukiyo-e painting collection, this pair of
handscrolls show Chōshun's mature style
at its most accomplished in scenes of
pleasure in Edo, indoors and out, in spring
and early summer. The first scroll opens
with auspicious scenes of New Year games
of shuttlecock and battledore, proceeds
through indoor games of backgammon and

cards, a pair of mendicant musicians, and
concludes with a scene of a woman
painting a standing screen (*tsuitate*)
surrounded by an audience of indolent
courtesans. The second scroll consists
entirely of outdoor scenes: a woman of a
noble household arriving in a palanquin
with her retinue to view the cherry blossom
and boisterous partying and a circle dance
under the trees; followed by puppet shows,
peepshows, a dressed monkey and magic
tricks for the benefit of groups of women
and children. The scene ends with the young
master of one household hoisted up on the
shoulders of a retainer hurrying in to join the
fun – hinting that these scrolls were
painted for some samurai household.

Particularly apparent is Chōshun's skill at
combining his figures into relaxed and
natural groupings which interact with
intelligence and grace in an entirely
convincing manner, setting up wonderful
flowing rhythms along the scrolls. Many of
these groupings, such as the three cherry-
viewing women who open the second
scroll, derive from the repertoire
established by Moronobu (compare no. 6).
Each ample figure is outlined with the
minimum number of fluid strokes, the
brilliant patterning of the robes used to
suggest the pose of the body underneath,
and these brilliant figures are set off against
a light and airy background of misty gold
washes and a succession of deftly drawn-in
trees which enter alternately from the top
and the bottom of the scroll. Every tiny
detail – be it picnic box or children's toy –
is a marvel of execution.

For other handscrolls by Chōshun on
similar themes see Kikuchi Sadao,
Kobijutsu, 36 (1971), pp. 94–8, and *UT*, vol.
10 (1987), no. 3.

37 detail (opposite)

38

MIYAGAWA CHŌSHUN

38 Parody of Fujiwara Teika's Cottage
at Mt Ogura

c. Kyōhō era
SIGNATURE: Nihon-e Miyagawa Chōshun zu
('Japanese picture drawn by Miyagawa
Chōshun')
SEAL: (?)Miyagawa
Hanging scroll; ink and colour on silk,
34.5 × 53.0 cm
PROVENANCE: Arthur Morrison
1913.5–1.0286 (Japanese Painting 1388). Given by
Sir W. Gwynne-Evans, Bt

Though in poor condition and bearing an
otherwise unrecorded seal (?Miyagawa in
white letters inside a gourd shape), this
small scroll certainly merits consideration
within the *oeuvre* of Chōshun or his
immediate atelier.

Legends concerning the love affair
between the poet Fujiwara no Teika
(1162–1241) and Princess Shokushi at
Teika's cottage Shigure no Chin ('Arbour of
the Autumn Showers') at Mt Ogura in
Kyoto had already formed the basis for the
Nō play *Teika*. In the seventeenth and early

eighteenth centuries these were adapted for
performance in more popular narrative
forms – in particular, Tosa *jōruri* versions in
which Princess Shokushi visits Teika's
cottage disguised as a young dandy.

The present painting is, as it were, a
'domestic' version of this colourful legend,
in which the events of history are merely
hinted at in an otherwise fashionable
modern scene (the device known as *mitate*,
see no. 29). A courtesan, accompanied by a
kamuro who shields her with an umbrella
from the autumn shower, approaches up a
maple-lined path towards a thatched retreat
where a party of men are making music.
Teika is supposed to have played the
shakuhachi, but one imagines that in the
case of Chōshun's painting it is the
handsome man of fashion playing the
shamisen and not the blind flute player who
is the courtesan's intended companion – an
added twist to the fun.

Chōshun painted similar horizontal
hanging scrolls of the *Akutagawa Scene from
Ise monogatari* (Kuwabara 1911, no. 25) and
Lady Murasaki at Ishiyama Temple (*Tanaka
1911–13*, vol. 2, no. 14).

38

39

MIYAGAWA CHŌSHUN

39 Courtesan Walking

Kyōhō–Kampō eras
SIGNATURE: Nihon-e Miyagawa Chōshun zu
  ('Japanese picture drawn by Miyagawa
  Chōshun')
SEAL: Chōshun no in
Hanging scroll; ink, colour and gold on paper,
  74.0 × 32.9 cm
PROVENANCE: Ernest Hart
LITERATURE: George Audsley, *The Ornamental Arts of
  Japan*, London, Sampson Low, 1882, pl. II;
  Morrison 1911, vol. 2, pl. XIII; UT, vol. 1 (1987),
  BW no. 8
1901.5–16.026 (Japanese Painting 1389)

Paintings of single figures of grand
courtesans set against a plain background
form a sizeable proportion of Chōshun's
oeuvre, sometimes with the woman
standing looking back over one shoulder,
sometimes, as here, hitching up her skirts
slightly at the front and walking forward.
The courtesan's under-kimono is of yellow
and black stripes, while the decoration of
the over-kimono is divided diagonally into
two separate designs – fishnets and reeds
against a black background and
chrysanthemums against white.

The present work does not match the
level of skill of Chōshun's best paintings in
terms of the line quality and details of the
patterning. The impression of the 'Chōshun
no in' seal is very ragged around the edges
(indeed, totally worn away in the corners),
suggesting a later period in Chōshun's
career when one can imagine him enlisting
the aid of pupils to meet the burgeoning
demand for works of this 'standard' type.

39

Miyagawa Isshō 1689–1779

Common name Kiheiji; alternative name
Fujiwara Andō (Yasumichi); *gō* Kohensai,
Sogan. Lived at Shiba, Tamachi nichōme. A
principal pupil of Miyagawa Chōshun,
together with Miyagawa Chōki, known for
his paintings of *bijin* and genre scenes in a
distinctive style, the figures having sloping
eyes and generally 'pinched' features. Isshō
often reused successful compositions: a
screen of *Pleasure-boats on the Sumida River*
exists in two versions, and there are at least
three versions of the hanging scroll *Street
Scene in Yoshiwara at the New Year*. In 1752,
after the dispute between Chōshun and
Kanō Shunga over payment for repair work
to the Nikkō Mausoleum and the
subsequent murder of Shunga, Isshō was
banished to Niijima, an island off the Izu
peninsula where he continued to paint for
local people and finally died in 1779.

MIYAGAWA ISSHŌ

40 Parody of Akutagawa

Before 1752
SIGNATURE: Kohensai Isshō
SEAL: Andō (Yasumichi)
Hanging scroll; ink and colour on paper,
    84.8 × 38.6 cm
PROVENANCE: Arthur Morrison
LITERATURE: *UT*, vol. 1 (1987), no. 105
1913.5–1.0346 (Japanese Painting 1406). Given by
    Sir W. Gwynne-Evans, Bt

In this unusual composition two samurai
carrying women piggy back are shown
running in opposite directions across a
landscape dotted with maples, while in the
distance servants search with lanterns in
front of a long curtain bearing the crest of a
noble family, hung between the trees. The
women have pulled over their heads a
special outer robe (*kinukazuki*) worn by
noblewomen to disguise their identity on
outings.

When the composition of an Ukiyo-e
painting or print seems unusual or odd, it
is often the signal that this is a *mitate*
rendition, alluding to some famous episode
in history or classical literature. Seeing a
woman carried on a man's back
immediately brings to mind the
'Akutagawa' (Akuta River) episode, chapter
6 of *Ise monogatari*, in which a man abducts
a young woman and carries her off to the
Akuta River, where as they shelter for the
night in a deserted house she is eaten by a
monster. Seeing men searching in the
distance for fleeing lovers also recalls the
'Musashi Moor' episode of the same novel
(no. 34). Perhaps Isshō intended the
painting simply to show games at some

40

40

40

autumn maple-viewing expedition of a
noble household, with simultaneous
references to *Ise monogatari*; or else it
illustrates the plot of some yet-to-be-
discovered contemporary drama.

The running figures have a spiky energy
never found in the work of Isshō's teacher,
Miyagawa Chōshun (?1682–1752; see p. 87),
and their distinctive 'pinched' features are
quite his own.

41

ANON. (Miyagawa school)

41 Courtesan and Kamuro

c. Kyōhō era
Hanging scroll (mounted on a panel); ink, colour
  and gold on paper, 98.5 × 42.0 cm
PROVENANCE: Yamanaka & Co.
1931.4–27.02 (Japanese Painting ADD 80)

The courtesan walks in a stately fashion, wearing a surcoat (*uchikake*) divided into irregular pale blue and white panels which are decorated with seasonal flowers – cherry and pine needles, (?)maple leaves and chrysanthemums – over a scarlet kimono. Her *kamuro*, dressed in a kimono with bold vertical stripes and a checked *obi*, follows in close attendance, turning to look behind her.

A restorer has skilfully cut around the outlines of the figures and glued them to a completely new background paper which has been toned to disguise the incongruity: a small piece of the original background left under the extending hairdo at the back of

the neck gives an idea of its former damaged state. In the case of paintings on paper the thick paint layer often serves to protect the background paper if this deteriorates as a result of poor storage conditions; and the restorer obviously sought to rehabilitate a scroll in generally poor condition but with the figures still relatively intact. Unfortunately, in the process he has also removed the signature from either the bottom right-hand or bottom left-hand corner.

Stylistically, however, the figures are firmly attributable to the school of Miyagawa Chōshun – probably to Chōki, his primary pupil, who seems to have worked from about the Kyōhō (1716–36) to Kampō (1741–4) eras, though the faces do not yet have the characteristic 'swollen' cheek beside the mouth seen in this artist's mature works. The present painting should be compared with a scroll by Chōki of similar configuration, but with the figures facing the other way, in the Freer Gallery of Art (Stern 1973, no. 36) and also one by Chōshun in the same collection (ibid., no. 35).

ANON. (Torii school)

42 The Actor Ichikawa Ebizō II in Four Roles

Mid-18th century, possibly 11th month, 1742
Hanging scroll; ink, colour and gold on silk,
  55.4 × 34.2 cm
PROVENANCE: Arthur Morrison
1946.2–9.035 (Japanese Painting ADD 185).
  Bequeathed by Arthur Morrison

The name Ichikawa Danjūrō was (and is) the most prestigious in the Kabuki world, the bombastic *aragoto* ('rough stuff') style of acting having been established by Danjūrō I (1660–1704) during the formative years of Edo Kabuki in the late seventeenth century. This painting shows the second incumbent, Ichikawa Danjūrō II (1688–1758) – who used the name Ebizō II after 1735 – in four roles: clockwise, from the top, dressed in the voluminous dark red costume, huge sword and white paper 'strength' wings in his hair of the *Shibaraku!* ('Stop one moment!') role; wearing a foot-soldier's hat as (?)Watari Shinzaemon, a role suggested by the character 'Watari' on his costume; Soga no Gorō, muscular hero of the plays on the theme of the revenge of the Soga brothers; and Hata Rokurōzaemon, a warrior role in plays of the *Taiheiki* cycle. It was Ebizō II who had established *Shibaraku* and Soga plays as annual festivities at the opening-of-the-season (*kaomise*) performances in the eleventh month and at

the New Year performances, respectively – a custom maintained to this day. Ebizō II acted the role of Hata Rokurōzaemon to great acclaim in Osaka in 1741, repeating it on his return to Edo in the play *Gaijin taiheiki* at the Kawarazaki theatre in the eleventh month, 1742. *Kabuki nendaiki* mentions that he also took the role of Watari Shinzaemon mentioned above, so it is possible the painting was done to

42

commemorate this occasion. On the other hand, it is very similar in style to a painting of Ebizō II in four roles by Torii Kiyomitsu (1735–85), formerly in the Takeoka Toyota collection (Kyoto 1923, pls not numbered), which would suggest a date late in Ebizō II's career, that is, in the 1750s.

The Torii school of artists founded by Kiyonobu I (1664–1729) and Kiyomasu I (dates unknown) at the end of the seventeenth century monopolised the production of images of Kabuki actors for theatre signboards, illustrated programmes and souvenir prints in a bold style described as 'gourd-shaped legs and wriggling worm line'. The vestiges of that grand style are visible in this painting.

43

Torii Kiyoshige

worked late Kyōhō (1716–36)–
Hōreki (1751–64) eras

Gō Seichōken (according to Yoshida Teruji). Lived in Koami-chō. Thought to be a late pupil of Torii Kiyonobu I (1664–1729). Known for hand-coloured actor prints in the Torii style and a small number of paintings of actors and beauties. A votive plaque by Kiyoshige of the *Kusazuri-biki* ('armour-pulling') scene in Kabuki, painted in 1730, is analysed in detail in two articles in the *Bulletin of the Azabu Museum of Art*, no. 2 (autumn 1986).

TORII KIYOSHIGE

43 The Actors Nakamura Tomijūrō I *(right)* and (?) Ichikawa Ebizō II *(left)* in 'Momiji-gari'

c. Hōreki era (before 1758)
SIGNATURE: Torii Kiyoshige ga
SEAL: Kiyoshige
Hanging scroll; ink, colour and gold on paper,
   87.0 × 27.5 cm
PROVENANCE: K. Murakami
1939.6–10.03 (Japanese Painting ADD 141)

The Nō play *Momiji-gari* (based in turn on a tale from the collection *Konjaku monogatari*) tells how Taira no Koremochi, at the Emperor's orders, subdued a demon that was haunting Mt Togakushi. In Kabuki versions of the story Koremochi goes to view the autumn maples deep in Mt Togakushi and encounters a beautiful woman, who offers him sake. Drifting into a pleasant stupour, he is brought to his senses by a warning from the mountain god just in time to see the woman taking on her real form as a she-devil. He manages to subdue her with his sword.

In this painting the great female impersonator Nakamura Tomijūrō I (1719–86), identified by his crest of a wheel of arrow flights, kneels holding up a demon mask amid falling scarlet maple leaves, while an Ichikawa actor, probably Danjūrō II (1688–1758) during the period he used the name Ebizō II (identified by the 'triple rice measure', *mimasu*, and lobster emblems on his costume), towers over her brandishing a signboard that reads 'Mt Togakushi'. His red face- and body-makeup, wide-legged stance and glaring expression indicate that this was an *aragoto* ('rough stuff') role, of which the Danjūrō line of actors were the chief exponents. Tomijūrō I was an actor of the Kyoto–

Osaka region who nevertheless visited Edo several times in his career for periods of several years at a time. The most likely time for this painting to have been done is during Tomijūrō I's extended stay between 1752 and 1759. In the play *Arigatashi yunzei Genji*, performed at the Nakamura theatre in the eleventh month, 1755, Tomijūrō I played the role of a mountain monster disguised as the courtesan Hatsuhana. Though Ebizō II was in the cast on this occasion, however, the role of Taira no Koremochi was played by Tomizawa Tatsujūrō. Present Kabuki records do not, therefore, permit a definite identification.

Torii Kiyomine (Kiyomitsu II)
1787–1868

Na Shōnosuke, later Kameji; *gō* Seiryūken, Genshinka. Grandson of Torii Kiyomitsu I, the third generation head of the Torii school; in 1795 became a pupil of Torii Kiyonaga, fourth-generation head of the school, using the name Kiyomine. Designed prints of beauties using this name. In 1815, upon the death of Kiyonaga, assumed fifth-generation leadership of the Torii school as Kiyomitsu II and ceased to design single-sheet prints.

TORII KIYOMINE (KIYOMITSU II)

44   The actor Ichikawa Danjūrō ?VII in the Shibaraku role

c. 1815–59
SIGNATURE: Seiryūken Kiyomitsu ga
SEAL: Kiyomitsu
Mirror pad; ink, colour and gold on paper,
    37.0 cm circumference (approx.)
PROVENANCE: Arthur Morrison
LITERATURE: *UT*, vol. 1 (1987), no. 152
1923.5–31.01 (Japanese Painting ADD 21).
    Presented by Arthur Morrison

Shibaraku is the famous set-piece scene, inserted into opening-of-the-season Kabuki performances in the eleventh month of each year, in which the hero comes on to the *hanamichi* (raised walkway through the audience) in voluminous persimmon-coloured robes, with white 'strength' paper decorations in his hair and wielding a massive sword. With a great cry of *Shibaraku!* ('Stop one moment!') he hurries on stage to rescue some hapless victim about to be done to death and cuts off the heads of a host of the foe with one sweep

44

44

of his weapon. This role was habitually performed by successive generations of the Ichikawa Danjūrō lineage, and on the basis of the artist Kiyomitsu II's period of activity it is probably Danjūrō VII (1791–1859) who is portrayed. The archaic style employed, imitating the Torii manner of the early eighteenth century which put little store in creating an actual likeness, makes it impossible to judge if this is Danjūrō VII on the strength of the features alone.

A decorated mirror pad would be used to protect a round mirror inside a case, and it is unusual for so ephemeral an object to have survived. It is tempting to imagine that this one may have been used by Danjūrō VII himself, but it was much more likely a gift to one of his many patrons.

Kawamata Tsuneyuki
worked *c.* Kyōhō (1716–36)–
Kampō (1741–4) eras

Kawamata Tsunemasa
worked *c.* Kyōhō (1716–36)–
Kan'en (1748–51) eras

Ukiyo-eshi den records a painting by
Tsuneyuki with a signature 'Tsuneyuki
aged sixty-five years' which had a box
inscription by the artist dating the work to
Kampō 1 (1741), suggesting that Tsuneyuki
was born *c.* 1677. *Gajō yōryaku* (1832)
includes the information that he was a
native of Niigata and studied under Kanō
Tsunenobu (1636–1713). A pair of six-fold
screens showing *Scenes of Pleasure* includes
a view of the Nakamura theatre with the
play *Iribune Hiru-ga-kojima* in progress,
which was performed in the eleventh
month, Kyōhō 15 (1730).

It was Fujikake Shizuya in his *Ukiyo-e no
kenkyū*, 1943, vol. II, p. 84, who first
suggested a tentative lineage for the
Kawamata artists of Tsuneyuki–
Tsunemasa–Tsunetatsu (very few works
known), and in terms of the fashions
portrayed in their respective paintings this
would seem to be borne out; most of the
several dozen works by Tsunemasa so far
recorded would appear to date from the
Kampō (1741–4) to the Kan'en (1748–51)
eras. One Tsunemasa painting is signed
with the *gō* 'Chōsetsusai'.

Stylistically, Tsuneyuki's figures are
generally larger and show the influence of
artists such as Okumura Masanobu.
Tsunemasa's paintings with their delicate
figures with small rounded faces and his
frequent choice of *mitate* themes must have
provided an important stylistic and
thematic precedent for the colour prints of
Suzuki Harunobu.

KAWAMATA TSUNEYUKI

45 Courtesan and Attendant

c. Kyōhō era
SIGNATURE: Tsuneyuki hitsu
SEAL: (?)Tsuneyuki
Hanging scroll; ink, colour and gold on silk,
  93.5 × 40.4 cm
PROVENANCE: K. Murakami
LITERATURE: *UT*, vol. 1 (1987), no. 113
1931.11–16.02 (Japanese Painting ADD 86)

A courtesan turns to face the *kamuro*
following her, her body arched to form a
perfect curve. Her hair is combed out and
hangs loosely down her back, tied together
at the ends with a red ribbon, and she
wears a purple *uchikake* over a kimono
decorated with maple leaves and (?)clematis
scattered over a winding river. The *kamuro*

45

45

carries a long stem of peach blossom,
perhaps intended to adorn a display in the
Yoshiwara quarter for the Dolls' Festival on
the third day of the third month.

Within Tsuneyuki's *oeuvre* this is thought
to be an earlier rather than later work,
dating from perhaps the middle of the
Kyōhō era (1716–36) (see Asano Shūgō's

comments in *UT*, vol. 1 (1987), no. 113), but
the face already has the oval shape, long
nose and rosebud mouth that are the
hallmarks of Tsuneyuki's style. The highly
modulated and flowing calligraphic outlines
to the drapery lend support to the
contention that Tsuneyuki may have
studied with the Kanō master Tsunenobu.

46

KAWAMATA TSUNEMASA

46 Courtesan and Attendant Sampling
Incense on a Verandah

Kampō–Kan'en eras
SIGNATURE: Tsunemasa ga
SEAL: Tsunemasa
Hanging scroll; ink, colour and gold on silk,
 88.9 × 33.0 cm
PROVENANCE: Arthur Morrison
LITERATURE: *UT*, vol. 1 (1987), no. 112
1913.5–1.0401 (Japanese Painting 1447). Given by
 Sir W. Gwynne-Evans, Bt

A courtesan stands at the corner of a
verandah, leaning against a pillar and
toying with her hairpin, while a young
shinzō kneeling beside her offers up an
incense burner for her mistress to sample
the fragrance. In the garden behind a
cherry tree is in full bloom. The accessories
for preparing the incense – a lacquer box
and tray and a folded paper packet – are
arranged on the tatami of the open room.

The 'incense guessing game' (*kō-awase*) in
which different aromatic woods were burnt
and teams competed to identify the
fragrance was a pastime dating back to the
courtly Heian period (794–1185). Even
though it does not appear to be a specific
mitate reworking of an historical theme,
Tsunemasa's painting certainly plays on
such courtly associations in what was to
become an increasingly important trend in
late eighteenth-century Ukiyo-e – the
identification of Yoshiwara courtesans with
the court women of Japan's classical past.
Sampling incense was a favourite theme of
Tsunemasa's paintings (compare, for
instance, Sendai 1988, no. 34), and a
woman standing on the corner of a
verandah a favourite compositional device.
The delicate figures, with their small,
round faces and slender wrists, must have
been an important stylistic precursor for the
colour woodblock prints designed by
Harunobu from 1765 to 1770.

46

ANON.

47 Parody of Chō Ryō and Kōseki Kō

Late Meiwa–early An'ei eras
Hanging scroll; ink and colour on paper,
    98.0 × 27.0 cm
PROVENANCE: Arthur Morrison
LITERATURE: Morrison 1911, vol. 2, pl. XIV;
    UT, vol. 1 (1987), no. 118
1913.5–1.0289 (Japanese Painting 1404). Given by
    Sir W. Gwynne-Evans, Bt

After his failed attempt to assassinate the
Qin dynasty emperor Shi Huangdi in 218
BC, the warrior Zhang Liang (Japanese: Chō
Ryō) went into hiding in Xiapei in Jiangsu
Province. There he was sought out by the
sage Huangshi Gong (Japanese: Kōseki Kō)
to lead a further campaign against the Qin
tyrant. The meeting of the two became
immortalised in legend. Huangshi Gong,
travelling incognito as an old man on
horseback, contrived to test Zhang Liang's
character by dropping his shoe into the
water as he crossed a small bridge. Zhang
returned the shoe with such perfect
courtesy that Huangshi Gong presented

him with a precious handscroll of secret
military strategies. In Japan the story of
Chō Ryō and Kōseki Kō became widely
known on all cultural levels, forming the
basis of the Nō play *Chō Ryō*, as well as
later, more popular theatrical versions in
which Chō Ryō has first to subdue a
dragon living in the river.

In this humorous *mitate* version a youth
crossing the bridge carrying an umbrella
has dropped a black lacquer clog, which
the young woman kneeling on the back of
the river dragon returns to him with an
amorous gaze. Behind the pair blossoms a
branch of auspicious red plum. The
dragon, drawn in Kanō style, lurks amid
broiling waves topped with spattered black
and white pigment, while the figures, in
contrast, are elegantly demure. Though
unsigned, the figure style is highly
reminiscent of Harunobu's latest works,
and the painting may be attributed to a
pupil such as Tanaka Masunobu, working
shortly after Harunobu's death.

47

48

ANON.

48 Women and Children in a Bamboo
Grove (Parody of the Seven Sages)

Meiwa–early An'ei eras
SEAL: (unread)
Hanging scroll; ink, colour and gold on silk,
  53.5 × 70.9 cm
PROVENANCE: Mrs Julino Spier
LITERATURE: *UT*, vol. 1 (1987), no. 115
1941.7–12.01 (Japanese Painting ADD 145). Given
  by Mrs Julino Spier

The scene is a bamboo grove beside a
winding stream. As a young man kneels to
dig up a bamboo shoot, a boy runs off to
the left brandishing one of the shoots, and
his younger brother is held back from
scampering after him by one of the women.
At the rear two women discuss the
contents of a letter. The odd setting signals
that this is parody (*mitate*) treatment.

'The Seven Sages of the Bamboo Grove'
(*Chikurin no shichi ken*) was a popular
subject for Kanō school and *bunjin* (scholar)
ink painters. It relates to the legend that in
the Jin dynasty (AD 265–419) in China seven
wise men would meet regularly in a
bamboo forest to drink wine, play musical
instruments and engage in conversation, as
a protest against the corruption of society.
Ukiyo-e reworkings of this subject generally
show a group of courtesans in place of the
seven wise men, and there are colour
prints by Toyonobu and Harunobu, among
others, showing the women grouped
around a long scroll they are studying.

Judging by the hairstyles, the present
painting follows shortly after the printed
versions by Toyonobu and Harunobu, at
the end of the Meiwa (1764–72) or
beginning of the An'ei (1772–81) eras. A
seal, which may be that of the artist, is just
visible in the bottom left corner of the
painting but is too faint to decipher. The

48

artist displays considerable skill in
suggesting the way the misty landscape
recedes into space and depicting the lively
actions of the children, and he should be
considered an important minor artist of the
generation immediately following the death
of Harunobu in 1770. Another anonymous
painting of a similar subject, though in a
somewhat different style, is in the
collection of the Azabu Museum of Arts
and Crafts, Tokyo (*Azabu Bijutsukan dayori*,
12 (May 1985), cover illustration).

Tōensai Kanshi

worked *c*. Hōreki (1751–64)–
Meiwa (1764–72) eras

Narazaki Muneshige discovered a *haiku*
poem signed Echigo Kanshi ('Kanshi of
Echigo Province') in an untitled anthology
compiled by Tōryūsō Enshi, published in
Meiwa 2 (1765), with illustrations and
poems by Toriyama Sekien and his pupils;
otherwise his biography is unknown. At
least a dozen or so paintings of beauties by
Enshi are known, all exhibiting the same
eccentric style – facial expressions of wide
eyes and raised eyebrows and billowing
lines to the drapery.

TŌENSAI KANSHI

49 Courtesan Reading a Letter

c. Meiwa era
SEAL: Kanshi (inside a long-eared rabbit)
Hanging scroll (mounted in board); ink and
  colour on paper, 73.3 × 15.7 cm
1989.4–20.01 (Japanese Painting ADD 891)

A woman wearing a slate-grey kimono with
a design of yellow plum blossom on the
sleeves and skirts sits on the edge of a
verandah reading a letter – a love-letter to
judge from the manner in which she bites
her collar with scarcely restrained passion.
On the *shōji* (sliding panel) behind is the
shadow of a figure spying through a hole
made in the paper screen. From the long
shadow cast by the sleeve it would appear
to be a young woman wearing a *furisode* (a
kimono with long, hanging sleeves), with
some kind of headscarf to disguise her. The
jagged plum-blossom pattern is one used
elsewhere by Kanshi on women's robes,
and the energetic white dotting just visible
on the skirting paper is typical of the
excitable, slightly bizarre character of his
work. The tall, narrow 'pillar-hider'
(*hashira-gakushi*) format is common in prints
of the period but rare in paintings.

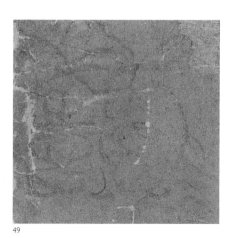

49

49

99

Tsukioka Settei 1710–86
and Tsukioka Sessai d. 1839

Settei used many different names: clan name Minamoto; family name Kida, *na* Masanobu; *azana* Daikei; common names Tange, Shinten'ō; *gō* Tsukioka, Settei, Rojinsai, Tōi, Kindō. Native of Ōtani, Hino, Ōmi Province, later lived and worked in Osaka. Studied with Takada Keiho (1674–1755), a painter of the Kyoto Kanō school.

Settei's earliest dated work is the printed book *Ehon Tatsutayama* of 1753, in which the figure style shows the strong influence of Nishikawa Sukenobu. Up to the end of the Meiwa (1764–72) era he designed over fifty illustrated books, many showing the manners and customs of women of the historical past, gradually developing his own style. From the early Meiwa era onwards he began to paint the hanging scrolls of beauties in contemporary fashions by which he is best known. A painting dated Meiwa 2 (1765) already bears the signature 'Shinten'ō Hokkyō Tsukioka Settei' ('Shinten'ō Tsukioka Settei of Hokkyō (Bridge of the Law) rank').

The classic painting by Settei shows a single figure or group of grand, tall courtesans and geishas, with particular attention paid to the gorgeousness of the bold patterning on their robes, invariably in high-quality pigments. Outlines of faces and limbs are always picked out in red, and the women sport the wide 'lantern-locks' (*tōrō-bin*) hairstyle that was fashionable in Osaka after *c.* 1769. Settei was also a master of painted and printed erotica of the utmost technical refinement: there was a superstition in the Edo period that they were an effective talisman against a house catching fire!

In about An'ei 1 (1772) Settei was elevated to the rank of Hōgen ('Eye of the Law'), which he generally used in his signature after this date, often in combination with his age. Paintings of the later period are numerous and, as Tanaka Tatsuya has pointed out (*NU*, vol. 9 (1982), p. 139), consequently somewhat lacking in invention. The figures become shorter and the patterning less bold – doubtless reflecting contemporary fashion. Courtly subjects come to form a significant proportion of the *oeuvre*.

Settei was succeeded by a number of pupils who faithfully replicated his style of painting beauties, notably his son Sessai (d. 1839), who was also elevated to both Hokkyō and Hōgen ranks and worked in Osaka and then Edo. Sessai used the following names: *na* Shūei; *azana* Taiso; *gō* Gikōsai. Other pupils include Katsura Munenobu, Sumie Buzen, Shitomi Kangetsu, Okada Gyokuzan and Inagaki Tsurujo.

TSUKIOKA SETTEI

50 Woman Collecting Mushrooms

c. late Meiwa era
SIGNATURE: Shinten'ō gihitsu ('Painted for amusement by Shinten'ō')
SEAL: Masanobu no in
Hanging scroll; ink, colour and gold on paper, 111.0 × 37.2 cm
PROVENANCE: Arthur Morrison
LITERATURE: Morrison 1911, vol. 2, pl. XVII
1913.5–1.0380 (Japanese Painting 1414). Given by Sir W. Gwynne-Evans, Bt

One of the great culinary delicacies of autumn in Japan is the fragrant and delicious *matsutake* mushroom. Here a woman has strung the mushrooms she has collected on to a stalk of *susuki* grass and turns on her walk home to gaze up at the bright orange foliage of a maple tree. Her black kimono is decorated with a discreet band of seasonal bushclover pattern around the hem, but she has shrugged off one sleeve, which hangs down at the back, to cool herself from her exertions and also, of course, to display a scarlet under-kimono that vies with the autumn leaves in brilliance. The carefree way in which she has draped a scarf around her head and shoulders, too, suggests her feelings of freedom on this country jaunt; Settei's women are otherwise immaculately (and constrictingly) attired.

Undoubtedly this large, confident painting dates from the late Meiwa (1764–72) era, after the introduction in the Kansai region of the wide 'lantern-locks' (*tōrō-bin*) hairstyle in 1769 – a period in Settei's career when the figures and costumes are at their grandest and he is most inventive in terms of unusual poses and compositions. The deft landscape setting in pale washes with accented ink outlines gives evidence of his Kanō training under Takada Keiho.

50

50

50 detail (*opposite*)

51

51

52

52

TSUKIOKA SETTEI

51 Geisha with a Shamisen

c. 1777

SIGNATURE: Shinten'ō ōju giga/jinen rokujū-nana
('Painted for fun at special request by
Shinten'ō, aged sixty-seven')
SEAL: (unread, in Chinese-style bronze tripod
vessel)
Hanging scroll; ink, colour and gold on silk,
71.5 × 33.4 cm
PROVENANCE: Arthur Morrison
LITERATURE: *UT*, vol. 1 (1987), no. 129
1913.5–1.0382 (Japanese Painting 1416). Given by
Sir W. Gwynne-Evans, Bt

A geisha engaged to entertain at a flower-
viewing party stands in front of a banded
curtain strung from a cherry tree, reading
from a small book open in one hand while
resting the other hand on her *shamisen*.
Perhaps she is memorising the words of a
new song one last time before entering the
flower-viewing enclosure to perform. Her
pale purple kimono is decorated with
motifs relating to the sea – plovers above
stylised waves on the top half and reeds
against drying fishnets picked out in gold
around the hem. The plump face and
hands have the characteristic red outlines
shared by all Settei's figures.

In comparison with no. 50 the figure has
become shorter and the execution of the
setting more cursory: this is a modest work
from *c.* 1777, a period when Settei's
paintings were increasingly in demand.

TSUKIOKA SESSAI (d. 1839)

52 Dancing Girl Holding a Drum

Bunka era (or earlier?)
SIGNATURE: Hōgen Tsukioka Sessai
SEALS: Taiso, Shūei no in (partly obscured by
worm-hole)
Hanging scroll; ink, colour and gold on paper,
76.7 × 24.9 cm
PROVENANCE: Arthur Morrison
1913.5–1.0377 (Japanese Painting 1411). Given by
Sir W. Gwynne-Evans, Bt

A young woman is caught in mid-
movement in a lively dance, her body
posed in a curve and right hand poised in a
delicate gesture, about to tap the hand-
drum (*tsutsumi*) she holds up to her
shoulder. The toes of one foot are raised as
if following the rhythm, and the ends of
her *obi* and sleeves – painted with rapid,
dry strokes – fly off to one side with the
momentum. The black over-kimono is
decorated with pine fronds in gold and
cherry-flower-shaped roundels in various

53

53

tie-dyed techniques, and both sleeves have
been pulled off to allow her more freedom
of movement, revealing a pink under-
kimono with a design of butterflies over
waving grasses. Her hair is twisted up into
a variant of the archaic *hyōgo-mage* style,
with a few stray locks allowed to dangle
down.

Women performers – dancers and
puppeteers – were a regular subject for
artists of the Tsukioka school, and it is
likely this painting is based on an older
composition by Settei, Sessai's father and
teacher. This scroll may be dated
tentatively to the Bunka era (1804–18) based
on similarities with the signature on a
Sessai painting, *Female Puppeteer*, inscribed
by Takizawa Bakin in 1812 (*NU*, vol. 9
(1982), no. 38), though, of course, Bakin
may have added the inscription some years
after that work was painted.

The bottom left-hand corner of the
painting has been patched and a small part
of the edge of the skirts repainted.

TANAKA KYŌSENSAI (dates unknown)

53 Woman Out Walking

Late 18th century
SIGNATURE: Kyōsensai giga ('Painted for
amusement by Kyōsensai')
SEAL: Tanaka-uji in
Hanging scroll; ink, colour and gold on silk,
66.0 × 33.1 cm
PROVENANCE: Arthur Morrison
LITERATURE: *UT*, vol. 1 (1987), no. 130
1913.5–1.0349 (Japanese Painting 1407). Given by
Sir W. Gwynne-Evans, Bt

A woman, dressed in a black kimono with
patterns of cherry blossom on the shoulder
and 'lucky treasures' around the hem,
pauses on a country walk and turns to
watch butterflies dancing around the
flowers of a blossoming mustard plant (*na
no hana*). The elegant curve of her leaning
pose is balanced in the composition by the
gesture of her raised left arm, the hand
pulled back into the sleeve.

Nothing is presently known of the artist,
Tanaka Kyōsensai, but the style of the face
with its full cheeks and red outlines shows
the strong influence of the Osaka painter
Tsukioka Settei (nos 50, 51), and it is likely
that he was a presently unrecorded pupil.
The wide 'lantern-locks' (*tōrō-bin*) hairstyle
became fashionable in the Osaka-Kyoto
area *c.* 1769, so the painting may be placed
in the last quarter of the eighteenth
century.

Isoda Koryūsai
worked *c*. 1766–88

Clan name Fujiwara; *na* Masakatsu; common name Shōbei. Probably a retainer (or *rōnin*) of the Tsuchiya family of Ogawa-chō, Edo. Later lived in Ryōgoku Yagenbori and appended the signature on his prints *Bukō Yagenbori inshi* ('Samurai recluse of Yagenbori in Edo, Musashi Province'). Earliest prints in the style of Harunobu, of whom he seems to have been a pupil, using the name Haruhiro. Beginning *c*. 1777, he designed the extended series of *ōban* prints of courtesans *Hinagata wakana no hatsu moyō* ('New [Kimono] Patterns for Young Leaves') for the publisher Nishimuraya Eijudō. He was also a prolific designer of pillar prints, an illustrator of books and erotic series.

Koryūsai's first paintings date from the early An'ei era (1772–81), before the fashion for wide 'lantern-locks' (*tōrō-bin*) arrived in Edo from the Kansai region *c*. 1774, and together with Utagawa Toyoharu he is the grandest and most prolific artist of *bijin* paintings of the 1770s. Around 1781 he was awarded the rank of Hokkyō, which invariably appears in his signature after this date, and in the following year contributed illustrations, together with Toyoharu, for a *waka* (classical poetry) anthology, *Shōyū gaei* ('Elegant Recitations by Friends of the Pine'), privately published by the Tsuchiya family. During the 1780s Koryūsai seems to have given up designing prints to concentrate on paintings, though his last datable work is a calendar print for the New Year, 1788.

The landscape elements that appear in the background to his scrolls give strong evidence of training in the Edo Kanō style, and he may have been the first Ukiyo-e artist to employ the 'red avoiding' (*benigirai*) technique of painting in monochrome, in a triptych of *mitate* paintings of *Matsukaze, Murasame and Yukihira* (Azabu Museum of Arts and Crafts; Sendai 1988, no. 36) that would appear to date from the late 1770s.

ISODA KORYŪSAI

54 Guan Yu, the Chinese God of War

c. An'ei era
SIGNATURE: Koryūsai ga
SEALS: Masakatsu in, Isoda
INSCRIPTION: Tōgarashi/seiryūken o/ushiro kana
INSCRIPTION SIGNATURE: Rissetsuan Goshin dai ('Inscribed by Rissetsuan Goshin')
INSCRIPTION SEALS: Go, Shin
Hanging scroll; ink and colour on silk, 86.1 × 31.8 cm
PROVENANCE: Arthur Morrison
LITERATURE: *UT*, vol. 1 (1987), BW no. 12
1946.2–9.037 (Japanese Painting ADD 191). Bequeathed by Arthur Morrison

Guan Yu (Japanese: Kan U) is worshipped in China as the god of war. As recounted in the novel *San guo zhi yan yi* ('Romance of the Three Kingdoms'), he swore blood brotherhood with Liu Bei (Japanese: Ryū Bi) and Zhang Fei (Japanese: Chō Hi) in a peach garden, and together the three fought successfully to establish Liu Bei as the first Emperor of the Shu kingdom in AD 221. Japanese versions of the story seem to have circulated by the early eighteenth century, and in 1737 in the Kabuki play *Urū-zuki ninin Kagekiyo* the characters of Taira no Kagekiyo and Shigetada switched to the guises of Kan U (played by Ichikawa Danjūrō II) and Chō Hi (played by Ichikawa Danzō I) respectively. Guan Yu's appearance in Ukiyo-e prints and paintings is based on Chinese folk imagery – an imposing build, florid facial colouring, long, flowing beard, and always with the 'blue dragon lance' (*seiryūken*) seen standing behind him here.

The meaning of the *senryū* (comic *haiku*) inscription is still obscure but seems to rely on likening Guan Yu's ruddy complexion to a red hot pepper:

> Do 'hot pepper' Chinese
> Put the Blue Dragon Lance
> Behind them?

Other poems by Rissetsuan Goshin appear on a *surimono* by Hokusai, *View of Enoshima*, dated 1799 (Matthi Forrer, *Hokusai*, London, Royal Academy of Arts, 1991, no. 9).

54

55

55

ISODA KORYŪSAI

55 Courtesan Walking with a Dog

c. late An'ei era
SIGNATURE: Koryūsai ga
SEALS: Masakatsu in, Isoda
Hanging scroll; ink and colour on paper,
  105.0 × 36.1 cm
PROVENANCE: Arthur Morrison
LITERATURE: Morrison 1911, vol. 2, pl. xv; *UT*, vol. 1
  (1987), no. 117
1913.5–1.0353 (Japanese Painting 1408). Given by
  Sir W. Gwynne-Evans, Bt

A courtesan walks her pet dog on a leash
beside a river, where large heaps of rocks
bound together with bamboo ropes prevent
the erosion of the bank. Above clouds in
the background is the silhouette of a
mountain somewhat reminiscent of Mt
Tsukuba, north-east of Edo (though this is
by no means certain). The woman wears a
purple-striped *haori* jacket with patches of
coloured brocade over a green kimono and
yellow *obi* tied at the front. The *haori* was
originally a man's garment, but was
adopted by courtesans and geishas in the
late eighteenth century and by women in
general in the early nineteenth.

Paintings on paper are often more
informal in terms of technique and
composition than those on silk, and here
Koryūsai has tried an unusual, and it has
to be said, somewhat awkward, pose, with
one shoulder jutting forward and the arm
bent behind. Pigments are not as thickly
applied as they would be on silk: the
cursive form of the signature, too, reflects
this slightly 'relaxed' approach. The wash
technique of the landscape, with 'pools' of
unpainted paper left in reserve to suggest
highlights, was the standard one used by
artists of the Edo Kanō school. If Koryūsai
was, indeed, once a retainer of the
Tsuchiya family, he would have been able
to enrol formally in the Kanō school, an
opportunity generally denied to Ukiyo-e
painters who were not of the samurai class.

56

Utagawa Toyoharu 1735–1814

Na Shōju (Masaki); common name Tajimaya
Shōjirō (later Shin'emon); *gō* Ichiryūsai,
Senryūsai, Sen'ō, Shōjirō. Almost no hard
evidence about his biography is known, but
said, variously, to be a native of Usuki,
Bungo Province, or Toyooka in Tajima
Province, or Edo. Early on may have
studied the Kanō style under Tsuruzawa
Tangei in Kyoto, then to Edo where his
earliest work is an actor print datable to
c. 1768. In Edo may have studied with
Toriyama Sekien. From the later Meiwa
(1764–72) era produced many 'perspective
prints' (*uki-e*) – views of Edo, foreign
scenes, historical and legendary scenes –
some of which have precedents in the work
of Maruyama Ōkyo in Kyoto. At about the
same time began to paint beauties in the
prevailing Harunobu style and went on to
become one of the most prolific painters of
the late eighteenth and early nineteenth
centuries, giving up print designing in the
1780s to concentrate exclusively on
painting. More than 100 paintings are
presently known.

For a few years in the late 1770s a feature
of the courtesans in Toyoharu's paintings is
their particularly wide girth. In the 1780s
and 90s his characteristic compositions
show courtesans and attendants under
cherry blossom or *mitate* works on themes
such as Matsukaze and Murasame, the salt
maidens. He was also responsible for some
large horizontal landscapes of figures in
Edo settings which are unparalleled in
Ukiyo-e painting (Stern 1973, no. 74; *Zaigai
hihō*, vol. 3 (1969), text vol. p. 75), as well
as lively indoor party scenes. Several
hanging scrolls are signed with Toyoharu's
age between sixty-one (1795) and sixty-six

(1800), and a single fan painting of *Tokiwa
Gozen in the Snow* gives his age as seventy-
seven (1811) (Ōta 1981, no. 198).

Toyoharu and his pupils Toyohiro
(nos 81, 82) and Toyokuni (nos 83–5)
established the Utagawa school as the
dominant lineage of artists in Ukiyo-e in
the nineteenth century.

Attributed to
UTAGAWA TOYOHARU

56 Courtesans of the Tamaya House

c. early Temmei era
Six-fold screen; ink, colour and gold on paper,
   144.1 × 314.6 cm
PROVENANCE: Ralph Harari
LITERATURE: Hillier 1970, vol. 1, no. 48; Smith 1990,
   no. 194; Tokyo 1990, no. 1
1982.6-1.02 (Japanese Painting ADD 687). Gift of
   Dr and Mrs Michael Harari

This grand screen shows the *harimise*, the
latticed display room facing on to the
street, of the Tamaya house of pleasure in
the Yoshiwara quarter. The high-ranking
courtesans are grouped on the red carpet in
the centre of the room, while around the
walls – paired in matching kimonos with
long, hanging sleeves – are their
apprentices (*shinzō*). This is probably the
midday session from roughly noon to four
o'clock, since business seems to be slack
and the women amuse themselves dressing
a doll, folding a paper crane, and smoking.
One even dozes off, her head lolling
forward while her neighbour prepares to
liven up the mood with jaunty *shamisen*
music in the *sugogaki* style.

Next to the smoking-set in front of the
courtesan wearing a black surcoat (*uchikake*)
decorated with blue and red tassels is a

small black lacquer box painted in gold
with the emblem of a single crane flying
with wings outstretched. Referring to the
printed guide to courtesans of 1788 by
Santō Kyōden, *Keisei kei*, we find that this
was the 'alternate crest' (*kaemon*) of
Komurasaki, one of the highest-ranking
women in the house run by Tamaya
Sansaburō, confirming the name of the
house which appears, half obscured by a
gold cloud, on the entrance curtain.

Considered in terms of its theme and
composition – a complex grouping of
figures in the corner of a room surrounded
by a certain number of accessories (even a
dropped hairpin beneath the *shamisen*) – the
screen clearly belongs to the sequence
established by the illustrated book *Seirō
bijin awase sugata kagami* of 1776 by Shunshō
and Shigemasa. It does not quite show the
mania for detail of Kitao Masanobu's album
Yoshiwara keisei shin bijin awase jihitsu kagami
of 1784, however, and this stylistic
evidence points to a date of execution in
the early 1780s. Though the screen is
unsigned, the manner of drawing the faces
and amplitude of the figure style require a
firm attribution to Utagawa Toyoharu.
Several large horizontal hanging scrolls by
Toyoharu are known, but this is the only
six-fold screen by him presently recorded.
The large scale, the sense of rhythm and
energy in the lines of the drapery and the
variety of gestures portrayed make this one
of the most important Ukiyo-e paintings to
have survived from the period, giving a
vivid sense of the glittering 'special world'
of the Yoshiwara pleasure quarter.

The face of the woman folding the paper
crane has been patched and completely
repainted at a later date.

57

UTAGAWA TOYOHARU

57 The Courtesan Katachino under a Cherry Tree

c. Temmei era
SIGNATURE: Utagawa Toyoharu ga
SEALS: Ichiryūsai, Toyoharu
Hanging scroll; ink, colour and gold on silk,
96.6 × 41.5 cm
PROVENANCE: Arthur Morrison
LITERATURE: Morrison 1911, vol. 2, pl. XXIII;
UT, vol. 1 (1987), no. 133
1913.5–1.0395 (Japanese Painting 1435). Given by
Sir W. Gwynne-Evans, Bt

A courtesan stands beneath a flowering cherry tree – probably planted in Naka-no-chō, the central street of the Yoshiwara pleasure quarter – the light from two large lanterns at her feet illuminating the blossoms. The rear lantern bears the triple-fan emblem of the Ōgiya ('Fan house'), while the one in front has triple oak-leaves in a circle, which, according to the printed guide to courtesans of 1788, *Keisei kei*, was the 'alternative crest' (*kaemon*) of the high-ranking courtesan Katachino. In this guide Santō Kyōden remarks that Katachino is vivacious, likes sake, and has a large following of admirers.

   Here she is shown from behind, turning to look over her right shoulder, wearing a sophisticated ensemble of a (?faded) purple kimono with roundels of seasonal plants and flowers – pinks, iris, bushclover and maple leaves – set off by a black *obi* decorated with small coiled dragons in gold. Her hands are held up inside her robe, and the right sleeve has been tossed over and hangs down in display. Toyoharu did many paintings of courtesans dressed in gaudy finery processing beneath cherry trees with attendants, but this work is set apart by the relative simplicity of the costume and the fact that Katachino is depicted alone in pensive mood.

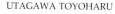

58

UTAGAWA TOYOHARU

58 Maids Seduced by Workmen

c. Kansei era
SIGNATURE: Ichiryūsai Toyoharu ga
SEAL: Shōju no in
(?)Hanging scroll, now mounted as a handscroll;
ink and colour on silk, 43.6 × 76.5 cm
1978.1–23.02 (Japanese Painting ADD 570)

No matter how impressed we are by Toyoharu's sure grasp of the human form and the freshness of his colouring, there is no avoiding the fact that this is a scene of rape, and violent rape at that. Two maids working in the service area of some restaurant or mansion (to judge by the

58

59

assorted paraphernalia stacked up behind
them – tatami, braziers, a flower vase, an
umbrella) have been set upon by three
burly workmen who clearly had been
sweeping the garden until they threw
down their brooms for the attack. Dropping
her tray of cups and dishes in terror, a
waitress still holds the sake kettle as she is
abused by two men at once. Her
companion has not even had time to stop
washing cloths in a tub on the verandah
before she, too, is violated.

There can be little doubt that the original
intent of the work was to titillate, and we
can only wonder why such elegant
accomplishment has been lavished on so
base a theme. Rape scenes are not unusual
as one of a series of (generally twelve)
otherwise affectionate scenes in late
eighteenth- and nineteenth-century erotic
prints and paintings. Only rarely do they
convey a real and direct sense of terror and
pain – as in the case of Utamaro's famous
scene of a woman biting her attacker in
Utamakura ('Poem of the Pillow', 1788) –
and all too often, as here, the aggressors
wear the characteristic smirk that is
evidence of pandering to fantasy.

The painting has clearly had a chequered
existence, as evidenced by the burn marks
along the top and bottom: either a previous
owner was about to commit it to the flames
and then thought better of it, or else it was
the first thing he rescued when there was a
fire! The positioning of the signature is
curious – one would generally expect to
find it in the bottom left-hand corner if the
original format were that of a handscroll –
and yet it is hard to imagine a subject such
as this being displayed as a normal hanging
scroll in a *tokonoma* (display alcove).

CHIKAKAZU (dates unknown)

59 Woman and Children

c. Temmei era
SIGNATURE: Chikakazu hitsu
SEAL: handwritten cipher (*kaō*)
Hanging scroll (now framed); ink and colour on
paper, 95.6 × 27.0 cm
PROVENANCE: H. S. Richards
1962.10–13.03 (Japanese Painting ADD 375).
Bequeathed by H. S. Richards

A woman struggles to control two lively
boys as the older hides in the long,
hanging sleeve of her kimono and the baby
in her arms wriggles to try and catch his
brother. This black *furisode* kimono is
decorated with roundels of autumn plants –
bushclover (*hagi*), pampas grass (*susuki*) and
chrysanthemums – and there is the crest of
a boat in full sail on the sleeve. A pigeon
sits on the branch of the cherry tree above.

Such an ambitious tangle of figures
would not normally be expected of an
otherwise unknown artist such as
Chikakazu, and in fact they prove to be
taken line for line from a hanging scroll by
Toyoharu, now in the collection of the
Museum of Fine Arts, Boston. The Boston
Toyoharu painting has a New Year
kadomatsu (gateway pine branch) decoration
behind the figures instead of the branch of
cherry (which is in any case the weakest
part of the Chikakazu composition), a *kyōka*
(crazy verse) poem inscribed above by the
female poet Chie no Naishi, and is signed
'Utagawa Toyoharu ga', with an early form
of the 'Shōju' seal, suggesting a date in the
1780s. Chikakazu's colouring, though not
as rich as Toyoharu's, follows the basic
black/scarlet contrast seen in the Boston
scroll, and the work probably dates from
soon after Toyoharu's original.

59

60

60

Katsukawa Shunshō ?1726–92

Imina Masateru; *azana* Senjin; common
name Yōsuke (changing to Yūsuke in the
spring of 1774; also given as Yūjirō); *gō*
Kyokurōsei, Yūji, Ririn, Rokurokuan,
Jūgasei. Lived in Edo. Pupil of Miyagawa
Shunsui; also collaborated with the
Hanabusa school artist Kō Sūkoku
(1730–1804) and may have studied with
him. His family name may be Hayashi,
which appears in a jar-shaped seal on his
earliest prints, though this is also said to
have been the accounts seal of Hayashiya
Shichiemon with whom Shunshō is
supposed to have lodged.

Scholars disagree on the dating of his
earliest works – a diptych of actor prints in
the Art Institute of Chicago has been linked
to a performance in Meiwa 1 (1764) – but
certainly by Meiwa 5 (1768) he was
regularly producing actor prints in the
small, narrow *hosoban* format and using the
new techniques of the full-colour
woodblock print (*nishiki-e*). Shunshō's actor
portraits were also revolutionary for the
degree of 'likeness' (*nigao-e*) to each actor's
actual facial features, as demonstrated
particularly in the colour-printed illustrated
book *Ehon butai ōgi*, showing half-length
portraits of actors in fan-shaped borders,
which he designed in collaboration with
Bunchō in 1770. A small number of prints
of beautiful women in the prevailing style

of Harunobu at the beginning of his career
were followed by increasingly confident
large-scale figures of women in the
kakemono-e print format that heralded the
development of his mature painting style.
The illustrated book *Seirō bijin awase sugata
kagami*, designed in collaboration with Kitao
Shigemasa and published in the New Year
of 1776, was a major landmark in the
increasingly extravagant cult of the
Yoshiwara courtesan, as well as showing
new skill at setting groups of figures in
complex interiors.

The earliest-surviving painting by
Shunshō that can be accepted with
confidence is a hanging scroll, *Standing
Courtesan*, formerly in the Bigelow
collection (Tokyo, Nihon Bijutsu Kyōkai
1933, no. 74), which can be dated to
c. 1779–80 on the basis of the unusual form
of the handwritten cipher (*kaō*) following
the signature. The paradox is that already
in a *sharebon* of 1775 there occurs the
remark that 'a scroll by Shunshō costs 1,000
gold pieces' ('Shunshō ippuku atai senkin'),
so clearly many early works have been lost.
Shunshō's mature paintings of beauties,
done mainly during the Temmei era
(1781–9) and up to his death in 1792, are
one of the glories of Ukiyo-e. Particularly
notable is a series of tall, narrow hanging
scrolls on the theme of 'Manners and
Customs of Women in the Twelve Months'

(MOA Art Museum; only ten of the scrolls
survive), datable to *c.* 1783, which was once
owned (and may even have been
commissioned) by Lord Matsura Seizan. In
terms of thematic inventiveness,
compositional sophistication, flawless
technique and the sheer beauty, refinement
and intelligence of the women portrayed
they are unrivalled in all Ukiyo-e painting.
After the New Year of 1789 the style of
Shunshō's signature changes dramatically
to the broad, mannered 'Teika' calligraphic
style, and the works of his last few years
show a tendency towards tall, slender
figures, often in large formats on paper. A
pair of six-fold screens of *Pleasures in Spring
and Summer* (Museum of Fine Arts, Boston)
date from these years.

More than 100 paintings by Shunshō are
presently known, and a convincing attempt
has recently been made by Naitō Masato to
arrange them chronologically on the basis
of the forms of the signatures and ciphers
and discuss the changes in his *bijin* style
(see Naitō 1989). Shunshō's pupils Shunkō,
Shun'ei (no. 65; Introduction, figs 6, 7, 11),
Shunchō (no. 63) and, of course, Hokusai
(nos 95–104) all became important painters
in their own right, developing personal
styles.

61

61

KATSUKAWA SHUNSHŌ

60 Cat Licking its Paw

(?)*c.* 1789–92
SIGNATURE: Katsu Shunshō ga
SEAL: Katsukawa
Hanging scroll; ink and colour on paper,
   39.2 × 51.7 cm
PROVENANCE: Ralph Harari
LITERATURE: Hillier 1970, vol. 1, no. 55; *UT*, vol. 1
(1987), BW no. 14
1982.7–1.016 (Japanese Painting ADD 701)

Japanese legends concerning cats often
portray them as malevolent creatures – the
cat-witch that terrified the town of Okabe
on the Tōkaidō Highway, for instance –
and there is definitely some such
undertone in this example, showing the
creature with staring saucer eyes. To paint
a cat on its own is highly unusual, and the
treatment here has the somewhat naïve,
searching realism usually associated with
artists experimenting in Western-derived
styles, such as Odano Naotake (1749–80)
and Shiba Kōkan (1747–1818). Shunshō
sometimes includes kittens and puppies
playing at the feet of his figures of
beauties, but these are in an altogether
more conventional style. The signature is
certainly in the 'Teika' style of Shunshō's
last four years, but the seal – a vermilion
circle with 'Katsukawa' in white reserve – is
unique, and until this can be confirmed
from a painting of a more orthodox subject
Shunshō's authorship remains uncertain.

KATSUKAWA SHUNSHŌ II
worked Bunka (1804–18)–Tempō (1830–44) eras

61 The Grand Shrine at Ise

Tempō era, after 1832
SIGNATURE: Kyokushōsei Shunshō kore [o]
  tsutsushinde sha [su] ('This was respectfully
  painted by Kyokushōsei Shunshō')
SEAL: Tokusai (in jar-shape)
Hanging scroll; ink, colour and gold on silk,
   44.7 × 72.5 cm
PROVENANCE: William Anderson
LITERATURE: Anderson 1886, no. 234
1881.12–10.0234 (Japanese Painting 281)

Shrouded in mist and surrounded by
ancient cypress trees are the Inner and
Outer Shrines at Ise, one of the two most
important Shintō sacred places, enshrining
the ancestral gods of the Imperial family.
Rebuilt every twenty-one years in
unpainted cypress wood, the distinctive
architectural style – with its platform raised
on stilts, extended finials (*chigi*) and cross-
pieces on the ridge pole (*katsuogi*) – is the
most ancient in Japan, said to date from the
third century. In the Edo period a
pilgrimage to Ise was one of the main
reasons for commoners to be permitted to
travel and was phenomenally popular. It is
recorded, for instance, that between March
and August 1830, a particularly auspicious
year, 4,579,000 pilgrims visited the shrine.

  Shunshō II was originally a pupil of
Shun'ei, using the name Matsui Shunkō
(written with a different character for 'kō'

from Shunshō I's famous pupil). In 1832,
the fortieth anniversary of Shunshō I's
death and the thirteenth anniversary of
Shun'ei's death, he took the name
Shunshō II and the *gō* Kyokushōsei in
imitation of Shunshō I's *gō* Kyokurōsei. He
is known principally for actor and warrior
prints: this hanging scroll shows his
modest skills as a painter in the later Edo–
Kanō blue and green landscape style.

62 (ADD 883)

62 (ADD 882)

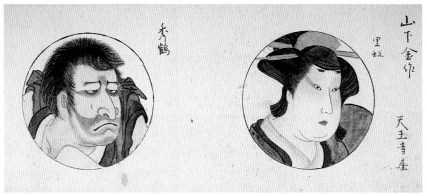

62 (ADD 884)

ANON. (Katsukawa school)

62 Portraits of Five Actors in Round Windows

c. 1789–90

(?)Three sections from a handscroll (mounted in board); ink and colour on paper, 18.5 × 19.9 cm (ADD 882), 18.5 × 42.1 cm (ADD 883), 18.5 × 43.2 cm (ADD 884)

1988.12–15.01–03 (Japanese Paintings ADD 882–4)

Portraits of five leading Kabuki actors in characteristic roles are painted in round windows and identified either by their acting name, *haiku* poetry name (*haimyō*), or 'trade' name (*yagō*), or all three. Based on their known dates of activity and assuming that the portraits were done during their lifetimes, it is possible to date the paintings to either 1789 or 1790.

The actors' names, roles and dates – where significant – are: Ichikawa Danjūrō V (*haimyō* Goi) as Matsuōmaru, possibly in the performance at the Kiri theatre in the seventh month, 1788 (ADD 882); Ichikawa Omezō I (*haimyō* Shinsha; used the name Omezō I from 1789 onwards); Sawamura Sōjūrō II (*haimyō* Nosshi; *yagō* Kinokuniya; died 1770) (ADD 883); Yamashita Kinsaku II (*haimyō* Rikō; *yagō* Tennōjiya); Nakamura Nakazō I as Sadakuro (*haimyō* Shūkaku; died 1790) (ADD 884). Sawamura Sōjūrō is

marked 'father' (*chichi*), clearly identifying him as the second generation to use the name, who died in 1770 and was the father of the actor who was the incumbent in 1789–90. No other actor is indicated as being deceased or of another generation in this way, suggesting that the paintings were indeed done after Omezō I's adoption of that name in 1789 and before Nakazō I's death in 1790.

Attention should be drawn to the marked similarity of the portrait of Danjūrō V to a full-length painting by Katsukawa Shunkō of the same actor in the same role of Matsuōmaru in the Freer Gallery of Art (Stern 1973, no. 68; *US*, vol. 16 (1981), no. 41), now thought to be related to a performance at the Kiri theatre in the seventh month, 1788. It was just at this time, too, that Shunkō was designing his revolutionary woodblock-print bust portraits of actors. Roger Keyes has identified seventeen of these, which he dates between the eleventh month, 1788, and the eleventh month, 1789 (see his comments in *US*, vol. 13 (1981), no. 67). Shortly after this – Keyes suggests around the third month, 1790 – Shunkō fell victim to a paralysis that affected his right hand and all paintings thereafter were done with

the left hand in a quite different style. The present paintings are simply and spontaneously executed and yet have that surety of line that does not suggest they are copies, and they may be tentatively attributed to Shunkō, or another Katsukawa pupil working closely with him.

Portraits of actors in round windows are rare, but there is a slightly later handscroll of such subjects by Utagawa Kunimasa in the collection of the Japan Ukiyo-e Museum Matsumoto 1985, nos 248–51). It is suggested that the present paintings were intended as studies for a more finished handscroll of this type, perhaps on silk. In general paintings of actors seem to have been put to much more practical, ephemeral uses than those of beauties – such as theatre signboards and fans with actors' inscriptions – which helps to explain their comparative rarity.

Katsukawa Shunchō

worked Temmei (1781–9)– Kansei (1789–1801) eras

Common name Kichizaemon; *gō* Yūshidō, Shien, Tōshien, Chūrin, Chūrinsha, Sankō, Jūgasei, Tansei, Tanseidō. Lived in Edo Bakuro-chō, then Nihombashi Daiku-chō and finally Setomono-chō. Studied under Shunshō, but curiously for a Katsukawa pupil designed no actor prints. His prints of beauties from the 1780s – often in triptych form – are very much in the Kiyonaga mould, as is his erotica, a genre in which he was prolific. In later years studied under Shumman, using the name Kichisadō Shunchō.

Presently about twenty paintings are known. The earliest (New Ōtani 1991, no. 51; Tokyo, Mainichi Shimbun 1990, no. 209) are virtually indistinguishable from works by Shunshō, and the technique equally flawless. In the 1790s, however, the figures become more slender and the compositions more original.

63

63

KATSUKAWA SHUNCHŌ

63 'Entering the Teahouse' (Ageya-iri)

Late Temmei–early Kansei eras
SIGNATURE: Tōshien Shunchō zu
SEAL: (damaged)
Hanging scroll (mounted on a panel); ink, colour
    and gold on silk, 63.4 × 105.0 cm
1980.12–22.01 (Japanese Painting ADD 631)

The most ambitious composition by
Shunchō yet discovered, this wide hanging
scroll shows the formal procession of a
grand courtesan as she comes from a house
of pleasure to one of the assignation
teahouses (*ageya*) that lined Naka-no-chō,
the central street in the Yoshiwara quarter,
where the client is waiting with a group of
entertainers. This ceremonial progress was
known as 'entering the teahouse' (*ageya-iri*).
The scene is a veritable catalogue of
Yoshiwara types: the courtesan is
accompanied by two apprentices (*shinzō*),
girl and boy attendants, and an elderly
couple who must be the brothel owner and
his wife; while on the teahouse platform
extending into the street another courtesan
is seated chatting with a teahouse waitress,
and beside her two geishas prepare their
shamisen and hand-drum, and a
professional jester (*hōkan*) is offered sake by

a second waitress. At the back, half
obscured by the shop curtain, with food
laid out before him, calmly smoking a pipe
and gazing at the approaching vision –
which must have appeared to him like the
descent to earth of a Buddhist deity and
heavenly host – is the handsome patron.
On the far left is one of the cherry trees
that was specially transplanted to line the
centre of Naka-no-chō each spring.

Scenes of parading courtesans are, of
course, one of the staples of Ukiyo-e
painting, and party scenes inside teahouses
are not uncommon. To have the two
combined into such a complex grouping,
however – one involving more than a
dozen figures – is probably unique, and it
may be that the sensitively rendered faces
were intended as portraits of real
individuals. The composition has been
skilfully orchestrated to focus on the central
figure of the courtesan, who mediates, as it
were, between the formality of the
procession and the convivial bustle of the
teahouse scene. All this is cut through by
the gaze of the client, amplified halfway by
the glance of the geisha with the drum who
faces in the same direction.

The painting has extensive repairs.

113

64

Katsukawa Shungyō
worked c. Kansei era (1789–1801)–1831

Family name Saitō; common name Shinzō;
gō Kakusensai, Kakei. Lived in Asakusa
Kotosuke-chō. Pupil of Shunshō known for
prints and paintings of beauties, originally
imitating Shunshō's style very closely. His
latest dated work appears to be a
contribution to the illustrated kyōka
anthology Hototogisu sanjū-rokkasen
published in 1831. Narazaki Muneshige has
proposed that Shungyō may be the same
individual as the painter Hishikawa
Ryūkoku, who used the gō Shungyōsai
(NU, vol. 4 (1982), pp. 62–3), but this
suggestion was not taken up by Tanaka
Tatsuya in his articles on Ryūkoku in
the Azabu bijutsukan dayori, nos 6–7
(May/July 1985).

64

KATSUKAWA SHUNGYŌ

64 Courtesan with a Dog under a
Maple Tree

c. early Kansei era
SIGNATURE: Shungyō zu
SEALS: Kakei, (unread)
Hanging scroll; ink, colour and gold on silk,
79.5 × 26.4 cm
PROVENANCE: Arthur Morrison
LITERATURE: UT, vol. 1 (1987), no. 136; Tokyo 1990,
no. 32
1913.5–1.0384 (Japanese Painting 1434). Given by
Sir W. Gwynne-Evans, Bt

Faithfully imitating the bijin style of his
teacher Shunshō's last years, c. 1789–92,
when the stature of the women became
doll-like and slender with sloping
shoulders, Shungyō produces a charming
small composition showing a beauty with
her little black dog beneath the scarlet
foliage of a maple tree in autumn. On the
bench behind are a writing-set and tanzaku
decorated poem cards, ready for her to
compose some seasonal poems, and in her
right hand she carries a bronze hand-
warmer containing charcoal with which she
will light her pipe. The figure is remarkably
close to Shunshō's mannerisms of style,
down to the characteristic contrast between
pale lilac kimono (covered in delicately
traced pinks in gold and white), bright
scarlet under-robe and black obi and lacquer
clogs often seen in Shunshō's paintings.
One cannot imagine, however, that a
master such as Shunshō would half-obscure
the figure with the trunk of a tree in this
way.

The shell-white pigment on the face has
been retouched in the area along the
hairline between the woman's right eye
and ear.

65

Katsukawa Shun'ei 1762–1819

Gō Kutokusai. Lived in Shin Izumi-chō,
Edo. Pupil of Katsukawa Shunshō. His
earliest work is an actor print datable to
1778, but most of his colour prints, mainly
of actors but some *bijin* and *sumō* wrestler
prints as well, are concentrated in the
decade between the late 1780s and late 90s.
His *hosoban* actor prints show a highly
individual style – excited and kinetic – in
comparison with those of his fellow (but
senior) pupil Shunkō, and his *ōban* series of
the 1790s a searching portrayal of
psychology that would set the tenor for
actor prints of his contemporaries.

Even fewer paintings by Shun'ei are
known – perhaps a dozen – than by
Shunkō, but in this field, too, he displays
interest in exploring a wider range of
psychological states than perhaps any of
his contemporaries, Utamaro included.
Particularly notable in this respect is a
hanging scroll, *Courtesan Seated Reading a
Letter* (Art Gallery of New South Wales;
Introduction, fig. 11).

Attributed to
KATSUKAWA SHUN'EI

65 Ten Scenes of Lovemaking

c. Kansei–early Bunka eras
Handscroll; ink and colour on paper,
  28.0 × 637.3 cm
LITERATURE: Smith 1990, no. 196
1980.3–25.04 (Japanese Painting ADD 615)

Though unsigned, features of the style
such as the racing dry brushwork of the
outlines of the drapery and sensuous faces
with thickly lashed eyes suggest a firm
attribution to Katsukawa Shun'ei. Erotic
handscrolls generally comprise twelve
scenes, so it may be that the artist's
signature was included on one of the two
sections which have probably been
trimmed from this work.

Shun'ei was at pains to extend the
boundaries of Ukiyo-e to express a wider
range of emotional and psychological states
than previous artists. In this handscroll of
ten erotic scenes, too, he contrives to avoid
conventional poses and situations in what
could all too easily become a stereotyped

genre, and explores a rich gamut of
sexuality ranging from a young woman
lying dreaming after reading a love-letter to
the contents of her dream in which a
couple make desperate love one final time
before they commit ritual suicide. In the
scene illustrated a husband steals up to
embrace his wife from behind as she
washes and combs her hair. Her surprise
and his powerful passion – conveyed by
narrowed and intently gazing eyes seen
above her shoulder – are utterly
convincing, and bodies, robes and the folds
therein, as well as accessories, are all
captured with unswerving precision and
the utmost sensitivity. It is hard to
determine a stylistic development within
Shun'ei's few known paintings, but the
relatively strong vestiges of Shunshō's
figure style still apparent in this work
indicate perhaps a date not too many years
after the latter's death in 1792.

Kubo Shumman 1757–1820

Family name Kubota (shortened to Kubo after 1783); common name Yasubei; *gō* Shōsadō; *kyōka-gō* Hitofushi Chizue; *haigō* Enshimbō; *gesaku-gō* Nandaka Shiran, Kōzandō. Lived in Kodemma-chō, then Kamei-chō and finally Kanda Tomimatsu-chō. A pupil of Katori Nahiko and later Kitao Shigemasa. His earliest work was a copy made in 1774 of an *ema* (votive plaque) by Nahiko. From *c.* 1779 to 1784 was active as an author of *gesaku* (popular literature) using the names Kubota Shumman and Nandaka Shiran. In 1782 changed the character with which he wrote 'Shun' of Shumman from 'spring' to 'excel', to distinguish himself, it is said, from the pupils of Katsukawa Shunshō. Studied *haiku* of the school of Tani Sogai and became a judge of *kyōka* ('crazy verse'), a passion he was to pursue from the early 1780s to the end of his life. Contributed to *kyōka* anthologies and became ever more involved in the production of single-sheet *kyōka surimono* (special edition prints bearing *kyōka* poems), devising designs for his fellow poets' poems and supervising their carving and printing himself. In the later Temmei era (1781–9) produced commercial prints of beauties heavily influenced by the prevailing Kiyonaga style, often in triptych format, and including several works in the 'red-avoiding' (*beni-girai*) palette of purples, greens and greys such as the six-sheet *Six Jewel Rivers* (*Mutamagawa*).

Shumman was the most prolific painter of the Kitao school, with an *oeuvre* presently totalling over seventy examples. One of the earliest of these is a painting of *Two Beauties and Morning Glories* (Narazaki and Yoshida 1970, vol. 2, BW no. 18), dated 1785, which is almost entirely in shades of *sumi* (ink), a technique already used occasionally by Koryūsai in the 1770s and which must have influenced the *beni-girai* prints mentioned above. In general in the early paintings, which often include the *gō* 'Enshimbō' in the signature, the figures have faces reminiscent of Shigemasa but are tall and elegant in stature in the manner of Kiyonaga. Moving into the nineteenth century Shumman was increasingly prolific as a painter, often repeating successful compositions several times. Many of these paintings were then inscribed with *kyōka* poems by such luminaries of the world of popular literature as Ōta Nampo, and Shumman regularly contributed to collaborative scrolls done spontaneously with other artists and poets assembled at *shogakai* (poetry and painting meetings).

66

67

66

KUBO SHUMMAN

66 Woman Washing Cloth in the Jewel River

c. mid Temmei era
SIGNATURE: Enshimbō Shumman ga
SEAL: (?)'Man' (handwritten cipher)
Hanging scroll; ink and *gofun* on silk,
  82.8 × 32.0 cm
PROVENANCE: Shōzō Katō
LITERATURE: *UT*, vol. 1 (1987), no. 125
1922.2–13.01 (Japanese Painting ADD 15)

The 'Jewel Rivers' (*tamagawa*) at Ide in Yamashiro Province, Noji in Ōmi, Noda in Rikuzen, Kōya in Kii, Chōfu in Musashi and Mishima in Settsu were place-names replete with poetic associations (*utamakura*), employed as they were in the composition of *waka* poetry since the eighth-century *Manyōshū* collection. In the Edo period they were collected together to form a set of six, the *Mutamagawa*, which became a theme for Ukiyo-e print series by artists such as Harunobu and Koryūsai. Shumman himself designed a six-sheet woodblock print in the muted 'red-avoiding' (*beni-girai*) colour scheme which combines the six rivers into a single composition and shows elegantly dressed townspeople watching humble country beauties at their work. This is thought to have been issued *c.* 1786, and the third sheet from the right, the design for the Chōfu Jewel River, shows a woman in a similar pose to the present painting, washing cloth prior to bleaching it. The conflation of the classical world of the Jewel Rivers with Ukiyo-e is another example of the phenomenon of *mitate* ('reworking in contemporary taste'; Introduction, p. 21).

Shumman uses Jewel River subjects in many of his paintings, often executed – as here – entirely in shades of *sumi* in a manner appropriate to the quiet elegance of the theme, but it is not possible at present to be sure if any of these predate the production of the six-sheet print. The woman's face is oval in shape in the manner of Shigemasa, suggesting a relatively early date, and the only colour in the work is a touch of rouge on the woman's lips and the red cipher (a combination of the *hiragana* (phonetic graphs) for 'ma' and 'n'?) beneath the artist's signature. The wilful abandonment of the glorious polychrome of Temmei era (1781–9) paintings and prints might be regarded as the ultimate in manneristic refinement.

Another, later version by Shumman of this subject in the Freer Gallery of Art (*US*, vol. 16 (1981), no. 46) introduces a second woman about to beat cloth in a mortar with a large wooden pestle and substitutes a pine tree for the willow.

KUBO SHUMMAN

67 Courtesan and her Attendant at the New Year

Kansei–early Bunka eras
SIGNATURE: Shōsadō Shumman gadai ('Painted to the theme by Shōsadō Shumman')
SEAL: Shumman
INSCRIPTION: Hatsukai wa/kotosara ōki/massha-tachi/kamiyo ni chikaki/haru no Yoshiwara
INSCRIPTION SEALS: Nan, Po
Hanging scroll; ink and colour on silk,
  92.0 × 30.4 cm
PROVENANCE: Arthur Morrison
LITERATURE: *UT*, vol. 1 (1987), no. 124
1913.5–1.0385 (Japanese Painting 1419). Given by Sir W. Gwynne-Evans, Bt

The auspicious New Year *kyōka* ('crazy verse') composed and inscribed on the painting by Ōta Nampo (1749–1823), doyen of popular cultural circles, may be translated:

A New Year engagement
Is particularly expensive
So the hired comedians
Are practically in heaven –
Yoshiwara in spring.

The 'first engagement' (*hatsukai*) of a courtesan at the New Year was an especially lavish affair, so the comedians hired to entertain at parties (*massha* or *hōkan*) stood to make a lot of money. There is also a string of word-play/associations involving the terms *massha*, which can also mean a small 'subsidiary shrine'; *kamiyo* ('the age of the Gods', 'heaven'); and the idea that the Yoshiwara pleasure quarter at the New Year holiday was like heaven on earth. The same inscription appears on another painting by Shumman, *Standing Courtesan Reading a Letter* (Tanaka 1911–13, vol. 2, pls not numbered).

As the signature suggests, Shumman took his lead from the poem and filled the painting, too, with auspicious New Year imagery: decked out in matching new robes with a lucky pattern of cranes flying over the tops of pine trees, the courtesan and her *kamuro* attendant are on their way to the first engagement of the New Year, passing in front of a New Year display of fresh pine boughs and bamboo. In her hair, too, the *kamuro* has arranged the first few red plum blossoms, with some tiny sprigs of pine. Broad strokes of ink wash have been skilfully used on the courtesan's surcoat to suggest the glossiness of the black silk.

Tanaka Tatsuya has suggested that the circular 'Shumman' seal on the present painting was used from the late Temmei (1781–9) to the early Bunka (1804–18) eras and that from mid-Bunka onwards Shumman switched to a different circular

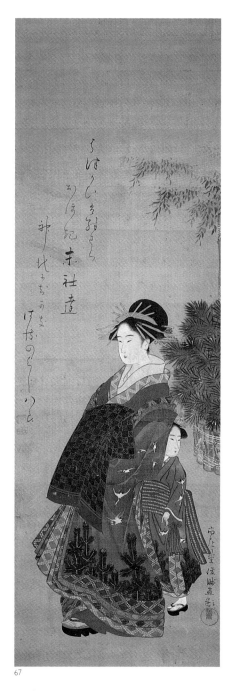

67

'Shumman' seal, one which includes the three strokes of the water radical on the left-hand side of the character 'man' (*NU*, vol. 5 (1983), pp. 77, 78). The face here has the pointed, slightly turned-up nose and narrow eyes which taper to slightly upturned points characteristic of Shumman's mature works.

In a second version of this subject by Shumman the composition is reversed and the courtesan has a *yoko-hyōgo* hairstyle (*Ukiyo-e taisei*, vol. 8 (1930), no. 143).

KUBO SHUMMAN

68 Two Women and a Girl Admiring
Cherry Blossom

Kyōwa–early Bunka eras
SIGNATURE: Shōsadō Shumman
SEAL: Shumman
Hanging scroll; ink, colour and gold on silk,
94.0 × 31.8 cm
PROVENANCE: Arthur Morrison
LITERATURE: Morrison 1911, vol. 2, pl. XIX; UT, vol. 1
(1987), BW no. 17
1913.5–1.0386 (Japanese Painting 1420). Given by
Sir W. Gwynne-Evans, Bt

Three women – the wife of a merchant
shielding her face from the sun with a fan,
her daughter and a maid – are walking
along some country path among
blossoming cherry trees, perhaps at
Gotenyama or some such other spot
famous in the city for flower viewing
(*hanami*). The pose of the maid, seen from
behind and staring off out of the painting,
is a visual means of indicating the
informality of the scene, a break from
normal custom and habit to enjoy an
outing at this special time of the year.

The chronology of Shumman's works has
so far been established in only its broadest
outlines (see the comments on the use of *gō*
and seals in nos 66, 67). The seal on the
present painting is thought to have been
abandoned after the early Bunka era
(1804–18), and the generally shorter
proportions of the figures in comparison
with Shumman's earlier works suggest
perhaps a date in the first decade of the
nineteenth century.

68

68

Kitagawa Utamaro ?1753–1806

Common name Yūsuke; *gō* Sekiyō,
Mokuen, Entaisai, Murasakiya; *kyōka-gō*
Fude no Ayamaru. Competing theories as
to his birthplace – Kawagoe, Kyoto, Edo,
etc. – but no firm evidence. From *c.* 1781
lived in Ueno Shinobugaoka, On-Sukiya-
chō; from *c.* 1783/4 lodged with the
publisher Tsutaya Jūsaburō in Tōriabura-
chō; later resided in Kanda Benkei-bashi,
Kyūemon-chō and Bakuro-chō sanchōme;
in his final years moved to (?)Demma-chō,
Daimaru Shindō. Pupil of Toriyama Sekien,
whose family name he very occasionally
adopted. By 1774 styling himself Kitagawa
Toyoaki. In 1781 the first use of the name
Shinobugaoka Utamaro in a *kibyōshi* for the
publisher Tsutaya, whose protégé he
became and by whom his career was
launched as an illustrator of luxury *kyōka*
anthologies and *bijin* prints in the later
Temmei era (1781–9). Dominated the
Kansei era (1789–1801) with hundreds of
woodblock half-length portraits of women,
done principally for Tsutaya (until his
death in 1795) but also for many other
publishers, which explore a range of types
of women and nuances of their moods in a
way not previously attempted in Ukiyo-e.
The compositions of prints of seated
women are also cleverly cropped in such a
manner as to suggest the figures coming
out at the viewer, a technique not used in
his paintings. Notable, too, are the double
half-length portraits of pairs of lovers taken
from the plays of Chikamatsu.

About two dozen paintings by Utamaro
are known, dating principally from the
mid-1790s onwards. Apart from his
standard compositions showing stylish
women seated or standing with generally
very little in the way of accoutrements or
background, there is a set of three very
large horizontal hanging scrolls on the
theme of 'Snow' (second-floor rooms
around a snowy courtyard garden in a
brothel in Fukagawa; present location
unknown), 'Moon' (large parlour room of a
Shinagawa brothel overlooking Edo Bay in
the moonlight; Freer Gallery of Art) and
'Flowers' (teahouse at Yoshiwara Naka-no-
chō with cherry blossom in bloom;
Wadsworth Atheneum) painted over a
period of years in the middle of his career,
formerly owned (and possibly
commissioned) by the family of Kamiya
Ihei in Tochigi. These grand compositions
involving whole crowds of figures in
complex architectural settings are unique
among Ukiyo-e paintings of the period.

69

69

KITAGAWA UTAMARO

69 Woman Washing her Face

c. late Kansei era

SIGNATURE: Utamaro hitsu

SEAL: Utamaro (framed by ascending and
descending dragons)

Hanging scroll; ink and colour on silk,
39.4 × 54.9 cm

PROVENANCE: C. Maresco Pearce ('acquired . . . in
Paris early in the century')

LITERATURE: *UT*, vol. 1 (1987), nos 119, 120; Smith
1990, no. 195; Tokyo 1990, no. 29

1965.7–24.04 (Japanese Painting ADD 380). Bequest
of C. Maresco Pearce

A woman has washed her face in a shallow
copper basin and is about to dry it with a
cotton hand-towel in preparation to
applying the white face makeup from the
small blue and white porcelain bowl beside

the basin. Utamaro presents the quiet,
intimate moment as she pauses, towel
spread between her hands, and glances
over to her right at a potted morning glory
in bloom. The pose of the kneeling figure,
back almost vertical and one knee raised so
the skirt of the kimono forms a tight U-
shaped curve which seems to come out of
the picture, is one seen in several of
Utamaro's colour prints; but here the effect
of placing this figure in the large horizontal
composition of the hanging scroll is quite
different. Instead of the tight cropping of
the figure found in the woodblock prints,
Utamaro displays his skill at clever
placement by putting the vertical line of the
woman's back almost in the very centre of
the scroll and then constructing around this
a stable triangular composition whose

points are the basin, the morning glory and
the top of her ballooning *marumage*
hairstyle. A similar strong triangular
composition is seen in other of the artist's
horizontal paintings of the late Kansei
period (compare, for instance, *NU*, vol. 6
(1981), nos 1, 8).

The patterns on the various textiles are
cleverly differentiated, the modulation of
the checks on her brown kimono, for
instance, used to suggest the shape of her
bent leg and the cloth collecting at her
elbow, while the blue lines and dots on the
printed cotton *yukata* (cotton kimono) and
towel are rendered correspondingly coarser
to suggest a rougher weave. The flash of
red undergarment around the naked knee
and the slightly open collar are typical
instances of Utamaro's subtle eroticism.

Kitagawa Hidemaro

worked *c.* Kyōwa (1801–4)–Bunka (1804–18) eras

Common name Haruji; *gō* Shōrinsai. Lived in front of the Shitaya Yanagi Inari Shrine. Pupil of Utamaro. Known by several series of colour prints following the late Utamaro style and collaborated with the latter in the famous illustrated book *Seirō ehon nenjū gyōji* (1804). Also illustrated novels. Only several paintings known (for example, *Geisha Holding a Shamisen*, Tokyo National Museum).

KITAGAWA HIDEMARO

70 Walking Courtesan

c. early Bunka era
SIGNATURE: Hidemaro ga
Hanging scroll; ink and colour on paper,
  119.0 × 28.5 cm
PROVENANCE: Arthur Morrison
1946.2–9.039 (Japanese Painting ADD 214).
  Bequeathed by Arthur Morrison

It must be the destiny of minor pupils of a great artist to find one aspect of their teacher's genius in which they are competent and then to exaggerate this to carve out for themselves a certain individual territory. Only once in his career did Utamaro crop a figure with the edge of a painting, in what is thought to be one of his latest works, *Courtesan Seated Playing a Shamisen*, in the Freer Gallery of Art (US, vol. 16 (1981), no. 48), and Hidemaro uses this compositional technique combined with the turned head with great effect to suggest that the woman is walking forward. Similar, too, to Utamaro's late painting style is the use of saturated colours, thickly applied; the *obi* with a design of coiling dragons in intense green and orange bands is a *tour de force*, and the same colours are used on the lips. In general, however, Utamaro's figure style – particularly the face – has been elongated in a mannered way. The fashion for bringing the two sections of the *yoko-hyōgo* hairstyle to a sharp point is seen in early prints by Eizan and would seem to date to shortly after the death of Utamaro in 1806.

70

70

Kitagawa Fujimaro

worked *c*. Kyōwa (1801–4)–
early Bunsei (1818–30) eras

Gō Kōkasai, Shien, Shihō, Shikasai, Hōshū,
Yōzan, Shusen. Presumed to be a pupil of
Utamaro. Nothing is known of his
biography. One of the most prolific
painters among Utamaro's followers, more
than a dozen paintings recorded – mainly
of *bijin* subjects – including an ambitious
six-fold screen showing *Beauties at Enoshima*
(formerly Nikaidō Bunko Collection; *NU*,
vol. 6 (1981), no. 22) in which the influence
of Utamaro's figure style is still strongly
apparent. The painting *Woman from Ōhara* is
dated Bunsei 2 (1819). In his later paintings
the figures become smaller and the
pointed, impish features and expressions of
childlike surprise more pronounced.

KITAGAWA FUJIMARO

71 Young Man

c. early Bunka era
SIGNATURE: Fujimaro hitsu
SEALS: Hōshū, (unread)
Hanging scroll; ink and colour on silk,
    94.0 × 33.0 cm
1989.6–24.01 (Japanese Painting ADD 894)

Bijin ('beautiful person') is a term of
approbation that can be applied to both
men and women, but Ukiyo-e *bijin*
paintings that feature handsome men, even
in the company of women, are extremely
rare. Here a youth who has not yet reached
maturity and shaven off his forelock is
shown dressed in striped brown *hakama*
leggings over a plain blue kimono and
sporting a single sword thrust through his
belt. The only touch of extravagance in his
clothing is a glimpse at the collar of a red
and white checked under-kimono. It is
hard to be sure what is his station in life.
Another painting of a young man by
Fujimaro seems to show a trainee Kabuki
actor of the Sawamura family (Cleveland
Museum of Art 1988, pl. 1) accompanied by
a boy attendant. Perhaps this young man,
too, is associated with the theatre in some
way.

   The large, broad face with its open,
appealing expression is typical of
Fujimaro's earliest works still showing the
strong influence of Utamaro, and the
painting may tentatively be dated to the
early Bunka era (1804–18). An almost
identical form of signature and seals is
found in *Parody of the Six Immortal Poets*
(Tobacco and Salt Museum, Tokyo; *NU*,
vol. 6 (1981), no. 23).

71

71

Hosoda Eishi 1756–1829

Na Tokitomi; common names Taminosuke, Yasaburō; *gō* Chōbunsai, Kaei, (?)Dokuyū. Lived in Hama-chō, later Honjo Wari-gesui. Eishi was of unusually high rank for an Ukiyo-e artist, his grandfather and great-grandfather having both served as Chief of Accounts (*kantei bugyō*) for the Bakufu, with a stipend of 500 *koku*, court rank of Lower Fifth Grade and the title Governor of Tamba Province. This permitted Eishi to study painting under Kanō Eisen'in Michinobu (1730–90), head of the Kanō school and Chief Painter in Attendance (*oku-eshi*) to the Shōgun Ieharu after 1781. The nineteenth-century compilation of painters' biographies, *Koga bikō*, even records that Eishi was appointed as Ieharu's 'painting companion' (*on-ga no tomo*), though he was forced to retire after only three years of service because of ill health, presumably before Ieharu's death in 1786.

It was at about this time that Eishi must have taken the decision to 'drop out' of the Bakufu bureaucracy and painting academy and become an artist of the popular Ukiyo-e school. Such a transformation was not entirely unprecedented: it was at this time that Sakai Hōitsu, second son of the Lord of Himeji, was studying Ukiyo-e painting with Utagawa Toyoharu. Eishi never relinquished his high status, however, and some of his best later Ukiyo-e paintings are signed with titles such as 'Painted by Eishi, High Official of the Ministry of Ceremonial, Tokitomi of the Fujiwara Clan' ('Jibukyō Eishi Fujiwara Tokitomi hitsu').

His earliest works in Ukiyo-e style were illustrations for a *kibyōshi* novel published in 1785, and in general his colour prints of the later 1780s follow the prevailing style of Kiyonaga, with a particular penchant for courtly themes, as in his series of triptychs reworking chapters from *Tale of Genji* in modern settings, printed entirely in muted colours. In the 1790s he produced a steady stream of prints of standing or seated beauties against simple backgrounds that show the influence of Utamaro, but have a particularly refined tone (often likening the courtesans to female poets from the Heian period) and a style that favoured broad sweeping curves in the drapery.

Eishi was one of the most prolific of Ukiyo-e painters, and although his corpus of several hundred paintings has yet to be studied systematically and in detail, there are a handful of dated works that fall between 1795 and 1826. The figures show the same elegant line and refined poses as in the woodblock prints and are often set in ink-wash landscapes deftly painted in the Edo–Kanō technique learned in his youth. Eishi was often prone to repeating successful compositions, and, for example, more than a dozen versions survive in various formal and informal painting styles of a handscroll, *The Gods of Good Fortune Visit Yoshiwara*, based on a comic essay of 1781, *Kakure-zato no ki* ('Record of the Hidden Village'), by Ōta Nampo. Nampo was a leading figure in popular literature from the 1780s to his death in 1823, and his *kyōka* (crazy verse) or *kanshi* (Chinese-style poem) inscriptions are often to be found on Eishi's paintings: Eishi did several versions of a portrait of the famous writer.

In addition to paintings on Ukiyo-e themes Eishi did several versions of a handscroll, *The Battle of Sekigahara* (fought in 1600), presumably for military patrons. It is with precisely the same touch Eishi used to paint the crests of Yoshiwara courtesans on their lanterns that he now painted the emblems of military families on their battle standards: nothing could illustrate more neatly the duality of the world he inhabited. It is further recorded that on one occasion the retired Emperor Gosakuramachi saw a painting by Eishi, *Sumida River*, and was sufficiently taken with it for the work to enter the Imperial collections. After this Eishi occasionally impressed a large seal on his paintings reading 'Viewed by the Emperor' (*tenkan*).

Almost thirty pupils of Eishi are recorded, the most prominent being Eishō, Eiri and Eisui, who are known for their colour prints of the 1790s showing bust portraits of famous courtesans. Most other pupils are known only by a few paintings in Eishi style, and it seems that after *c.* 1800 the new, brash tenor of commercial printing – epitomised by the Utagawa school – was no longer in tune with Eishi's fine sensibilities. After this time he produced only paintings.

72

72

HOSODA EISHI

72 The Chinese Beauty Yang Guifei

Late Kansei–Bunka eras
SIGNATURE: Chōbunsai Eishi hitsu
SEAL: Eishi
Hanging scroll; ink, colour and gold on silk,
43.9 × 60.3 cm
PROVENANCE: Arthur Morrison
LITERATURE: Brandt 1977, painting no. 478; TNM
1987, no. 24; *UT*, vol. 1 (1987), no. 126; Smith
1990, no. 197
1913.5–1.0405 (Japanese Painting 1424). Given by
Sir W. Gwynne-Evans, Bt

Yang Guifei was the fabulously beautiful
consort of the Tang Emperor Xuanzong
(AD 685–762). At his command the poet Li
Bo composed poems likening her beauty to
the peony, most prestigious of flowers, and
comparing her to female deities and
immortals. Eishi did several paintings of
Yang Guifei, on one occasion pitting her
against the equally fabled Japanese court

beauty Ono no Komachi and a Yoshiwara
courtesan in *Parody of the Three Vinegar
Tasters* (Museum of Fine Arts, Boston).
Here, however, perhaps taking his idea
from Li Bo's poem likening her to female
mountain hermits, Eishi has painted Yang
Guifei playing the flute, seated alone on an
elaborate Chinese-style throne, surrounded
by flowering trees and peonies in an
otherwise open mountain landscape. He
also did two upright versions of this
composition (Freer Gallery of Art; *Kokka*,
487 (1931), p. 178).

The skilful overlaying of washes in the
landscape to produce an effect of light seen
through appropriately mythical clouds
gives evidence of Eishi's early training in
the Edo–Kanō style, and combines with his
hyper-refined figure drawing and the
wealth of chinoiserie accessories to produce
a work with an exceptionally rich range of
tonalities.

73

73

HOSODA EISHI

73 Four Women and a Boy Viewing Cherry Blossom

Late Kansei–Bunka eras
SIGNATURE: Chōbunsai Eishi hitsu
SEALS: Eishi, (?)Dokuyū
Hanging scroll; ink, colour and gold on silk,
    40.7 × 72.5 cm
PROVENANCE: Arthur Morrison
LITERATURE: Morrison 1911, vol. 2, pl. XXI; Brandt
    1977, painting no. 486; UT, vol. 1 (1987),
    BW no. 22
1913.5–1.0410 (Japanese Painting 1429). Given by
    Sir W. Gwynne-Evans, Bt

In this slight but charming work four women and a boy are shown gesticulating excitedly as they wander along winding paths amid banks of flowering cherry trees. They are seen from above as if from further up the hill, and the location is probaby Gotenyama, a hilly beauty spot at Shinagawa on the south-eastern outskirts of Edo, famous for its views over Edo Bay and the cherry trees, which had been transplanted from Yoshino in the seventeenth century. This is confirmed by a painting on a similar theme in the Ujiie Collection (Ujiie 1974, no. 59, dated 1811) which shows boats on the horizon in the bay. Several more compositions by Eishi based on this subject are known.

The figures are small but animated in a manner not found in more formal works, and they have been surrounded once again by a soft landscape in limpid Kanō-style washes, the spiky branches and blossoms of the cherry trees drawn with considerable lively flourish.

HOSODA EISHI

74 'Palace Emanating from the Clam'
(Shinkirō)

Late Kansei–Bunka eras
SIGNATURE: Chōbunsai Eishi hitsu
SEAL: Eishi
Hanging scroll; ink and colour on silk,
  81.0 × 31.2 cm
PROVENANCE: Arthur Morrison
LITERATURE: Brandt 1977, painting no. 443; UT, vol. 1
  (1987), BW no. 19
1913.5–1.0404 (Japanese Painting 1423). Given by
  Sir W. Gwynne-Evans, Bt

Two *kamuro* attendants of a Yoshiwara
courtesan are shown in a cloud emanating
from a parcel of clams, a New Year gift
attached to a branch of flowering white
plum. This curious subject must derive
from a pun on a phrase in the ancient
Chinese Han dynasty chronicles, the *Shi ji*
(Japanese: *Shiki*), in which occurs the
assertion that palaces can be created from
the air (or 'breath') which emanates from
clams. In Edo-period Japan *rō* (palace) had
the specific secondary meaning of one of
the grand licensed brothels of the
Yoshiwara pleasure quarter. Probably
through some *kyōka* poet's witty word-play
this gave rise to a series of images by Eishi
in which a courtesan or her attendants (or
both) are shown in clouds coming out of
clams. Big clams send out courtesans, while
little ones (as here) produce only child
attendants. The title given this subject in
Japanese, paraphrasing the original
Chinese, is *Shinkirō* ('Palace Emanating
from the Clam'). Perhaps the recipient of a
present of clams also hoped to get a
courtesan.

As with the painting *Kamuro Shaving the
Pate of Fukurokuju* (no. 76), the figures are
in Ukiyo-e polychrome, while the clams
and plum branch are very much in Kanō
ink-wash style.

74

74

75

HOSODA EISHI

75 Woman Dreaming of 'Tales of Ise'

Late Kansei–Bunka eras
SIGNATURE: Chōbunsai Eishi hitsu
SEAL: Eishi
Hanging scroll; ink, colour and gold on silk,
 88.7 × 31.2 cm
PROVENANCE: Arthur Morrison
LITERATURE: Brandt 1977, painting no. 444; UT, vol. 1
 (1987), BW no. 18
1913.5–1.0407 (Japanese Painting 1426). Given by
 Sir W. Gwynne-Evans, Bt

The convention in Ukiyo-e is to show the content of a dream in a cloud-like emanation from the head. Here a young woman has been reading *Ise monogatari* ('Tales of Ise'), the title clearly legible on the book in her drooping hand and on the book box on which she rests her elbow. The episode which has fuelled her imagination and features in the dream is chapter 12 in which lovers hide in the tall grasses of Musashi Moor from guards of the Provincial Governor, who threaten to set fire to the moor with their torches (see also no. 34). Doubtless she imagines herself the heroine in many-layered brocade robes being held in the protective arms of the handsome courtier. Images such as this provide an interesting complement to the device frequently employed in Ukiyo-e of *mitate* (reworking classical themes in a contemporary guise) in as much as they suggest that people of the period had no difficulty transporting themselves in imagination back to inhabit the classical past too, a kind of *mitate* in reverse.

Two further versions of this subject are known, in the Azabu Museum of Arts and Crafts (Azabu 1986, no. 39) and Chiossone Museum (Tokyo, Mainichi Shimbun 1990, no. 212), identical save for minor differences in the patterning of the robes, in the dressing of the hair and in the positioning of the figures in the dream. Though certain artists of the period such as Shunshō never repeated a composition, Eishi frequently did, and in this instance all three versions appear equally authentic.

HOSODA EISHI

76 Kamuro Shaving the Pate of Fukurokuju

Late Kansei–Bunka eras
SIGNATURE: Chōbunsai Eishi hitsu
SEAL: Eishi
Hanging scroll; ink and colour on silk,
  71.7 × 30.3 cm
PROVENANCE: William Anderson
LITERATURE: Brandt 1977, painting no. 445; *UT*, vol. 1
  (1987), BW no. 20
1881.12–10.02045 (Japanese Painting 1430)

76

Fukurokuju, a smiling old gentleman short in stature with a high forehead and bushy whiskers and carrying a handscroll tied to a staff or flat fan, was one of the Seven Lucky Gods (*Shichifukujin*), originally a Chinese popular deity thought to be an embodiment of the South Pole stars. Paintings of the Seven Lucky Gods became a popular theme for Kanō artists in the eighteenth century as Kanō painting became increasingly 'domesticated' and lost much of its earlier lofty seriousness. A hanging scroll of Fukurokuju would often be flanked in a triptych by scrolls of a crane and a long-tailed tortoise, emblems of long life, and hung in the *tokonoma* at the New Year holiday.

In this work Eishi cleverly mixes the two styles at his disposal – Kanō and Ukiyo-e: Fukurokuju, rendered, of course, in the ink wash and highly inflected outline of Kanō painting, is having his mammoth pate shaved by a tiny *kamuro* perched at the top of a ladder, she, by contrast, painted in the delicate outline and brilliant polychrome of Ukiyo-e figure work. Her companion holds a flat basin of water at the ready. The rope hung with New Year decorations above suggests that the Lucky God is having a spruce up in preparation for the holiday festivities in the Yoshiwara quarter. The handscroll *Three Gods of Good Luck Visiting Yoshiwara*, frequently painted by Eishi, ends with scenes of Ebisu, Daikoku and Fukurokuju revelling with courtesans in the houses of pleasure. The theme seems to derive from a comic essay, *Kakurezato no ki* ('Record of the Hidden Village'), written by Ōta Nampo in 1781.

76

77

77

HOSODA EISHI

77 Cocks Fighting

c. late Kansei–Bunsei eras
SIGNATURE: Eishi hitsu
SEAL: Eishi
Hanging scroll; ink, colour and gold on silk,
 86.5 × 36.1 cm
PROVENANCE: William Anderson
LITERATURE: Anderson 1886, no. 1403; Brandt 1977
 painting no. 518; *UT*, vol. 1 (1987), no. 127
 1881.12–10.01403 (Japanese Painting 1431)

The court blind at the top of the painting
suggests that this is a cock fight staged as
one of the annual rituals of the Imperial
court, held by tradition in the south garden
of the Seiryōden Palace on the third day of
the third month each year. This would
coincide with the blossoming of the cherry
trees. Perhaps the implication is that some
august person, maybe the Emperor himself,
is viewing the match (which had divinatory
implications and was not just sport) from
behind the blind. Eishi has captured an
instant when the white cock leaps in the air
to drop on its multicoloured opponent and
several petals are knocked from the tree by
the beating of its wings.

As pointed out by Brandt (1977, painting
no. 518), the signature 'Eishi hitsu' is very
rare, found on several other paintings in
purely Kanō style; the 'clog-shape seal'
(*geta-in*) reading Ei-shi in white reserve is
unique. None the less, the trunk of the
cherry tree is done with a flourish in just
the combination of fluid washes of colour
and dark accents of *sumi* that are found in
the background landscapes of many of
Eishi's paintings, and there seems no
reason to doubt the work's authenticity. A
more precise dating, however, must await
the appearance of other subjects signed
with this form of signature and seal.

HOSODA EISHI

78 Bird, Hanging Flower Bucket and
Morning Glory

Late Kansei–Bunsei eras
SIGNATURE: Chōbunsai Eishi ?ga (in gold)
SEAL: handwritten cipher (*kaō*) in gold
Hanging scroll; ink, colour and gold on silk,
33.2 × 43.1 cm
PROVENANCE: Arthur Morrison
LITERATURE: Brandt 1977, painting no. 520
1913.5–1.0408 (Japanese Painting 1427). Given by
Sir W. Gwynne-Evans, Bt

Like a *haiku* poem, which can suggest a
whole world with a few carefully selected
fragments of reality, this modest, rapidly
executed work conveys the feeling of a
bright, fresh morning in early summer as a
small bird has come to take a drink from a
hanging flower bucket. Down the string of
the bucket twines a morning glory, its
tendrils forming pleasing arabesques as
they venture out to fill the space of the
painting around them. The bird looks up at
the large open trumpet of the blue flower.

Leaves, bucket and bird are all done in
broad, moist washes, and the signature has
been hidden on the side of the bucket so as
not to impinge on the overall sense of
lightness – though it is written in gold
paint, giving a touch of discreet luxury.
This unpretentiousness points to the scroll
having been used as a decoration for a
rustic tearoom.

78

78

79

HOSODA EISHI

79 View of the Sumida River

Bunka–Bunsei eras
SIGNATURE: Chōbunsai Eishi hitsu
SEAL: Eishi
INSCRIPTION: Sumidagawa/me ni tsuku mono wa/
  akebono no/murasaki tateru/Tsukubayama kana
INSCRIPTION SIGNATURE: Shokusanjin
Hanging scroll; ink and slight colour on silk,
  82.6 × 28.9 cm
PROVENANCE: Arthur Morrison
LITERATURE: Brandt 1977, painting no. 516; UT, vol. 1
  (1987), BW no. 21
1913.5–1.0403 (Japanese Painting 1422). Given by
  Sir W. Gwynne-Evans, Bt

Eishi's landscapes of Edo centre on the
Sumida River, the main artery of the city,
and are generally made up of
impressionistic collages of vignettes of
famous places looming out of Kanō-style
ink-wash mists. Most impressive is a pair
of six-fold screens, dated 1826, in the
Azabu Museum of Arts and Crafts (Sendai
1988, no. 55) which show a vast panorama
along the Sumida all the way from
Shinagawa to Asakusa.

The view of the present painting is
looking north-east along the upper reaches
of the Sumida, from Ōkawa (Azuma)
Bridge in the foreground (with a large
emblematic sail) to Mt Tsukuba on the
distant horizon. In between are fishermen,
pleasure-boats and a ferry close to the
shallows off Imado, and on the far bank
the top of the stone gateway to Mimeguri
Shrine, just visible above the embankment,
and Shirahige Shrine and Chōmyō Temple
surrounded by trees beyond. The *kyōka*
poem above, which contains word-play on
the name Mt Tsukuba and the expression
me ni tsuku (to catch the eye), may be
translated:

> Sumida River –
> What catches the eye
> Is the mist
> Rising from Mt Tsukuba
> At dawn.

In the painting a v-shaped formation of
geese is leaving Mt Tsukuba.

Simple works such as these could be
quickly executed in response to the huge
demand which must have been directed at
Eishi and Nampo in their later years
(Nampo used the name Shokusanjin after
1801). Under such circumstances, however,
the level of inspiration of both paintings
and poems was bound to suffer.

79

Formerly attributed to
HOSODA EISHI

80 Portrait of a Seated Man

Dated equivalent to 1815, but probably mid-19th
century
SIGNATURE: Chōbunsai Eishi gyōnen rokujussai
hitsu ('Painted by Chōbunsai Eishi, aged sixty')
SEAL: (?)Ketsuei, or (?)Tei'ei
INSCRIPTION: Utamaro zō ('Portrait of Utamaro')
Hanging scroll; ink and colour on silk,
33.0 × 39.8 cm
PROVENANCE: Arthur Morrison
LITERATURE: Arthur Morrison, 'Yeishi's Portrait of
Kitagawa Utamaro', *Ostasiatische Zeitschrift*, vol.
1 (1912–13), pp. 475–8; Binyon and Sexton 1923,
p. 137; Fujikake 1943, fig. 353; Hayashi
Yoshikazu, 'Utamaro ga aishita Tochigi', *Kikan
ukiyo-e*, 50 (Sept. 1972), p. 94; Hillier 1979,
fig. 98, text pp. 143–5; Ueno 1985, no. 123; *UT*,
vol. 1 (1987), BW no. 23; Smith 1988, no. 123
1913.5–1.0402 (Japanese Painting 1421). Given by
Sir W. Gwynne-Evans, Bt

This purported portrait of Utamaro by Eishi
has, periodically, attracted considerable
interest and debate since its introduction by
Arthur Morrison in the *Ostasiatische
Zeitschrift* in 1912 and its 'rediscovery' by
Fujikake Shizuya and reproduction in many
pre-war Japanese catalogues. Since it has
been possible to establish Eishi's birthdate
with some certainty as 1756, it is now
known that the inscription 'painted by
Chōbunsai Eishi, aged sixty', if it were
genuine, would date the painting to 1815,
nine years after Utamaro's death in 1806.
Some of the many theories and counter-
arguments concerning this painting may be
briefly summarised as follows: 'It was
painted as a memorial after Utamaro's
death' (Fujikake 1943) – 'there is nothing
significant about the ninth anniversary of
somebody's death' (Hayashi 1972); 'it is a
portrait of Utamaro II' (Hayashi 1972) –
'Eishi was too eminent a painter to
commemorate an insignificant artist such as
Utamaro II' (Hillier 1979); 'the signature is
not genuine' (Narazaki in Ueno 1985); 'it
has many problems' (Narazaki 1987).
   The present writer is not inclined to
accept it as a portrait of Eishi for the
following reasons: (1) this style of
portraiture is not otherwise found in Eishi's
oeuvre – his famous portrait of Shokusanjin
is much more schematic; (2) the general
style (which is not at all characteristic of
Eishi) and the use of thick pigments

80

suggest a later date of execution, *c.* Tempō
era (1830–44); (3) the seal, which may be
read (as two characters) 'Ketsu'ei' or 'Tei'ei'
is not found on any other Eishi painting
and does not relate to any of his known
names; (4) the *mon* (crest) on the black *haori*
jacket of crossed falcon feathers in a circle
is not known to relate to Utamaro; (5) the
likeness does not resemble any of the self-
portraits in Utamaro's prints. In summary it
seems that a false inscription, Eishi
signature and seal may have been added to
a painting done several decades later than
1815.
   It should be noted in passing that in
Kikan ukiyo-e, 50 (September 1972), p. 94,
Hayashi Yoshizaku illustrates another
purported portrait of Utamaro by Eishi,
showing an older man seated wearing a
black *haori* jacket and holding a rosary in
his left hand. Unfortunately, the present
whereabouts of this painting is unknown
and the photograph too small and blurred
to permit any useful assessment.

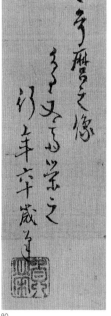

80

81

81

Utagawa Toyohiro d. 1829

Family name Okajima; common name Tōjirō; *gō* Ichiryūsai. Lived at Shiba Katamonzen-chō. Pupil of Utagawa Toyoharu, together with Toyokuni. Earliest work a calendar print for 1788, but other datable works rare until *c.* 1800. From 1800 to *c.* 1810 illustrations for *kibyōshi* and *gōkan* ('combined volume' illustrated novels); from *c.* 1806 to 1827 illustrations for *yomihon* (didactic novels with frontispieces). From late Kansei (1789–1801) to Bunka (1804–18) eras a small number of *bijin* and landscape prints. Accomplished painter of beauties, of which at least thirty examples are known. Teacher of Utagawa Hiroshige.

UTAGAWA TOYOHIRO

81 Geisha with a Shamisen

Mid Kansei–Kyōwa eras
SIGNATURE: Toyohiro ga
SEAL: handwritten cipher (*kaō*) in red
Hanging scroll; ink, colour and gold on paper,
    105.0 × 42.1 cm
PROVENANCE: Arthur Morrison
LITERATURE: Morrison 1911, vol. 2, pl. xxv; *UT*, vol. 1
    (1987), no. 135; Tokyo 1990, no. 33
1913.5–1.0397 (Japanese Painting 1437). Given by
    Sir W. Gwynne-Evans, Bt

Her elongated body arched into a single, sweeping curve, a geisha stands in front of a free-standing screen (*tsuitate*) tuning her *shamisen* and seeming to listen to what is being said on the other side of the screen, before she enters some party group to perform. She wears the slightly sombre ensemble that was customary for geishas – a blue kimono with a pattern of small plant fronds scattered around the hem and a wide brown *obi* with a design of large banana leaves picked out in green. The bottom half of the screen is painted with autumn vine leaves in Edo Rimpa style, and this is where Toyohiro playfully chooses to place his signature, as if he were the artist of the screen and not of the figure.

   The manner of drawing the face and the elongated proportions are highly reminiscent of the mid–late Kansei era (1789–1801) style of Toyokuni, a fellow, but somewhat senior, pupil of Toyoharu, who was much more prolific than Toyohiro at this time. Toyohiro had followed Toyokuni in the style of his paintings from his very first works done probably in the early Kansei era (1789–1801), often signed 'Utagawa Toyohiro'. Later, however, in the Bunka (1804–18) and Bunsei (1818–30) eras Toyohiro's figures would develop their own, much more fragile and idiosyncratic style with long necks and narrow faces.

82

UTAGAWA TOYOHIRO

82 Promenading Courtesan

Bunka era
SIGNATURE: Ichiryūsai Toyohiro ga
SEAL: Toyohiro
Hanging scroll; ink and colour on silk,
    94.7 × 29.7 cm
PROVENANCE: Arthur Morrison
LITERATURE: *UT*, vol. 1 (1987), BW no. 24
1913.5–1.0398 (Japanese Painting 1438). Given by
    Sir W. Gwynne-Evans, Bt

Dressed in all her finery, a courtesan makes the stately, ceremonial procession in the quarter, from the brothel where she lives to an assignation teahouse to greet a client. The costume – a kimono decorated with plovers and waves and a surcoat of a foaming waterfall – is dominated by the extraordinarily large bow of the *obi*, tied in front, which is even wider than the woman's body itself. This, together with the fashion for wearing the hair long, loosely combed out and gathered at the ends with a ribbon, as well as the complex aureole of hairpins surrounding her head, is reminiscent of the colour prints of Eizan, dating from the decade following the death of Utamaro in 1806.

    The technique of the present painting is unusual in as much as the angular 'hooked' outlines of the drapery, the calligraphic flourishes of the patterning and the generally thin, transparent colouring are much more characteristic of cheaper works on paper rather than paintings on silk. Perhaps this was to speed up production to meet burgeoning demand.

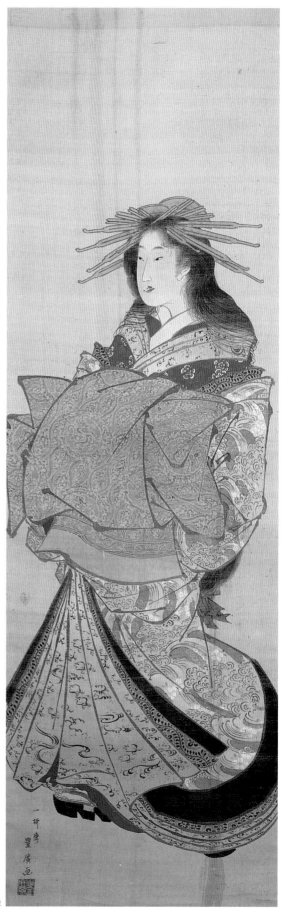

82

83

Utagawa Toyokuni 1769–1825

Family name Kurahashi; common name Kumayoshi; *gō* Ichiyōsai. Son of a doll-carver, Gorōbei, in Shiba Jimmei-mae Mishima-chō, later lived in Yoshi-chō and Horie-chō, finally by 1808 in Nihombashi Kamimaki-chō. Pupil of Utagawa Toyoharu. Earliest work illustrations for *kibyōshi* novels, *c.* 1787–8. From *c.* 1790 triptychs of beauties in the style of Kiyonaga, sometimes with perspective backgrounds in the style of Toyoharu. About this time began an association with the publisher Izumiya Ichibei, for whom he began a revolutionary series of actor portraits in the spring of 1794, the *Yakusha butai no sugata-e* ('Pictures of Actors on Stage'), sometimes in diptych and triptych format with one figure to each *ōban* sheet – which would become the standard format in the nineteenth century. From *c.* 1796 an important group of bust portraits of actors and from 1799 illustrated books of actor portraits that would constitute the 'standard likeness' (*nigao-e*) for the Utagawa school. Leading designer of illustrations for *gōkan* and later *yomihon* novels. At least thirty paintings of beauties known, dating from the Kansei era (1789–1801) onwards.

UTAGAWA TOYOKUNI

83   The Kabuki Actor Segawa Ronosuke as Shizuka Gozen

(?)1803
SIGNATURE: Ichiyōsai Toyokuni ga
SEALS: Utagawa, Toyokuni
INSCRIPTION: Sakura saku/koro wa shizuka ni/hokō kana
INSCRIPTION SIGNATURE: Segawa Ronosuke
Hanging scroll; ink and colour on silk,
   93.8 × 25.5 cm
PROVENANCE: Arthur Morrison
LITERATURE: Morrison 1911, vol. 2, pl. XXIV;
   UT, vol. 1 (1987), no. 134; Smith 1990, no. 198
1913.5–1.0399 (Japanese Painting 1439). Given by
   Sir W. Gwynne-Evans, Bt

Standing beneath branches of cherry in full bloom, the young actor Segawa Ronosuke (who used this name from 1801 to 1807) is dressed for travelling. The female character he plays has a bundle tied around her shoulders and carries a large, flat, black lacquer hat and a long walking-stick. The kimono, one sleeve of which has been shrugged off to accommodate the bundle, is decorated with a dazzling pattern of yellow blossoms scattered on stylised flowing water.

A short *haiku* poem, written (and probably composed) by the actor himself, is inscribed in elegantly trailing lines of calligraphy at the top of the painting:

   In the season of
   Blossoming cherry
   Why not proceed more slowly?

Aside from the obvious invitation to linger in one's travels and admire the blossoming cherry, the poem contains a punning allusion to the name of Princess Shizuka, who is probably the character portrayed here by Ronosuke. Shizuka's flight to Mt Yoshino, famous for its cherry trees, was the most poignant scene in the play *Yoshitsune sembon-zakura* ('Yoshitsune and the Yoshino Cherry Trees'), and Shizuka a role particularly associated with Ronosuke's great predecessor, Segawa Kikunojō III. Ronosuke is recorded as having played the role of Shizuka only once – at the Ichimura theatre in the eighth month of 1803 – and it is likely that this is the performance Toyokuni has painted.

In comparison with paintings of beauties paintings of actors are rare, and since this example is actually inscribed by Ronosuke one can imagine that it was intended as a gift for one of his important patrons.

UTAGAWA TOYOKUNI

84   Parody of Sugawara no Michizane Seated on an Ox

Late Bunka–early Bunsei eras
SIGNATURE: Utagawa Toyokuni ga
SEALS: ?Ichiyōsai, Toyokuni
Hanging scroll; ink, colour and gold on silk,
   94.6 × 32.5 cm
PROVENANCE: Shōzō Katō
LITERATURE: *UT*, vol. 1 (1987), BW no. 25
1927.10–13.07 (Japanese Painting ADD 47)

When an Ukiyo-e painting shows a beauty in a somewhat unusual setting, this is often a clue that there are other layers of meaning intended – allusions to episodes from history or classical literature – a device known as *mitate* (see Introduction, p. 21). This painting has in the past gone by the title of *Geisha on a Pilgrimage to Enoshima* (an

island linked to the shore by a causeway near Kamakura where there was a famous shrine to Benten, a popular destination for tourists from Edo), and, indeed, that is certainly its ostensible subject. An immaculately dressed geisha does not normally ride side-saddle on an ox, however, and there are additional references here to: (1) the goddess Benten who is sometimes portrayed seated on an ox (no. 124); and (2) an episode in the life of the ill-fated courtier and statesman Sugawara no Michizane (845–903), who died in lonely exile at Dazaifu in Kyūshū as a result of the machinations of his rival, Fujiwara no Shihei. Legends concerning the life of Michizane (or Tenjin, as he was deified to placate his angry spirit shortly after his death) abounded in the Edo period and formed the basis of one of the most popular puppet and Kabuki plays ever written, *Sugawara denju tenarai kagami* ('Sugawara's Secrets of Calligraphy'), first performed in 1746.

A colour woodblock-print diptych by Toyokuni records a scene in this play, not now generally performed, in which Yae, the faithful maid of his daughter, Princess Kariya, leads by a rope an ox on which Michizane (or Kan Shōjō, as he is called in the play) is mounted (see Tokiwayama Bunko (eds), *Kankō*, exh. cat., 1965, fig. 70). The manner of drawing the ox is identical, down to the way in which one foreleg is bent back, and there can be little doubt that it is also Yae and Michizane who are being impersonated by the boy and the geisha in the present painting. The beach at Enoshima is presumably supposed to evoke Michizane's forlorn place of exile.

The painting can be placed in the last decade of Toyokuni's career, based on the similarity in signature and seals to a painting thought to relate to the visit to Edo by the actor Nakamura Utaemon III in 1818–19 (*NU*, vol. 8 (1981), no. 6), and exhibits the characteristic brilliant colouring and immaculate attention to detail of works of this period. The unusual sense of modelling in the treatment of the waves derives ultimately from Western-style paintings by such artists as Shiba Kōkan, possibly through the intermediary of Hokusai, who experimented with this style in woodblock prints during the decade *c.* 1800–10.

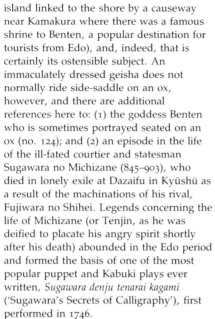

84

85

85

UTAGAWA TOYOKUNI

85 Woman Comforting a Baby

Bunka era
SIGNATURE: Toyokuni ga
SEAL: Ichiyōsai
Hanging scroll (mounted in board); ink and
 colour on paper, 36.6 × 54.2 cm
1986.8–1.01 (Japanese Painting ADD 831)

A woman wearing a thin cotton kimono
with checked blue and red ikat-dyed design
and black *obi* is seated holding a reluctant
baby boy up to her cheek. On the floor
behind is a fan decorated with painted iris,
suggesting the time of year is the fifth
month, midsummer.

To suit the light-hearted subject the
handling of the outlines is spontaneous,
the colouring rudimentary (except for a few
small accents of brilliant tie-dyed fabrics)
and the forms loosely composed. Rapidly
executed paintings on paper such as this
must have been frequently painted to
request on the spot by Ukiyo-e painters,
but perhaps because they were not so
highly valued as more finished paintings
on silk they are less frequently encountered
today.

86

Santō Kyōden (Kitao Masanobu)
1761–1816

Family name Iwase; *na* Samuru; *azana* Yūsei; common name Kyōya Denzō; childhood name Jintarō, later Denzō; *gō* Sensai, Sogo, Santōan, Seisai, Seiseisai, Seisei Rōjin, Kikutei, Kikuken; *kyōka-gō* Migaru no Orichika. Born at Fukagawa Kiba, the son of Denzaemon Nobuaki, a pawnbroker. Ran a pipe and pipe-case shop called Kyōya at Kyōbashi Ginza itchōme. Pupil of Kitao Shigemasa. Earliest dated work illustrations for a *kibyōshi*, *Kaichō riyaku no meguriai*, published in 1778; would become one of the leading authors and illustrators of this genre, creating the famous, pretentious playboy character Enjirō in *Edo-umare uwaki no kabayaki*, published in 1785. From the beginning of the 1780s designed illustrated books and illustrations for *kyōka* anthologies, as well as colour prints of beauties and a handful of paintings. In 1783–4 produced lavish double-*ōban* prints of courtesans which were bound together into the album *Yoshiwara keisei shin bijin awase jihitsu kagami* (Introduction, fig. 13). In 1789 during the Kansei Reforms for his satirical *kibyōshi* illustrations, and modified his acerbic style. Ceased using the name Kitao Masanobu and his activities as an Ukiyo-e painter and printmaker at about this time. Thereafter paintings are generally slight works in abbreviated styles, signed Kyōden.

SANTŌ KYŌDEN

86 Woman Returning from the Bath

Kansei–Bunka eras, before 1816
SIGNATURE: Santō Kyōden hitsu
SEAL: Kyōden
INSCRIPTION: Mono omou/ori ya hito koe/mezura-dori
INSCRIPTION SIGNATURE: Muhi Mushi Dōjin
INSCRIPTION SEALS: ?Suirin'an, Muhi Mushi Dōjin
Hanging scroll; ink and slight colour on paper, 108.0 × 27.5 cm
PROVENANCE: Arthur Morrison
1946.2–9.038 (Japanese Painting ADD 188). Bequeathed by Arthur Morrison

In this loosely and sketchily executed work a woman stands in the corridor on the way back from the bath, absent-mindedly piling up her hair with one hand and pulling her cotton robe around her with the other. At her feet is a shallow wooden bucket and washcloth. Up in the space above, by convention in the sky outside, flies a cuckoo. The *senryū* poem inscribed by one who signs himself 'Sage of Neither This Nor That' reads:

When something's on your mind,
How wondrous!
A single cry of the cuckoo.

The poem contains a pun on the word *mezurashi* which means 'wondrous' and is also the beginning of *mezura-dori*, one of the many poetic names for the cuckoo (*hototogisu*) that calls in the fifth month, midsummer.

The style is refreshingly inelegant and down-to-earth in comparison with the generic poise and polish of most Ukiyo-e paintings. It has not yet been possible to ascertain the 'real life' identity of Muhi Mushi Dōjin.

SANTŌ KYŌDEN

87 Zen Priest's Fly Whisk

Kansei–Bunka eras, before 1816
SIGNATURE: Kyōden gasan ('Painted and inscribed by Kyōden')
INSCRIPTION: Ikan zo kore tsūshi sairai no iki/yazen no kashiwa-mochi chokibune ni neburu
Fan painting; ink and colour on mica-covered paper, 17.3 × 47.5 cm
PROVENANCE: Hosomi Ryō; Ralph Harari
LITERATURE: Hillier 1970, vol. 1, no. 70
1982.7–1.017(9) (Japanese Painting ADD 7021)

A *hossu* is a ceremonial fly whisk used by Zen priests and, more particularly in the context of this painting, is an attribute of Daruma (Bodhidharma), founder of the Zen sect. *Daruma* was a slang word for 'prostitute' in the Edo period (no. 93), which might explain the humorous mixing of the sacred and profane worlds in the inscription on this fan, phrased as if it were a Zen *kōan* (philosophical riddle):

How chic for the rebirth/revisit of a Man of Fashion –
Last night's sweetmeats licked in the ferry.

This is undoubtedly a parody of some Zen proverb well known at the time, but it has not been possible to discover what. The word *sairai*, as well as being the Buddhist term for rebirth, could also mean a second visit to a courtesan by a favoured customer; and the ferry is more specifically a *choki-bune* ('boar's tusk' boat), which carried customers along the Sumida River to and from the Yoshiwara pleasure quarter.

86 87

87

Kuwagata Keisai
(Kitao Masayoshi) 1764–1824

Family name Akabane (later Kuwagata); *na* Tsuguzane (Shōshin); *azana* Shikei; common name Sanjirō; *gō* Keisai, Sankō; *kyōka-gō* Mugino Orochimaro; *gesaku-gō* Kishō Tengō. His father was Tanaka (?)Yoshiharu, of Okitsu in Suruga Province. Later adopted by the Akabane family of Shimotsuke Province, who ran a tatami business in Edo. Masayoshi was born in Edo and lived first in Sugimori Shindō, then Shin Himono-chō and finally Kanda Benkeibashi. Pupil of Kitao Shigemasa, later Kanō Yōsen'in Korenobu. Prolific illustrator of *kibyōshi* (about 180) and other (about sixty) books from *c.* 1780 onwards. From early 1780s paintings of *bijin* and views of Edo, at first signed Sanjirō, and from mid-1780s colour prints of beauties, warriors and perspective views. Used the *gō* Keisai after *c.* 1785. In fifth month, 1794, appointed as painter in attendance to the Lord of the Tsuyama fief and from sixth month, 1797, took his grandmother's family name of Kuwagata, began study with Kanō Yōsen'in Korenobu at the orders of his Lord, and devoted himself entirely to painting and book illustration, developing the *ryakuga-shiki* (abbreviated painting style). In 1803 painted handscroll of *Scenes of Edo Prosperity* (*Tōto hanjō zukan*) for Matsudaira Sadanobu, and in the following year three handscrolls of *Scenes of Craftsmen* (*Kinsei shokunin-zukushi ekotoba*) for the same patron. In 1810 accompanied his Lord to the Tsuyama fief and painted a bird's-eye panorama of Edo on *fusuma* (sliding-door panels) in the castle which was reproduced in numerous printed and smaller painted versions. Masayoshi had, however, consistently experimented with bird's-eye panoramas since a small fan painting of Nakazu dated the fifth month, 1783 (Ōta Memorial Museum of Art). His later paintings, signed Shōshin (Tsuguzane), are a mixture of Ukiyo-e, Kanō and his own 'abbreviated painting' style, and often the figures revive archaic fashions from earlier in the Edo period (Introduction, fig. 22).

88

88

KUWAGATA KEISAI

88 Courtesan and Attendant

Mid Kansei–early Bunka eras
SIGNATURE: Shōshin (Tsuguzane) hitsu
SEAL: handwritten cipher (*kaō*)
Hanging scroll; ink on paper, 41.7 × 17.1 cm
PROVENANCE: Ralph Harari
LITERATURE: Hillier 1973, vol. 3, no. 214; Hillier 1980, no. 42; UT, vol. 1 (1987), BW no. 16
1982.7–1.025 (Japanese Painting ADD 712)

After all the meticulous, highly finished paintings in this catalogue it comes as something of a relief to encounter this lightning sketch of a courtesan and her *kamuro* attendant, done with the minimum of rapidly brushed lines in the 'abbreviated painting style' (*ryakuga-shiki*) perfected by Masayoshi after the middle years of the Kansei era (1789–1801). In a series of colour-printed illustrated books of beguiling humour and utter originality, all with the title ending . . . *ryakuga-shiki*, he captures the individual essence of figures, birds, beasts, fish and even landscapes with just a few telling strokes and colour washes.

Many of the figures in Masayoshi's later paintings wear archaic fashions – perhaps to indicate that he had distanced himself from the up-to-date world of Ukiyo-e – and abbreviated though the drawing is here, the courtesan clearly has the seventeenth-century *hyōgo-mage* hairstyle, in which the hair is twisted into a knot on top of the head.

89

JORAN (dates unknown)

89 Beauty with a Cat

Late Kansei–early Bunka eras
SIGNATURE: Joran
SEALS: Jo, Ran
INSCRIPTION: Kagerou no/omoi ni soete/karaneko
   no/tsuma kou koe mo/yowa ni yawa kiku
INSCRIPTION SIGNATURE: Chikage
Hanging scroll; ink, colour and gold on silk,
   45.7 × 62.9 cm
PROVENANCE: William Anderson
LITERATURE: Anderson 1886, no. 1705; *UT*, vol. 1
   (1987), BW no. 10
1881.12–10.01705 (Japanese Painting 1597)

A beauty wearing her hair in the 'Shimada'
style of the bygone Genroku era
(1688–1704) reclines fondling a pet cat that
nestles in the open neck of her kimono at
her breast. Outlined with luxuriant black
brushstrokes that taper and swell around
the contours of her body, the brilliant
scarlet kimono is decorated with bold
patterns in blue, green and gold, tied with
a blue *obi* with a design of curling plant
fronds in gold. A *waka* poem suggesting

her thoughts is inscribed above by the
noted poet, calligrapher and scholar Katō
Chikage (1735–1808):

   Why do I hear
   The kitten mewing for its mate
   At dead of night?
   Is it because he matches
   My own darkening thoughts?

The woman's cheerful expression,
however, hardly indicates that she is
sleeplessly waiting for a lover who does not
come.

Nothing is recorded of the artist Joran,
though the high level of technical
accomplishment suggests he must have
been a professional painter. The style is so
close to the archaising works of
Masayoshi's later career (compare, for
instance, Introduction, fig. 22) that it is
tempting to suggest that Joran must be an
alternative name used by him; though this
hypothesis must, of course, await
confirmation from some other source.

89

90

90

TAKESHIBA GENKEI (dates unknown)

90 Courtesan Painting Fans

4th month, Kansei 7 (1795)
SIGNATURE: Kinoto u shuka motome [ni] ōji/
Takeshiba Genkei gisho ('Written for
amusement by Takeshiba Genkei, at special
request in the 4th month, 1795')
SEALS: Zuiko, Takeshiba ?gihitsu ('Painted for
amusement by Takeshiba'), Hakkei no in
INSCRIPTION: Yun xiang yi shang hua xiang rong/
Chun feng fu jian lu hua nong
Hanging scroll; ink, colour and gold on silk,
33.0 × 50.5 cm
PROVENANCE: W. L. Behrens; Miss M. H. Turner
LITERATURE: Henri L. Joly, *W. L. Behrens Collection,
Part IV: Buddhistic Section and Chinese Antiquities*,
London, Glendenning & Co., 1913–14, p. 36,
pl. XLIV.
1944. 10–14.01 (Japanese Painting ADD 168).
Presented by Miss M. H. Turner

A courtesan seated at a Chinese-style black
lacquer table pauses to think what she will
paint on the blank folding fan she has open
in one hand. On the other side of the table
her *kamuro* attendant holds a fan already
painted with a branch of flowering cherry
and appears to turn and talk to the
courtesan. A young boy brings in
refreshment on a tray. All of the painting
accessories – brush pot with peacock
feathers, ink-stone, brush-rest and tray of
pigments in jars and saucers – have been
meticulously delineated.

The inscription above quotes part of a
Chinese verse by the poet Li Bo from the
Qing ping diao anthology written in AD 743
at the command of the Tang Emperor
Xuanzong about his beautiful concubine
Yang Guifei. It is signed by one Takeshiba
Genkei and dated 1795, has been written in
reverse – presumably from the back of the
silk before the painting was mounted – and
has been translated:

> The glamor of colored clouds gleams in
>   her raiment,
> And a flower's ravishing beauty radiates
>   from her face;
> The spring breezes gently sweep the
>   dew-drenched balustrade.

> (Sun Yu, *Li Po: A New Translation*, Hong Kong,
> The Commercial Press, 1982, p. 152)

A painting in the Japan Ukiyo-e Museum,
Courtesan and Kamuro, painted in a
comparable style also has an inscription in
seven-character Chinese couplets, in a very
similar hand, also written backwards
(Matsumoto 1985, no. 344). Judging by the
fashions, this looks to have been painted
five to ten years after the British Museum
scroll, but similarities in the spiky line
quality, the slightly aquiline nose, and the
manner, commented on by Kobayashi
Tadashi (ibid.), in which the pigments are
rather roughly applied, all suggest that the
two paintings were done by the same artist

and that he was probably the same
individual who wrote the inscriptions. The
inscription on the Japan Ukiyo-e Museum
painting is signed 'Shibamizu Sekigei', who
Kobayashi suggests may be the same
individual as Senseki Shibamizu, a
calligrapher mentioned in a directory of
famous Edo artists of the early 1830s, *Edo
genzon meika ichiran*. The name Takeshiba
on the British Museum painting shares the
same 'shiba' character and may be yet
another name used by the same individual,
who seems to have been primarily a
calligrapher and only an amateur, yet fairly
accomplished Ukiyo-e painter.

Attributed to
EISHŌSAI CHŌKI
worked late Temmei era (1781–9)–*c*. 1813

91 Courtesan and Asahina

Mid–late Kansei era
Hanging scroll; ink and colour on paper,
129.0 × 53.0 cm
PROVENANCE: box inscription by 'Yōrōken'
attributing the painting to Chōki
LITERATURE: *UT*, vol. 1 (1987), no. 123
1985.6–29.01 (Japanese Painting ADD 739)

Wada no Saburō Yoshihide, generally
known by the name Asahina, was a fabled
warrior of the early Kamakura period
(1185–1333), who in the Edo period was

adopted as a popular hero into early Kabuki drama, appearing as the henchman of the Soga brothers Gorō and Jūrō in New Year Soga plays. Asahina's moment of glory comes when he grabs the skirt of the armour worn by Gorō to prevent him impetuously dashing off after their enemy Kudō Suketsune, in a trial of strength known as the 'armour-tugging' (*kusazuri-biki*) scene. In a performance of 1759, however, a new variation on this standard treatment was introduced in which Gorō's place was taken by his sweetheart, the courtesan Kewaizaka no Shōshō of the Ōiso pleasure quarter. Learning that the evil Kudō Suketsune is in the same quarter, she determines to rush off and challenge him but is restrained by Asahina who grasps the end of her *obi* (*obi hiki*). This was a chance to introduce a softer mood and display the talents of the great female impersonator Segawa Kikunojō II. Since the figures in this painting do not bear actors' crests on their costumes, it is unlikely that it relates to a theatrical performance. Rather the idea may be to match a courtesan of the day with the muscular hero in a kind of *mitate* treatment.

The figure of the courtesan is executed entirely in shades of *sumi* with shell white on her face and hands and just a touch of colour in her hair ornaments. The butterfly pattern on the end of her sleeve is the emblem of her lover, Gorō. Asahina, in contrast, is portrayed in whiskery, full-blooded colour, holding a large sake cup and grimacing with somewhat befuddled determination. He wears his standard voluminous blue costume, white 'strength' papers in his hair and a massive curved sword. The lines of the drapery are executed with a kind of mannered nervousness.

The painting has in the past been attributed to Eishōsai Chōki, and certainly the face of the woman is reminiscent of the woodblock-print bust portraits of courtesans with mica backgrounds designed by Chōki in the middle years of the Kansei era (1789–1801). No other signed paintings by Chōki from this period are known at present, however, and for the time being the attribution must remain tentative. His woodblock prints never employ such mannered brushwork.

91

92

ANON.

92 Parody of Zhuang Zi's Dream of Butterflies

Bunka era
Hanging scroll; ink, colour and gold on silk,
32.3 × 40.5 cm
PROVENANCE: Arthur Morrison
LITERATURE: *UT*, vol. 1 (1987), no. 128
1913.5–1.0406 (Japanese Painting 1425). Given by
Sir W. Gwynne-Evans, Bt

Zhuang Zi (Zhuang Zhou; Japanese: Sō Shi or Sō Shū) was a Chinese philosopher of the Warring States period (403–222 BC), preoccupied with the nature of human consciousness within a material world. He told of a dream in which he imagined himself as a butterfly, but on waking could not decide whether he really had become the butterfly or whether it was the butterfly who had now taken on his form. What was the distinction between dream and reality, the nature of individual consciousness?

There are several paintings by Eishi showing a courtesan seated leaning on a Chinese writing-table, on which there is always a vase of peonies, looking up at a butterfly (or butterflies), and it is clear that these were intended as a parody (*mitate*) of Zhuang Zhi's dream. It is doubtful if any searching philosophical meaning were intended, however; as with so many *mitate* reworkings, this simply seems to have been one more unusual setting in which to paint a courtesan. Here she wears an elaborate surcoat decorated with hanging coloured wistaria blooms and a green brocade *obi* with a design of water-wheels and the trailing leaves of the aquatic candock plant (*kōhone*). The title of the book on the desk reads *Kogetsushū*, perhaps a variant on *Kogetsushō*, which was a famous commentary on *Tale of Genji* published in 1673, and the poem which the woman has just copied on to the tasselled slip in her hand is by the Monk Saigyō from the *Shin kokinshū* anthology: 'Yoshinoyama/kozo no shiori no/michi kaete/mada minukata no/hana o tazunemu' ('Last year, Yoshino,/I walked away bending branches/To point me to the blossoms – /Which now are everywhere and I can/Go where I've never been before'. William LaFleur (trans.), *Mirror for the Moon*, New York, New Directions, 1977, p. 75).

Though the composition is taken from Eishi, the figure style is not quite his and difficult to place. The high, pointed *yoko-hyōgo* hairstyle suggests the decade after Utamaro's death in 1806.

TSUTSUMI TŌGETSU (dates unknown)

93   Daruma Dressed as a Courtesan

(?)Kansei–Bunka eras
SIGNATURE: Tsutsumi Tōgetsu hitsu
SEAL: handwritten cipher in the shape of a dancing
   crane
INSCRIPTION: Makoto wa uso no kawa/uso wa
   makoto no hone/mayoeba uso mo makoto to
   nari/satoreba makoto mo uso to naru/uso to
   makoto no Nakanochō/mayou mo Yoshiwara/
   satoru mo Yoshiwara/keisei no makoto mo uso
   mo/Ariso-umi no hama no masago no kyaku no
   kazukazu
Hanging scroll; ink and colour on paper,
   88.0 × 28.0 cm
PROVENANCE: Mrs W. Bateson
1926.4–10.037 (Japanese Painting ADD 40).
   Presented by Mrs W. Bateson

Having the monk Daruma, the founder of
Zen Buddhism, dress as a Yoshiwara
courtesan (wearing a robe patterned with
holy sceptres, no less!) may seem
scurrilous, but this was not an unusual
subject in Ukiyo-e, deriving perhaps from
the fact that the word *daruma* was Edo
slang for 'prostitute'. In a broader sense
Zen philosophy had always challenged
accepted thinking with a provocative
mixture of the sacred and the profane. This
theme is taken up in the inscription, which
comically ponders the nature of 'truth'
versus 'lies', 'reality' versus 'illusion' in the
context of the pleasure quarter, in a style
reminiscent of Zen riddles:

> Truth is the skin of lies; lies are the
> bones of truth. When you are
> bewildered, lies seem like the truth;
> when you are enlightened, the truth
> seems like lies. It is all right to be
> bewildered, it is all right to be
> enlightened on Main Street, Yoshiwara,
> amid lies and truth. The pledges of
> courtesans may be truth or lies and are
> as myriad as their customers, like grains
> of sand on a beach.

A similar inscription appears written by
Ōta Nampo on a painting by Takao
Shōroku (a pupil of Eishi) dating from the
Bunka era (1804–18) (Kumamoto 1989, no.
38), and the playful, topsy-turvy logic of
the text suggests that he may have
composed it in the first place.

Nothing is known of Tōgetsu, but from
his art surname he is certainly a painter of
the Tsutsumi line established by Tōrin I
some time in the middle of the eighteenth
century. Tōrin III is said to have been one
of Hokusai's teachers, and he and other
Tsutsumi painters collaborated with Ukiyo-
e artists in the production of several colour-
printed *kyōka* anthologies during the 1790s.
The very rough line suggests Tōgetsu was a
painter of only amateur status.

93

93

94

ANON.

94 Wistaria Maiden

(?)Mid-19th century
Hanging scroll; ink, colour and gold on paper,
  53.1 × 20.8 cm
PROVENANCE: Arthur Morrison
LITERATURE: *UT*, vol. 1 (1987), no. 131
1913.5–1.0394 (Japanese Painting 1367). Given by
  Sir W. Gwynne-Evans, Bt

The 'Wistaria Maiden' (*fuji musume*), a
young woman in brilliant costume and
black lacquer travelling hat carrying a
branch of flowering wistaria, was one of
the stock subjects of folk painters in Ōtsu
since the seventeenth century. It enjoyed a
new vogue in the nineteenth century after
the theme was adapted in 1826 for the
Kabuki stage, as a dance sequence in which
the young woman came alive out of an
Ōtsu painting.

The costume and the manner in which
the work is decorated have many elements
associated with anonymous paintings of
beauties done in the Kambun era (1661–73,
nos 3, 4), particularly the extensive use of
tie-dyed dots on the outer-kimono and
tight gold and silver arabesques in frilled
roundels on the inner-kimono. The face,
too, has the cool, aloof gaze reminiscent of
figures in early genre paintings.
Nevertheless, as Kobayashi Tadashi has
suggested (*UT*, vol. 1 (1987), no. 131), the
way in which the drapery lines flare
sharply at the ends and the particular
combination of brilliant pigments suggest a
much later date of execution, probably
some time in the middle of the nineteenth
century. Another painting of the subject in
a similar archaising style and probably from
the same workshop is in the Los Angeles
County Museum of Art (Price Collection).

Katsushika Hokusai 1760–1849

Son of a certain Kawamura of Honjo Wari-
gesui, adopted by Nakajima Ise, a mirror
polisher in the service of the Bakufu.
Childhood name Tokitarō; from *c.* 1769
Tetsuzō; in later years used the name
Miuraya Hachiemon. *Gō* and other art
names (as given by Suzuki Jūzō in *GUDHJ*,
vol. 2 (1982), p. 90): Shunrō (*c.* 1779–93),
Gummatei (1785–93?), Sōri (1795–8),
Hyakurin Sōri (1795–7), Hokusai Sōri (1797–
8), Kakō (1798–1811), Hokusai (1797–1819),
Tokimasa (Tatsumasa) (1799–1810),
Kintaisha (1805–9), Gakyōjin (1800–8),
Kukushin (1805), Taito (1811–20), Raishin
(1811–15), Getchi Rōjin (1828), Zen Hokusai
Iitsu (1821–33), Iitsu (1820–34), Fusenkyo
Iitsu (1822), Gakyō Rōjin (1805–6, 1835–49),
Manji (1834–49), Miuraya Hachiemon
(1834–49), Tsuchimochi Ninsaburō (1834);
gesaku-gō Tokitarō Kakō; art surnames
Katsukawa (to 1792/3?), Katsushika
(1807–49). Pupil of Katsukawa Shunshō,
also said to have studied with Kanō Yūsen,
Tsutsumi Tōrin III, Sumiyoshi Hiroyuki.

Ever-innovative as he was, Hokusai's
long period of artistic activity of some
seventy years gives the appearance of a
succession or combination of many careers
as a painter, print designer and book
illustrator, any one of which would have
been the envy of lesser men. His corpus of
several hundred paintings, more than 1,000
prints and more than 250 illustrated books
stand as the achievement of one whose
brush never seems to have ceased its
restless experimentation.

After a fairly long and unremarkable
apprenticeship as a designer of actor prints
in the Katsukawa manner and an illustrator
of *kibyōshi* novels, Hokusai's career finally
took a dramatically new and personal
direction in the later Kansei era (1789–
1801), when he began to design landscape
and figure illustrations for poetry books
and albums (characterised as 'poetic
topography' by Jack Hillier in his *The Art of
Hokusai in Book Illustration*, London,
Sotheby, 1980, ch. 4) and large numbers of
surimono (a genre which he all but created
and continued to work in for much of the
rest of his career) signed 'Sōri'. He also
began to paint hanging scrolls of majestic
beauties in a new broad ink-wash style and
experiment with small landscape prints in a
style influenced by Western engravings.

During the Bunka era (1804–18) Hokusai
was active as one of the most prolific
designers of illustrations for serial *yomihon*
novels, collaborating with writers such as
Takizawa Bakin. A trip to Nagoya and the
Kansai region in 1811 saw the genesis of
the *Hokusai Manga* project with the

publisher Eirakuya Tōshirō which finally ran to fifteen volumes until after his death. Throughout this period he produced paintings on an increasingly wide range of themes as he explored Chinese and Japanese history and legend, as well as contemporary genre themes and landscapes in his illustrated books.

From the late 1820s another major new departure was the series 'Thirty-six Views of Mt Fuji' (*Fugaku sanjū-rokkei*) which established landscape as a new and vital genre for the Ukiyo-e colour woodblock print. This was followed quickly by more landscape series, as well as flower and bird and flower prints. So much wider, indeed, was the range of Hokusai's interests than traditional Ukiyo-e subjects that when considering his works one is challenged to widen the definition of Ukiyo-e and also conclude, perhaps, that he was much more than just an Ukiyo-e artist. The *bijin* paintings of the Taito and Iitsu periods develop increasingly mannered 'crinkled' outlines to the drapery; then in the Manji period, the last fifteen years of Hokusai's life, he explores evermore grand and transcendent themes in his paintings – tigers, eagles, phoenixes, waves, dragons – often imbuing them with a highly personal sense of lonely nobility.

Aside from his major pupils – Hokuba, Hokkei, Hokuju, Shinsai and Shigenobu – Hokusai had a host of lesser followers and imitators (almost 200 by the present tally), listed by Nagata Seiji in articles in *Kobijutsu*, 82–4 (April, July, October 1987).

KATSUSHIKA HOKUSAI

95 Flowering Plum Tree

c. 1795–8
SIGNATURE: Hokusai Sōri ga
SEAL: Kanchi
INSCRIPTION: Uguisu no/hatsune o oya no/iken yori/ kikeba mi ni tsuku/haru no asaoki
INSCRIPTION SIGNATURE: Yomo no Utagaki Magao
Hanging scroll; ink and *gofun* on paper,
   116.5 × 34.0 cm
PROVENANCE: Louis Gonse; Janette Ostier; Ralph Harari
LITERATURE: Goncourt 1896, p. 291; Paris, Hôtel Drouot, *Collection Louis Gonse (Troisième Vente): Oeuvres d'Art du Japon*, sale cat., April 1926, no. 662, pl. IV; Hillier 1966, no. 6; Hillier 1970, no. 102; Clark 1990, fig. 1
1982.7–1.03 (Japanese Painting ADD 688). Given by Dr and Mrs Michael Harari

A single bough of white plum blossom with smaller offshoots breaking into flower has been arranged so as to appear bursting with spring vigour beyond the confines of the scroll, despite its venerable age. It was

95

a long-established convention in Far Eastern painting to use fragmented ink strokes for the trunks of old plum trees, the white areas providing a visual metaphor for their gnarled, crusty bark; but here they are executed with particular speed and bravura. Although the brushwork appears completely spontaneous, the way in which each flower is open at a different stage and painted with lines of different character demonstrates a level of control that is formidable. Even in this early painting many of the basic elements of Hokusai's painting style are apparent – a grand, even eccentric conception and yet an unflagging attention to detail. No single line looks quite like another. Even in his most 'finished' works Hokusai was incapable of painting a boring dot or line, thus giving them a marvellously energised character.

The inscription on the scroll is a 'crazy verse' (*kyōka*) by the poet Yomo no Utagaki Magao (1752–1829):

The first singing of the warbler
Is more impressive
Than listening to parents' objections
To getting up early
On a spring morning.

The wit of the poem, which hovers like the missing warbler above the branch, is matched by the sophistication of the painting, executed in *sumi* and shell white, with the only touch of colour provided by Hokusai's large red 'Kanchi' seal. A related plum branch appears in the printed album *Miyama uguisu* ('Warbler Deep in the Mountains') of *c.* 1798. Although Hokusai writes that this design is copied after a painting by Ogata Kōrin (1658–1716), it bears little resemblance to this earlier master's work; Hokusai could not help but be an innovative stylist in almost all the many genres he explored.

95

96

KATSUSHIKA HOKUSAI

96 Tametomo and the Demons of
Onigashima Island

1811
SIGNATURE: Katsushika Hokusai Taito hitsu
SEAL: Raishin
INSCRIPTION: Ichigo ai-yorokobu dankin ri su/
haigun ima ni itari kunshin o shiki su/Hachirō
byōshoku su tōkai no sho/nao amari tōnen
tokutaku fukashi/kumo no matou/kokoro no
Onigashima harete/yumihari-zuki no/kage ōku
nari
INSCRIPTION SIGNATURE: Bunka kanoto hitsuji ryūtō
joya Kyokutei Bakin dai ('Inscribed by Kyokutei
Bakin on the last night of the year in deep
winter, Bunka 8 (1811)')
INSCRIPTION SEALS: Kyokutei, Bakin, (?)
Hanging scroll; ink, colour and gold on silk,
54.9 × 82.1 cm
PROVENANCE: Box inscription by Hirabayashi
Shōgorō III, dated 1854; William Anderson
LITERATURE: Anderson 1886, no. 1747; Gray 1948,
no. 162; Hillier 1955, no. 77; *Zaigai hihō*, vol. 3
(1969), no. 88; *NU*, vol. 7 (1982), no. 26; Ueno
1985, no. 166; TNM 1987, no. 25; *UT*, vol. 1
(1987), no. 140; Forrer and Goncourt 1988,
no. 151; Smith 1988, no. 166; Smith 1990,
no. 199; Clark 1990, fig. 3; Tokyo 1990, no. 35
1881.12–10.01747 (Japanese Painting 1479)

As the researches of Suzuki Jūzō have
shown (*Zaigai hihō*, vol. 3 (1969), no. 88,
text vol. p. 91), this painting is known to
have been specially commissioned by the
publisher Hirabayashi Shōgorō to celebrate
the highly profitable completion of the
serial novel *Chinsetsu yumihari-zuki* ('Strange
Tales of the Bow Moon', 29 vols, 1807–11),
with text by Takizawa Bakin (1767–1848)
and illustrations by Hokusai. In his *Edo
sakusha burui* Bakin describes how the
publisher paid him an extra ten gold *ryō*
and asked Hokusai to paint this hanging
scroll in the spring of 1811. It was finally
inscribed and dated by Bakin on the last
day of that year with a *kambun* text that
toasts his friendship with the publisher
using 'military' metaphors appropriate to
the subject and likening his influence
perhaps to the sway Tametomo holds over
the demons.

A word gives great pleasure and
   friendship profits.
The distribution of forces at this time,
Observes the wishes of the Lord.
On the island in the Eastern Sea where
   Hachirō holds court,
Truly this year blessings are so profuse
   that
The clouds of the devil-ridden heart clear
   away
And the light of the bow moon shines
   bright.

96   97

KATSUSHIKA HOKUSAI

97 Cockerel and Chick

c. 1815–20
SIGNATURE: Zen Hokusai Taito hitsu ('Painted by
  Taito, formerly Hokusai')
SEAL: Fuji no yama ('The mountain Fuji')
Fan painting; ink and colour on mica-covered
  paper, 16.6 × 48.0 cm
PROVENANCE: James Martin White
LITERATURE: Tokyo 1901, no. 100; Gray 1948,
  no. 179; Hillier 1955, no. 94; Clark 1990, fig. 5
1950.11–11.017 (Japanese Painting ADD 338).
  Presented by the Trustees of the late James
  Martin White

In contrast to the painstakingly detailed
Tametomo (no. 96) this spontaneously
executed fan painting reveals a completely
different side to Hokusai's talents. Here he
employs the minimum of broad strokes in
wet crimson ink and *sumi*, in some places
freely blending the two shades. In spite of
the simple forms the essential inquisitive
character of the birds is faithfully captured.
Writing in the catalogue of his 1900 Tokyo
exhibition of Hokusai paintings, Ernest
Fenollosa suggested that this was animal
painting on a par with Landseer or Sosen
but without the elaborate detail. In fan
painting an artist often reveals a genial,
humorous side to his personality which is
on the whole set aside in more 'serious',
full-scale pieces, and the fan format also
requires particularly careful arrangement of
the composition around its central vertical
axis. This fan paper seems to have been
painted after already having been mounted
and folded on its bamboo spines, since
colour has run down the folds in certain
places.

As Hokusai's painting demonstrates,
Minamoto no Tametomo, the master
archer, is so strong that not even three
demons from Onigashima Island tugging
together can bend his mighty bow. The
composition is essentially a mirror image of
one of the frontispieces of the novel (series
1, volume 1), with the landscape elements
adapted from another illustration in the
novel from the section when Tametomo
visits Onigashima (series 2, volume 2).

The execution seems to reflect the
publisher's desire for ostentatious
celebration: the elaborately layered and
modulated richness of the pigments and
all-over sprinklings of cut gold leaf suggest
a 'no expense spared' commission. As with
Flowering Plum Tree (no. 95), no one line is
quite like another, even in the most highly
worked passages, and the strokes in the
more freely rendered landscape are
energised and inspired. Hokusai's
compositions are frequently strongly
condensed in this way with a kind of
centripetal force his pupils could rarely
match. Although others could imitate (and
exaggerate) elements of his style, their
compositions frequently seem flaccid and
weak in comparison.

97

98

98

KATSUSHIKA HOKUSAI

98 Cormorant and Morning Glory

c. 1821–33
SIGNATURE: Zen Hokusai Iitsu hitsu ('Painted by
    Iitsu, formerly Hokusai')
SEAL: Katsushika
Hanging scroll; ink and colour on silk,
    36.5 × 55.8 cm
PROVENANCE: William Anderson
LITERATURE: Anderson 1886, no. 1899; *UT*, vol. 1
    (1987), no. 141; Clark 1990, fig. 6; Tokyo 1990,
    no. 36
1881.12–10.01899 (Japanese Painting 1485)

The ungainly cormorant stands with its
head drawn back and turned to one side so
that a large oval eye stares upwards,
making the creature seem half demented. A
kind of lonely superiority can also perhaps
be detected in the bird, as if Hokusai were
making it the focus of deeply personal

feelings, and it is unusual to find such
strong expressive content in normally
demure Ukiyo-e paintings. The edge of the
folded wing is sharply accented in deep
black, and the broken strokes used to
suggest the wing and tail feathers have
elements in common with *Cockerel and Chick*
(no. 97). A few spiky feathers stick up
perkily at the bridge of the beak. The
execution of the back feathers is noticeably
coarser, however, and not as impressive as
the related *Cormorant on a Rock* in the
Okayama Museum (Ōta (Hokusai) 1985,
no. 556). This has led to suggestions that
the British Museum scroll may be the work
of a pupil authorised with Hokusai's
signature and seal; certainly these are of a
standard type for the period *c.* 1821–33,
and the 'Katsushika' seal appears identical
with that on the famous *Seller of Fortune-
telling Poems* (no. 100).

99 (ADD 224)

99 (ADD 223)

(?)KATSUSHIKA HOKUSAI

99 Mountain Landscape in Chinese Style *(right)* and Li Guang's Arrow in Tiger Rock *(left)*

(?)1820s

SIGNATURES: Katsushika Iitsu hitsu (right); Zen Hokusai Iitsu hitsu (left)

SEALS: Fumoto no sato ('Village at the foot of the mountain', right); ?Iitsu, Iitsu (left)

Pair of hanging scrolls; ink and colour on silk, each 93.5 × 32.5 cm

PROVENANCE: Arthur Morrison

1946.2–9.041 (Japanese Painting ADD 223, right); 1946.2–9.042 (Japanese Painting ADD 224, left). Bequeathed by Arthur Morrison

No artist did more than Hokusai to introduce themes from classical Chinese literature into popular Japanese culture during the first half of the nineteenth century. Here two disparate compositions are paired, apparently, on the basis of their both having Chinese subjects. The theme of the right-hand scroll remains somewhat obscure: a Chinese figure is praying at an outdoor altar which faces a distant lofty peak. Henri Joly in his *Legend in Japanese Art* (London, John Lane, 1908), p. 207, lists a certain Kyō Chi (Chinese: Kuang Zhi) who '. . . was led to Mount Gi by a divinity disguised as a wood cutter. He built an altar and learnt Taoism', but it has not yet been possible to verify this legend from Japanese sources. The left-hand scroll illustrates the episode when Li Guang (Japanese: Ri Kō), a commander of the Han armies and famous archer, thought he saw a tiger hiding in the grass and let fly an arrow. Upon closer inspection, however, it proved to be a tiger-shaped rock into which the arrow had miraculously sunk. As well as the scrolls' common Chinese theme, the shape of the tiger-rock echoes perhaps the

configuration of the peak in the right-hand composition.

It is hard to come to a definitive judgement on the authenticity of these scrolls. The execution of the left scroll – in particular the crispness and energy of the birds and the elegant spikiness of the flowering pinks – shows many elements of Hokusai's style; but the mountain landscape, though generally well composed, is curiously lacking in focus and somewhat lack-lustre in execution. The cursive 'Iitsu' signature is unusual but not unprecedented. The 'Fumoto no sato' seal is found on about half a dozen paintings of Hokusai's 'Taito' period (1811–20) but not as yet on any other from the Iitsu period (1820–34). The seal on the left scroll, which might possibly read 'Iitsu, Iitsu', also appears on *Woman Dancing with her Hands Raised* (Obuse 1985, p. 9).

99 (ADD 224)

99 (ADD 223)

100

KATSUSHIKA HOKUSAI

100 Seller of Fortune-telling Poems

Dated 2nd day, 1st month, 1827
SIGNATURE: Hokusai Iitsu keiga ('Respectfully
   painted by Hokusai Iitsu')
SEAL: Katsushika
INSCRIPTION: Bunsei jū hinoto i nen/shōgatsu
   futsuka fude-hajime ('First use of the brush on
   the second day of the first month, Bunsei 10
   (1827)')
Hanging scroll; ink and colour on paper,
   124.2 × 50.5 cm
PROVENANCE: Arthur Morrison
LITERATURE: Morrison 1911, vol. 2, pl. XXVI; Hillier
   1955, no. 80; NU, vol. 7 (1982), no. 32; Ueno
   1985, no. 167; Forrer and Goncourt 1988,
   no. 327; Smith 1988, no. 167; Clark 1990, fig. 7
   1913.5–1.0317 (Japanese Painting 1450). Given by
   Sir W. Gwynne-Evans, Bt

The subject has been identified by Endō
Takeshi (NU, vol. 7 (1982), no. 32) as the
character Watarai Ietsugu from the Nō play
Utaura written by Kanze Motomasa in the
early fifteenth century. A similar, though
not identical, figure appears in *Hokusai
manga*, vol. 11 (1834), p. 3 verso. The
affecting expression on the downcast face
suggests that Watarai Ietsugu is reflecting
sadly on the home at Ise he has left behind
to roam the country selling the fortune-
telling poems that are hanging from the
string of his bow. Perhaps the hint of a
self-portrait projected on to this depiction
of a character from remote history can be
detected. Hokusai notes that this was the
first painting of the New Year of Bunsei 10
(1827), and it is signed 'respectfully
painted' which, together with the generally
abbreviated style using broad lines of
different ink tonality, suggests that this
may have been a *sekiga*, a 'painting done on
the spot' at a New Year party for some
illustrious patron with classical tastes. This
technique of broad lines with rich, dark
accents originated in the figure paintings of
Hokusai's 'Sōri' period (*c.* 1795–8) and
always remained an alternative to his more
meticulous style.

100

101

101

KATSUSHIKA HOKUSAI

101 Young Man Seated on a Bench

1840
SIGNATURE: Gakyō Rōjin Manji hitsu/yowai hachijū-ichi ('From the brush of Manji, old man mad with painting, aged eighty-one')
SEAL: Katsushika
INSCRIPTION: Shunpū Shun'u kyōshi o utsushi/tsuyu toka ni omoku ichiryōshi/nan zo nin kajin no omou tokoro ōku/moha namida o obi shō ni yoru toki ni/Sessen kun no tame ni daisu
INSCRIPTION SIGNATURE: yakko ('your servant')
Hanging scroll, ink and colour on silk,
  80.4 × 32.7 cm
PROVENANCE: Arthur Morrison
LITERATURE: Clark 1990, fig. 8; Tokyo 1990, no. 31
1913.5–1.0318 (Japanese Painting 1451). Given by Sir W. Gwynne-Evans, Bt

A young man dressed in a feminine-looking blue kimono with long, flowing sleeves decorated with white cherry blossoms and striped green *hakama* trousers sits on a bench in an alluring pose with one foot resting in his lap and head inclined coyly forward. To judge by the content of the inscription he is on an outing to admire the flowering cherry trees in spring. The scroll seems originally to have formed a pair with another showing a young man reading a letter (reproduced in Kamakura 1974, no. 22), and both were probably painted for a patron who was homosexual. The British Museum painting has an inscription in Chinese-style couplets by one who calls himself simply 'yakko' ('your servant') addressed to 'young Sessen (or Yukibune)', who must be the object of his affections:

Spring breezes and spring rains imitate his lovely form
The dew sits heavy on a branch or two of blossom by the wayside
To so many things I would liken this beautiful one
[My eyes] brim with tears like waves
As he rests there on the bench.

The drawing of the face, hands and lines of the young man's costume is similar to paintings from Hokusai's preceding 'Iitsu' period, such as *Woman Dancing with her Hands Raised* (Obuse 1985, p. 9), and it is interesting to see that the artist continued to work in this style into his eighties. The details of the accessories – the dots of the sharkskin scabbard and cord of the jacket –

are meticulously rendered, yet each stroke is unique in character. The 'Katsushika' seal is completely different from that on works of the 'Iitsu' period (nos 98, 100) but seems to be comparable with that on the late masterpiece *Eagle and Cherry Blossom* (Ujiie

Collection; *NU*, vol. 7 (1982), no. 33). While Japanese artists did not as a rule recut their seals, Hokusai used different 'Katsushika' seals in his 'Iitsu' and 'Manji' periods. Much work remains to be done on the use, variants and the forged versions of this seal.

102

KATSUSHIKA HOKUSAI

102 Traveller Viewing a Distant Landscape

1843
SIGNATURE: Hachijū-yon rō Manji hitsu ('Painted by Manji, old man of eighty-four')
SEAL: Fuji above clouds
Fan painting; ink and colour on mica-covered paper, 14.2 × 44.6 cm
PROVENANCE: Hosomi Ryō; Ralph Harari
LITERATURE: Hillier 1970, vol. 2, no. 144; Clark 1990, fig. 9
1982.7–1.017(1) (Japanese Painting ADD 702A)

102

It has been suggested that the aged traveller, whose rapt expression commands our attention despite the modest size of the painting, may be the itinerant monk-poet Saigyō (1118–80). The distant landscape with a shrine gateway amid hills has not, however, been identified. His tattered black monk's robes are crisply executed in deep, rich black, contrasting with the pale wash landscape – the two elements once again perfectly balanced about the central axis. Hokusai uses a miniature version of his stylised picture seal showing Mt Fuji above clouds, and it seems to have been an occasional practice for smaller versions of an artist's well-known seals to be cut especially for fans and small paintings.

KATSUSHIKA HOKUSAI

103 Ducks in Flowing Water

1847
SIGNATURE: Yowai hachijū-hachi Manji ('Manji, aged eighty-eight')
SEAL: Hyaku
Hanging scroll; ink and colour on silk, 111.0 × 40.0 cm
PROVENANCE: Arthur Morrison
LITERATURE: Morrison 1911, vol. 2, pl. XXVII; Hillier 1955, no. 82; Ueno 1985, no. 168; Smith 1988, no. 168; Forrer and Goncourt 1988, no. 441; Clark 1990, fig. 10
1913.5–1.0320 (Japanese Painting 1453). Given by Sir W. Gwynne-Evans, Bt

Two male mallards paddle against the current, one diving to fish amongst the water-weed. Fallen red maple leaves float by on the surface. The unusual optical effects – the modulation of washes across the sweeping bands of the current and the pond weeds painted in different shades of varying intensities depending on their depth from the surface – are evidence of Hokusai's long-standing interest in and experimentation with techniques derived from Western paintings and prints, although these never become obtrusive. Some of the maple leaves are also painted less distinctly to suggest they are sinking into the water. They are deftly drawn with a crispness and variety of tints that provide evidence of authenticity as certain as any signature or seal.

At a recent International Conference on Hokusai's paintings (University of Venice, May 1990) Kobayashi Tadashi proposed the intriguing theory that from about the age of eighty-seven Hokusai was no longer able to sustain the control necessary to paint drawn-out or sweeping lines. When viewed close up, any seemingly long lines on an authentic work of his late period are found

103

to be made up of a series of overlapping shorter strokes – a moving testament to the old man's fierce determination to disguise a shaking hand. In this painting the plumage of the birds (the most detailed part of the painting) are in fact built up with a variety of small strokes, in a manner that would accord with Professor Kobayashi's theory, and coloured in a brilliant palette. Hokusai gives detailed instructions for painting ducks and, indeed, illustrates a very similar bird in his painting manual *Ehon saishiki tsū* ('On the Use of Colour', 1848, vol. 1, p. 13 verso). The poses of the birds have that characteristic combination of the bizarre and the closely observed that makes all Hokusai's birds and beasts so entertaining.

103

103 detail

104

104

KATSUSHIKA HOKUSAI

104 Cormorant on a Stump

1847
SIGNATURE: Hachijū-hachi rō Manji hitsu ('From the brush of Manji, old man of eighty-eight')
SEAL: Hyaku
Hanging scroll; ink and colour on paper, 126.1 × 47.8 cm
PROVENANCE: James Martin White
LITERATURE: Tokyo 1900, no. 211; Forrer and Goncourt 1988, no. 440; Clark 1990, fig. 11
1950.11–11.016 (Japanese Painting ADD 336).
Presented by the Trustees of the Late James Martin White

In what is certainly the strangest work by Hokusai in the collection an ungainly cormorant perches on a breakwater, while a candock plant (*kōhone*) below pushes up its yellow flowers and heart-shaped leaves from roots in the riverbed. At first the relative proportions of the bird and its surroundings seem eccentric and the composition curiously empty and lacking in obvious focus; yet the more closely one observes the details and the technique, the more its qualities are revealed. Rich washes of pink, green and grey underlie the scumbled texture of dots and lines on the posts and the riverbank. The leaves of the candock plant have deeper tonalities of green, blue and black, their outlines formed by inked, dry strokes, each of which has its own character and sensitivity. The flowers are open at different stages, and one lies half-submerged in the water resembling the maple leaves in *Ducks in Flowing Water* (no. 103). Once again Hokusai gives detailed instructions for painting candock plants in *Ehon saishiki tsū* (vol. 1, p. 10 recto).

Finally one notices the flowering (?)reed which reaches up towards the bird; the dry, halting lines of the leaves are stretched as taut as elastic, and each stamen of the flower is like a tiny exploding star. The overall impression is of an irrepressible life force – a formidable tribute to the undiminished powers of the 'old man of eighty-eight'.

An inferior version of this composition is illustrated in Tokyo, Gotō Bijutsukan 1969, no. 31.

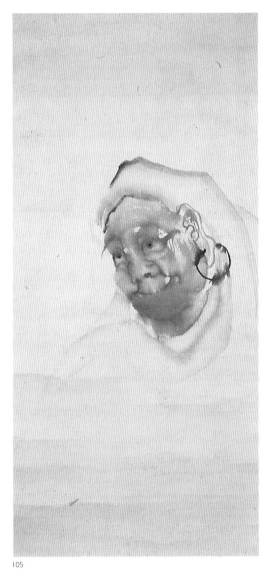

105

KATSUSHIKA SCHOOL

105 Daruma

c. mid-19th century
Hanging scroll; ink and colour on paper,
  59.0 × 27.5 cm
PROVENANCE: Louis Gonse
LITERATURE: Goncourt 1896, p. 292; p. 316; Hillier
  1955, no. 79
1945.11–1.054 (Japanese Painting ADD 182)

Half-length portraits of Daruma
(Bodhidharma), the patriarch of Zen
Buddhism, his crusty features wrapped
around with Indian monk's robes and
wearing a large earring, were painted by
followers of Zen as part of their spiritual
training and later taken up as a popular
subject by painters of the Kanō school. In
the Edo period the word *daruma* was slang
for 'prostitute', and Daruma is often shown
in Ukiyo-e in the company of courtesans,
on occasion even exchanging clothes with
them (no. 93)! Here the technique of using
washes to half-obscure the outlines of the
face makes Daruma appear like some
ghostly apparition. Some of the lines
appear to have been painted with a long
fingernail, in the manner of eccentric
Chinese scholar-artists.

The traditional attribution is to Hokusai,
and certainly the bulbous nose and smiling
expression have elements in common with
various of his male portraits (no. 100).
Hokusai is known to have painted massive
portraits of Daruma as outdoor spectacles
in Edo in 1804 and Nagoya in 1817, the
latter measuring some 240 square metres.
To the present writer, however, the British
Museum portrait lacks the intensity and
concentration of composition to be expected
in a work by the master and should be
attributed to a Hokusai pupil.

106

Ryūryūkyo Shinsai
worked 1799–1823

Na Masayuki; common name Hanjirō, also
Mannō Hanji; *gō* Ryūryūkyo, Ryūkaen,
Yūsenkyo. Lived at Kanda Koyanagi-chō,
later Shin'ishimachi. An early pupil of
Katsushika Hokusai, deriving the name
Shinsai from Hokusai's *gō* Tatsumasa
(Shinsei) and Ryūryūkyo from Hokusai's
predecessor Tawaraya Sōri I, who had used
the same name. Shinsai's earliest datable
work is *Keiseikai neko no maki*, a *kibyōshi*
published in 1799. In the early 1800s,
following Hokusai, he became one of the
most prolific designers of *surimono*,
particularly of still-life subjects such as in
the *Kasen-awase* series of 1809. After the
mid-1810s his *surimono* were almost
exclusively in the square format. He is also
known for two series of accomplished
landscapes in Western-influenced style and
a small number of paintings of beautiful
women, in both genres again following the
lead of Hokusai.

RYŪRYŪKYO SHINSAI

106 Standing Beauty Seen in Profile

Kyōwa–early Bunka eras
SIGNATURE: Yūsenkyo Shinsai ga
SEAL: Masayuki
Hanging scroll; ink, colour and gold on paper,
   90.0 × 30.5 cm
PROVENANCE: Hayashi Tadamasa; Shōzō Katō
1926.7–26.01 (Japanese Painting ADD 45)

About the time that Hokusai changed from
the name Sōri to Hokusai in 1798 he began
to perfect a suave style of painting beauties
uniquely his own that was characterised by
long, tapering outlines in strong, dark ink,
light washes of colour and occasional
passages of crisp detailing of accessories or
drapery patterns. This style, which he
continued to practise throughout his forties
in the Kyōwa (1801–4) and early Bunka
(1804–18) eras, is the one here imitated by
Shinsai, one of Hokusai's earliest pupils.

   The woman, perhaps a geisha, is shown
from the side, her face in full profile,
raising her right arm in an apparent gesture
to someone out of the picture. The pale
washes of the lilac kimono and black fabric
of the long hanging *obi* contrast with the
opaque white of her powdered white face
and the occasional accents of brilliant

scarlet in her hair and at her collar, sleeve-opening and skirts. The *obi* is overlaid with a design of the leaves of a trailing water plant (*kōhone*) subtly picked out in gold. Her proportions are tall and slender, and her attitude refined and intelligent. Though the pose is straight, even stiff and correct, the flowing lines of the kimono skirts collect in a sensuous eddy at her feet, and attention focuses on her fashionable *décolletage*, the nape of the neck being considered particularly erotic. Comparison may be drawn with paintings by Hokusai from the early Bunka era (1804–18) such as *Beauty at the Time of the Tanabata Festival* (*NU*, vol. 7 (1982), no. 8).

RYŪRYŪKYO SHINSAI

107 Two Women

Late Bunka–early Bunsei eras
SIGNATURE: Shinsai
SEAL: Shinsai
Hanging scroll; ink, colour and gold on paper,
   100.1 × 26.5 cm
PROVENANCE: Kegan Paul; Ralph Harari
LITERATURE: Hillier 1970, vol. 2, no. 150
1982.7–1.01 (Japanese Painting ADD 690). Given by
   Dr and Mrs Michael Harari

A young woman, probably the daughter of a wealthy samurai family, is out walking accompanied by a maid. She wears an *age-bōshi* cloth to protect her oiled hairdo from the dirt and dust. Her black kimono with long, flowing sleeves is decorated with a design of delicately painted autumn plants and grasses beside a winding river, and there is much use of gold, both to follow the ink contours of the drapery with slender gold outlines and also in the roundels of the thick brocade *obi*.

   The proportions are elongated to a mannered degree, as seen in paintings by other Hokusai pupils such as Hōtei Gosei who made a speciality out of exaggerating certain elements of the master's style, and the faces – with their rosebud lips, long noses and dark, tiny eyes – are doll-like and impassive in comparison with the intelligent features of the woman in Shinsai's painting from an earlier era (no. 106). None of Hokusai's pupils could keep pace with his restlessly evolving style.

   A comparison with the forms of signatures on datable *surimono* by Shinsai would suggest a date of *c.* 1815–20.

107

Yanagawa Shigenobu 1787–1832

Family name Suzuki; common name Jūbei; *gō* Rinsai, Kinsai, Ishōsai, Raito. Lived in Honjo Yanagawa, from which he took his art surname. A pupil of Hokusai, whose eldest daughter he married, following which he was adopted by Hokusai. After a separation, however, returned to his own family. From 1822 to the spring of 1823 visited and worked in Osaka. Designed *surimono* from the later 1810s and did a number of single-sheet prints and paintings, but mainly active as an illustrator of *yomihon* and *kyōka* poetry anthologies.

Attributed to
YANAGAWA SHIGENOBU

108 Geisha from the Fukagawa District

Late Bunka–early Bunsei eras (before 1823)
INSCRIPTION: Haru aki ni/Tomigaoka tote/ippon no/ ume o kazashite/hairu Obanaya
INSCRIPTION SIGNATURE: Shokusanjin
Hanging scroll; ink and colours on silk,
   81.0 × 25.5 cm
PROVENANCE: Hirano family, Akita (box inscription); box inscription by Inoue Kazuo
LITERATURE: Kruml 1991, no. 17
1991.7–1.02 (Japanese Painting ADD 981)

The *kyōka* poem composed and inscribed at the top of the painting by Ōta Nampo (1749–1823) reads:

> In spring and autumn
> Thinking [she's visiting] Tomigaoka
>   Shrine
> She puts a sprig of plum
> Into her hair
> And enters the Obanaya [Teahouse of
>   Flowering Pampas]

The Fukagawa district on the far, east bank of the Sumida River was the location for one of the major unlicensed pleasure quarters in Edo, operating, in particular, in the teahouses around Tomigaoka Shrine. The poem opens by mentioning spring and autumn and then weaves in punning references to the names of two well-known teahouses – Umemotoya ('Source of the Plum') and Obanaya ('Flowering Pampas Grass') – named after flowers of these seasons. The woman is clearly a *Tatsumi geisha* ('geisha of the south-eastern quarter', that is, Fukagawa) working out of one of these teahouses.

Though unsigned, the painting is firmly attributable on stylistic grounds to Shigenobu and exhibits the same painstaking technique and jewel-like qualities associated with his work as a designer of de luxe *surimono* prints. Particularly unusual is the absence of outlines and sense of three-dimensional

108

modelling in the pale green kimono lined with pale blue, suggesting Western-style painting techniques learned from Hokusai. The narrow face with its fine, long nose reflects the combined influences of Hokusai and the Utagawa school.

A painting of similar composition, *Geisha Looking Back*, in the Japan Ukiyo-e Museum, Matsumoto (Matsumoto 1985, vol. 2, no. 196), actually bears Shigenobu's signature and seals, though the woman's kimono is black, she has a toothpick in her mouth, and the details of her costume and hairstyle are quite different. The colour-printed *kyōka* anthology *Kyōka momo chidori* illustrated by Shigenobu also contains a similar figure, except that she faces to the front rather than over her shoulder. This book was published in 1830 (according to *Kokusho sō mokuroku*), however, so the British Museum painting must have been produced earlier, bearing as it does the inscription by Nampo, who died in 1823. When creating compositions for his paintings and prints, Shigenobu was clearly not as inventive as his great teacher.

Totoya Hokkei 1780–1850

Family name Iwakubo; *imina* Tatsuyuki; *azana* Kyōsai; common name Hatsugorō (Shōgorō), later Kin'emon; *gō* Aoigaoka, Kyōsai, Aiogazono, Go. Originally a fishmonger at Yotsuya Samegahashi, hence the art surname Totoya/Uoya (fish shop). *Edo hōgaku-wake* gives his address as Akasaka Nagai-chō and name as Hatsutarō (Shōtarō). His address also given as Akasaka Kirabatake. A pupil of first Kanō Yōsen'in Korenobu, then Hokusai. His earliest dated work an illustrated *kyōka* anthology, *Kyōka shakushi-guri*, published in 1799, making him one of Hokusai's earliest pupils. From *c.* 1810 onwards a major designer of *surimono* and illustrator of poetry anthologies. A small number of paintings of beauties and Chinese warrior subjects, the compositions often derived from Hokusai but the style progressively more individual.

TOTOYA HOKKEI

109 The Six Immortals of Poetry

Bunsei era
SIGNATURE: Hokkei
SEALS: Aoi, Oka [Aoigaoka]
INSCRIPTION: Utayomi no/kashira to kashira/ uchiyoseshi/oto wa Kokin no/jo ni kikoekeri
INSCRIPTION SIGNATURE: Rokujuen/ōju Baita sho ('Rokujuen, written at special request by Baita')
Fan painting; ink and colour on mica-covered paper, 16.5 × 49.5 cm
PROVENANCE: Hosomi Ryō; Ralph Harari
LITERATURE: Hillier 1970, vol. 2, no. 157
1982.7–1.017(3) (Japanese Painting ADD 702C)

The poet Ki no Tsurayuki's preface to the *Kokin waka shū* Imperial anthology of the early tenth century begins with the immortal lines about warblers chirping and frogs croaking: '... every living creature has its song' ('iki to shi ikeru mono izure ka uta o yomazarikeri'). Rokujuen's cheeky poem suggests that there were other 'noises' to be heard:

> The sound of luminaries
> At a poetry gathering
> Knocking their heads together
> Could be heard
> In the preface to the *Kokinshū*.

Hokuba's genial painting shows the Six Immortals of Poetry (*Rokkasen*): from left to right, Ariwara no Narihira, Funya no Yasuhide, Kisen Hōshi, Ōtomo no Kuronushi, Ono no Komachi, Sōjō Henjō, sitting facing away from us with their heads together in a poetic huddle. The Six Immortals were first so named in the *Kokinshū* preface, but the reference to heads knocking together may reflect the fact that Tsurayuki was less than generous in his criticisms of each.

Rokujuen (Ishikawa Masamochi, 1753–1830) was one of the leading *kyōka* poets of his generation, noted for his wide-ranging scholarship in both Japanese and Chinese matters. Here the inscription was written by a stand-in who has imitated well the mannerisms of his calligraphy, one Baita, who is probably Rokujuen's pupil Baitarō.

109

109

110

110

TOTOYA HOKKEI

110   Courtesan and Child

Early Bunsei era
SIGNATURE: Aoigaoka Hokkei
SEAL: Kyōsai
Hanging scroll; ink and colour on silk,
  55.0 × 104.8 cm
PROVENANCE: William Anderson
LITERATURE: Anderson 1886, no. 1906; Ueno 1985,
  no. 178; UT, vol. 1 (1987), no. 149; Smith 1988,
  no. 178; Tokyo 1990, no. 37
1881.12–10.01906 (Japanese Painting 1501)

A courtesan has finished applying her
makeup and is now dressing in elaborate
attire – a black gauze kimono with blue-
patterned lining over layers of frilly
undergarment, with a stiff brocade *obi* on
the floor beside her. Her young baby boy is
amusing himself writing the graph 'no' on
the steamed-over mirror on the makeup

stand, next to which is an elaborately
enamelled porcelain bowl of water
containing a single sprig of flowering
cherry.

   In addition to being the largest scroll by
Hokkei yet introduced this is also one of
the most ambitious in terms of its complex
composition and elaborate technique.
Hokkei has taken elements of the figure
style of Hokusai's Taito/early Iitsu period
and exaggerated these to a highly
mannered, almost overblown, result: the
contorted poses of the limbs, crinkly edges
to the draperies of the underclothes, the
sense of modelling to the flesh and above
all the dense patterning of the saturated
colours produce a very rich and opulent
combination. The form of the signature
would suggest a date early in the Bunsei
era (1818–30), *c.* 1820.

III (ADD 708)

III (ADD 709)

III (ADD 710)

III (ADD 708)

III (ADD 709)

III (ADD 710)

TOTOYA HOKKEI

III   Three Figures Reading

Mid–late Bunsei era
SIGNATURE: Hokkei
SEAL: Aoigaoka
Three album leaves; ink and colour on paper,
    each 27.0 × 41.5 cm (approx.)
PROVENANCE: Felix Tikotin; Ralph Harari
LITERATURE: Hillier 1970, vol. 2, no. 156; Hillier
    1980, no. 76; UT, vol. 1 (1987), BW nos 36–8
1982.7–1.023(1–3) (Japanese Paintings
    ADD 708–710)

These three small paintings in rapid ink
outline and wash technique, all apparently
taken from the same album, are linked by
the common theme of people reading. In
the first a woman is shown from behind,
her body forming a graceful curve as she
stands engrossed by the book she is
reading (ADD 708); in the second a man
lying outdoors, with his sword and bamboo
flute on the ground beside him, looks up
from his book to watch a flock of birds fly
past (ADD 709); and in the third a scholar
wearing a mob-cap crouches close to an oil-
lamp to make out the characters on the
page (ADD 710). The style is a loose, rather
genial version of Hokusai's quick ink and
wash technique.

Another album leaf of similar size and
with a similar signature and seal, *Reclining
Deer*, is in the collection of the Azabu
Museum of Arts and Crafts.

112

112

TOTOYA HOKKEI

112 Woman from Ōhara with an Ox

Late Bunsei era
SIGNATURE: Hokkei
SEAL: Aoigaoka
Hanging scroll; ink and colour on silk,
  77.0 × 32.5 cm
PROVENANCE: James Tregaskis
1925.11–18.01 (Japanese Painting ADD 30)

Ōharame ('women from Ōhara') were country women from the villages of Ōhara and Yase north of Kyoto, who would bring into the markets of the city bundles of firewood or charcoal carried on their heads or laden on oxen. Decorating the bundles with wild flowers and wearing distinctive costumes of tie-dyed cotton with cloth armbands (*tekkō*) and leggings (*kyahan*), they were considered a picturesque subject for Shijō-school and occasionally, as here, Ukiyo-e painters.

The composition of this painting is almost a line-for-line copy of an important work by Hokusai now in the Chiossone Museum, Genoa, dating from the Kyōwa (1801–4) or early Bunka (1804–18) eras. In his commentary on the Hokusai painting Nagata Seiji mentions the existence of two more versions with Hokusai signatures (which he does not consider genuine), as well as yet another Hokkei version with a 'Kyōsai' seal (see UT, vol. 10 (1987), no. 29). There was also a version by Hokkei formerly in the Ikeda Seisuke collection (Ikeda 1906, no. 74, pl. 38). In addition, Narazaki and Yoshida (1970, BW vol. nos 11, p. 78, and 20, p. 80) illustrate versions signed 'Hōtei Hokuei' and unsigned, respectively.

All this might not normally augur well for the authenticity of the present painting, which is clearly inferior to the Chiossone Hokusai in execution (the cut ends of the firewood on the woman's head are handled clumsily, the hairline is perfunctory, and the modelling of tones on the body and head of the ox less sophisticated). However, other instances are known of Hokkei having made several versions of Hokusai compositions at different stages in his career (see the comments concerning two Hokkei paintings in the collection of the Azabu Museum of Arts and Crafts, in Sendai 1988, nos 80, 81). In its favour, too,

is the fact that the face of the woman is painted with the small eyes tilted at different angles, a mannerism of style used in other, apparently genuine, paintings by Hokkei (for instance, Azabu 1986, no. 49). The form of the signature of the present painting, if genuine, would match most closely with signatures on *surimono* dating from the later 1820s.

Yashima Gakutei
worked 1815–52

Family names Sugawara, Yashima; *na* first Harunobu, later Sadaoka; *azana* Hōkyō; common name Maruya Onokichi; *gō* Gakutei Sanjin, Ichirō, Gogaku, Kyūzan, Nanzan, Yōtei, Yōsai, Kōen, Shinkadō, Shinkyūdō, Ryōsa; poetry name Horikawa Tarō. The illegitimate son of a Bakufu retainer, one Hirata of Kasumigaseki. His mother then married into the Yashima family of Aoyama Midorigaoka (or Kubo-chō), by whom he was adopted. Later lived in Minami Demma-chō; Ningyō-chō; Nihombashi Sakamoto-chō. Said to be a pupil of Tatsumi Shūei, then studied with Hokkei. Gakutei's first illustrations to popular fiction appeared in 1815, and the following year the first of his *surimono*, in which genre he would become a leading designer during the 1820s and 30s. An important author and illustrator of popular fiction, including the *yomihon Ehon saiyū zenden* (completed in 1835) based on the Chinese novel *Xi you ji* ('Record of the Westward Journey'). Gakutei made visits to the Osaka/Kyoto region in *c.* 1818–20 and 1831–2; in 1836 was living close to the Kamo River in Kyoto and in 1837–9 in Osaka. The most famous product of his time spent in Osaka is the folding colour-printed album *Naniwa meisho Tempōzan shōkei ichiran* ('Selected Views of Mt Tempō [Park], a Famous Place in Osaka'), published in 1834. According to Keyes (1985, p. 71), his last dated work was a contribution to *Chaban imayō fūryū*, published in 1852. Books published between 1856 and 1860 by an author, Okabe Sukezaemon, using the name Gakutei should be ascribed to Gakutei II.

113

YASHIMA GAKUTEI

113 Courtesan Wearing a Kimono
Decorated with Swimming Carp

Bunsei era
SIGNATURE: Gakutei
SEALS: Yashima, Sadaoka
Hanging scroll; ink, colour and gold on silk,
  120.0 × 41.5 cm
PROVENANCE: Arthur Morrison
LITERATURE: Morrison 1911, vol. II, pl. XXXI;
  UT, vol. 1 (1987), no. 150
1913.5–1.0288 (Japanese Painting 1500). Given by
  Sir W. Gwynne-Evans, Bt

In the Bunsei era (1818–30) the fashions
worn by courtesans became evermore
gaudy and elaborate: veritable aureoles of
tortoiseshell hairpins with flowers carved
on the ends (*hana-kanzashi*); surcoats
(*uchikake*) with designs of dragons and
tigers, padded to give a three-dimensional
effect and embroidered with gold thread;
wide brocade *obi* tied in an ostentatious
knot at the front; and high black lacquer
clogs. We can only marvel at the taste of
the times which undoubtedly found such
extravagances attractive and at the stamina
of the courtesans who managed to carry
them off.

Here the woman is turning so as to
display the fabulous design of swimming
carp that was probably painted directly in
sumi on to the silk of her *uchikake*. These
are reminiscent of the famous *surimono*
showing a carp leaping up a waterfall
which Gakutei designed in *c.* 1828. She lifts
the scarlet end of her geometrically
patterned *obi* with a flourish behind her
head, the more to show off the radiating
hairpins. Her gritted teeth and squint
suggest a formidable character, and again
we can savour the peculiarity of late-Edo
aesthetics, like exotic hybrids of cultivated
flowers.

The painting is technically extremely
accomplished and in an individual style not
dominated by either of the prevailing
Hokusai or Utagawa idioms.

113

Teisai Hokuba 1771–1844

Family names Arisaka, Hoshino; *imina*
Mitsutaka; common name Gorōhachi; *gō*
Teisai, Shunshunsai, Shunshuntei, Shūen.
Lived first in Kanda, then Shitaya Misuji-
machi. Already by 1818 he had taken lay
religious orders and lived in Shitaya Nichō-
machi. Retired retainer of the Bakufu (*go
ke'nin*). One of the earliest pupils of
Hokusai, together with Hokkei and Shinsai.
First dated work an illustration for *Kyōka
kachō shū*, published in 1800. Up to 1812
produced illustrations for at least sixty titles
of *kyōka ehon*, *yomihon* and *gōkan*, bringing
him into contact with many of the leading
men of letters including Asakusa-an
Ichindo (1755–1820) who was Hokuba's
teacher in *kyōka* poetry. Frequent
participator in *shogakai* (poetry and painting
meetings) and contributor to collaborative
paintings done on these occasions.
Designed a small number of *surimono* but
otherwise no woodblock prints; known
mainly for his prolific output of paintings
of beauties.

Hokuba was one of the few pupils of
Hokusai to establish a truly independent
style, and the poised, highly polished
paintings of beauties in brilliant pigments,
set in ink-wash landscapes of famous
places in Edo that became his standard
output, are the antithesis of Hokusai's
restless, energetic experimentation with an
encyclopaedic range of subject-matter.
Hokuba seems to have travelled frequently
to the provinces to paint for country
patrons, and his occasional portraits, such
as a pair of hanging scrolls showing the
elderly Noguchi Chōhei and his wife who
ran a general store at Honjo on the Tōkaidō
Highway, are refreshingly candid. Large-
scale works include a pair of six-fold
screens showing the Sumida River and
fishmarkets of Nihombashi teeming with
traders (Takanawa Art Museum), and a
pair of six-fold screens formerly in the
collection of the Matsudaira, *daimyō* of
Fukui (now Fukui Local History Museum),
which have recently come to light, showing
holiday crowds in the precincts of the
Asakusa Kannon Temple (*Kokka*, 1138
(1990), pp. 41–5).

A chronology for Hokuba's large corpus
of paintings has yet to be established, and
the dates proposed here are only tentative.
His earliest paintings from the Bunka era
(1804–18) have the signature 'Hokuba'
written fairly boldly and clearly, and the
figures show the residual stylistic influence

114

114

of Utamaro. His mature works of the
Tempō era (1830–44), which are most
frequently encountered, have the signature
'Teisai', often combined with the seal
'Hokuba gain' and sometimes giving the
artist's age.

TEISAI HOKUBA

114 The Six Immortal Poets (Rokkasen)

(?)Bunka era
SIGNATURE: Hokuba
SEALS: Tei, Sai
Hanging scroll; ink and slight colour on paper,
116.0 × 50.0 cm
PROVENANCE: Arthur Morrison
1913.5–1.0308 (Japanese Painting 1489). Given by
Sir W. Gwynne-Evans, Bt

The Six Immortal Poets (*Rokkasen*) were six
poets of the early Heian period, first
grouped together and critically appraised
by Ki no Tsurayuki in the preface to the
early tenth-century Imperial anthology
Kokin waka shū ('Collection of Poems Past
and Present'). Though in several cases only
the barest details of their biographies are
known, revered as they were by later
generations as the archetypal classical
poets, legends about them abound, and
they were assimilated widely into popular
culture in paintings and prints and even as
characters in historical Kabuki plays. Ukiyo-
e depictions are often humorous,
sometimes with characters from
contemporary society such as famous
courtesans and *kyōka* poets shown in the
guise of the famous six.

In this large, fluidly composed scroll
Hokuba shows the six poets in historical
costume seated beneath a furled court
blind, but in some decidedly odd poses –
each apparently oblivious of the other. The
most dignified, seated at the rear, is Funya
no Yasuhide, with Ariwara no Narihira, the
celebrated lover, dressed in hunting
costume leaning forward beside him.
Ōtomo no Kuronushi, the villain of so
many Kabuki pieces and dressed
appropriately in black, is seen seated from
the rear, while Ono no Komachi, her long
hair combed out over twelve-layered
brocade robes, is shown in profile. Bishop
Henjō, with shaved head and ecclesiastical
garb, racks his brains as he leans forward
on his fan, while Kisen Hōshi seems to
crawl forward with a pained expression on
his face!

115

TEISAI HOKUBA

115 The Six Immortal Poets Fighting

c. Bunka era
SIGNATURE: Teisai Hokuba ga
SEAL: Teisai
Fan painting; ink and slight colour on mica-
covered paper, 18.2 × 43.9 cm
1990.3–5.02 (Japanese Painting ADD 922). Given by
Jack Hillier

The unorthodox poses of the Six Immortal
Poets seen in the previous painting
(no. 114) have dissolved still further into a
chaotic brawl among the literary rivals.
Ono no Komachi, stripped to the waist,
sticks out her tongue at Bishop Henjō.
Narihira, also bare to the waist, is
restrained by Kisen Hōshi from beating
Funya no Yasuhide with a stick. All Ōtomo
no Kuronushi, seated at the back dressed
in black court robes, can do is scratch his
head in bewilderment. The battered court
fan lying in the foreground suggests that
Komachi has already used it to hit the head
of her fellow poets.

TEISAI HOKUBA

116 Courtesan and Kamuro

Bunka era
SIGNATURE: Teisai Hokuba ga
SEAL: Teisai
INSCRIPTION: Yo no naka ni akatsuki ni ukinagori/sa
mo nakariseba kaku tsura/karamaji o ika ni
ukikawatake/no mi ni shinareba tote – okite
yuku/hito yori ato no/matsuri kana
INSCRIPTION SIGNATURE: Yūjo Somenosuke ('The
courtesan Somenosuke')
Fan painting; ink and colour on mica-covered
paper, 16.9 × 44.5 cm
PROVENANCE: Hosomi Ryō; Ralph Harari
LITERATURE: Hillier 1970, vol. 2, no. 161
1982.7–1.017(7) (Japanese Painting ADD 702G)

The painting by Hokuba in quick, fluid ink
and colour shows a parading courtesan
seen from behind with her young *kamuro*
attendant facing back towards us. A cuckoo
sings out as it flies across the top right-
hand corner of the fan, suggesting that the
season is midsummer.

The main part of the fan, however, is
given over to an inscription by the

courtesan Somenosuke, the name used by
successive generations of high-ranking
women in the prestigious Matsubaya house
of pleasure in Yoshiwara. High-ranking
courtesans were expected to perfect a witty
turn of phrase and have elegant flowing
handwriting, both of which Somenosuke
demonstrates in this inscription. Such a fan
would be highly prized by a man of fashion
who wished to demonstrate to the world
that he was intimate with so grand a lady.
The opening preamble containing poignant
reflections upon the uncertain life of a
prostitute is then deflated by the comic
senryū poem which follows, in which the
word *matsuri* in the proverbial phrase *ato no
matsuri* ('the festival that follows') has the
secondary meaning of sexual intercourse:

If in this world there were no partings at
dawn, it would not be so hard to bear.
No matter how uncertain this life of a
prostitute . . .
Rather than the man
Who gets up and goes,
The fun and games that follow!

116

116

117

118 (1492)

establishments at the entrance to Yoshiwara where patrons who wished to enter the quarter incognito could cover their heads with a deep woven basket-hat.

Juppensha Ikku (1765–1831) was an author of comic novels and amateur painter best known for *Dōchū hizakurige* ('Shanks's Mare') and its various sequels, published from 1802 onwards for most of the rest of his life. The form of Hokuba's signature suggests a relatively early date for the fan in that painter's career, probably during the Bunka era (1804–18).

TEISAI HOKUBA

118 Procession of a Courtesan of the Ōgiya House

Bunka era
SIGNATURE: Hokuba ga
SEAL: Hokuba
Triptych of hanging scrolls; ink and colour on paper, each 102.0 × 27.7 cm (approx.)
PROVENANCE: Arthur Morrison
LITERATURE: UT, vol. 1 (1987), BW nos 31–3
1913.5–1.0309–0311 (Japanese Paintings 1490–2).
   Given by Sir W. Gwynne-Evans, Bt

As has already been seen (no. 63), even after the abolition of the two highest ranks of courtesan in the mid-eighteenth century, it was still the custom for women of the *sancha* and *yobidashi* grades to process out from the houses of pleasure to greet wealthy customers in the teahouses that lined Naka-no-chō, the main street of Yoshiwara. Here the grand retinue has been spread over a triptych of hanging scrolls – a *shinzō* apprentice courtesan and manservant carrying a lantern on the left, the high-ranking courtesan shielded by an umbrella in the centre, and a lesser courtesan and maid on the right. The loose manner of painting in fluid ink outlines and rapid washes of colour is matched by relatively informal poses, such as the leading *shinzō* shown from behind, and a touch of humour in the way in which the courtesan's face is teasingly hidden from view, reminding us, by contrast, just how poised and formal most Ukiyo-e paintings are.

The lantern carried by the leading manservant seems to bear the triple folding-fan crest of the prestigious Ōgiya house, together with the written character 'hana', suggesting that the courtesan in the kimono with a design of blooming irises in pools is probably Hanaōgi or Hanabito of that house. The hairstyles of the women are characteristic of the Bunka era (1804–18).

118 (1491)

117

TEISAI HOKUBA

117 Courtesan Under a Snow-Covered Umbrella

c. Bunka era
SIGNATURE: Hokuba hitsu
SEALS: Hoku, Ba
INSCRIPTION: Hyakkan no/kata ni nagameshi/ Yoshiwara ni/amigasa chaya no/yuki-geshiki oba
INSCRIPTION SIGNATURE: Juppensha Ikku
INSCRIPTION SEALS: Tei, Ichi
Fan painting; ink and colour on mica-covered paper, 17.1 × 46.5 cm
PROVENANCE: Hosomi Ryō; Ralph Harari
LITERATURE: Hillier 1970, vol. 2, no. 160
1982.7–1.017(2) (Japanese Painting ADD 702B)

In this witty and eccentric composition just the head of a parading courtesan is shown in one corner of the fan, all but hidden by the large snow-covered umbrella held by a servant over her head, the shape of the umbrella echoing the curve of the fan paper. The *kyōka* poem by Ikku likens her struggle through the snow to being weighed down by debt:

   Looking like a debt
   Of a hundred *kan*
   In Yoshiwara
   A scene at the basket-hat teashop
   In the snow.

The proverb *Hyakkan no kata ni kasa ikkan* ('Only a hat as surety for 100 *kan*' (1 *kan* was a string of 1,000 copper coins)), referring to a loan in which the risk is great for only a paltry reward, is punned with *amigasa chaya* ('basket-hat teashop'), the

118 (1490)

118(1492)   118(1491)   118(1490)

119

TEISAI HOKUBA

119 Boat Prostitute at Asazuma (Asazumabune)

Bunsei–Tempō eras
SIGNATURE: Hokuba
SEAL: Hokuba
Hanging scroll; ink, colour and gold on silk, 80.0 × 32.2 cm
PROVENANCE: Arthur Morrison
LITERATURE: *UT*, vol. 1 (1987), no. 146
1913.5–1.0314 (Japanese Painting 1495). Given by Sir W. Gwynne-Evans, Bt

Until the Edo period Asazuma was an important port on the eastern shore of Lake Biwa. The prostitutes who worked there in boats were even celebrated in classical poetry. In the Genroku era (1688–1704) this was adapted as a subject for painting by Hanabusa Itchō (1652–1724), the renegade Kanō painter, who portrayed an Asazuma prostitute seated in a shallow boat beneath the hanging branches of a willow gazing at the full moon, dressed in the costume of a *shirabyōshi* dancer – gold court hat (*eboshi*), court hunting robe (*suikan*) and fan – and carrying a small hand-drum (*ko-tsutsumi*). There is a tradition that the reason for Itchō's banishment to the island of Izu Miyakejima was that he had painted a picture parodying the habit of the fifth Shōgun Tsunayoshi for playing the drum and singing *nagauta* (recitative chanting) with his concubine Oden no kata in a boat on the lake in Fukiage Park. Itchō is supposed to have modified the subject into the prostitute from Asazuma after this incident, and certainly it was a popular theme for painters of the later Hanabusa school, as well as Ukiyo-e artists such as Harunobu, Eishi, Hokusai and, here, Hokuba.

At least five versions of the subject by Hokuba are known – two horizontal scrolls in which the prostitute is joined by an attendant in the prow of the boat (Ōta 1985, no. 121; Nagoya 1987, no. 27) and two more vertical versions in which the prostitute admires her reflection and that of the full moon in the water (Idemitsu 1988, no. 142; Azabu Museum of Arts and Crafts). Apart from the British Museum painting, which may be slightly earlier, the other four versions all date from Hokuba's last period of activity during the Tempō era (1830–44), when he used the signature Teisai (the Azabu painting is dated in his seventy-first year, 1841).

TEISAI HOKUBA

120   Geisha beside the Sumida River

Bunsei–Tempō eras
SIGNATURE: Teisai
SEAL: Teisai Hokuba no in
Hanging scroll; ink, colours and gold on silk,
   105.5 × 43.5 cm
PROVENANCE: William Anderson
LITERATURE: Anderson 1886, no. 1763; UT, vol. 1
   (1987), BW no. 29
1881.12–10.01763 (Japanese Painting 1498)

120

Perhaps the most common composition for
a Hokuba painting is that of a woman,
often a geisha, walking on the embankment
beside the Sumida River, the figure done in
high polychrome with a characteristically
long, oval face and the landscape done in
abbreviated Kanō wash style. Here a geisha
walks beneath a bare willow tree in winter,
wearing a purple kimono with a design
around the hem of fallen cherry petals on a
river where trout are swimming, together
with a striped brown *obi* of carp leaping up
a waterfall. To judge from the boat-houses
to the right on the far bank this is the
section of the Sumida between Ryōgoku
and Shin'ō Bridges, and the river flowing
off the Sumida from the far bank is the
Tatekawa.

   As so often, Hokuba uses a similar
composition, but set at a different beauty
spot in Edo at a different season, in several
other of his paintings – for instance, two
paintings of beauties in almost identical
poses, with distant landscapes of the
Masaki Inari Shrine (*NU*, vol. 7 (1982),
no. 59; Azabu Museum of Arts and Crafts).
Clearly Hokuba was content to ring the
changes in this way to meet the strong
demand for his works.

120

121

TEISAI HOKUBA

121 Geisha on a Landing Stage in the Snow

Tempō era
SIGNATURE: Teisai
SEAL: Hokuba gain
Hanging scroll; ink, colour and gold on silk,
102.9 × 14.4 cm
LITERATURE: *UT*, vol. 1 (1987), BW no. 30
1980.6–30.05 (Japanese Painting ADD 620)

In this, for Hokuba, unusual cropped composition a geisha wearing a costume similar to that in no. 120 – the kimono has a design of flowering plum trees around the hem, but the *obi* of carp leaping a waterfall is almost identical – waits on a landing stage in the snow for the ferry boat which will carry her across the Sumida River, perhaps to the unlicensed pleasure quarter at Fukagawa. In the distance is a *choki-bune* ('boar's tusk' boat) transporting the previous customer. This severe cropping of the format, in a manner derived from pillar prints (*hashira-kake*), heightens the sense of spontaneity of the scene, as if she has been captured in mid-movement, turning her head to look back.

Paintings by Hokuba are known to have entered the collections of high-ranking *daimyō* such as those of the Nabeshima and Fukui fiefs, and although it is not known whether these works were directly commissioned by the feudal aristocracy, it is certain that there was considerable demand for Hokuba's works in such circles towards the end of his career.

121

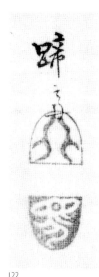

122

TEISAI HOKUBA

122 Parody of Xu You and Chao Fu

Tempō era
SIGNATURE: Teisai
SEALS: Hoku, Ba
Hanging scroll; ink and colour on silk,
   90.0 × 29.5 cm
PROVENANCE: Arthur Morrison
LITERATURE: Morrison 1911, vol. II, pl. xxx
1913.5–1.0313 (Japanese Painting 1494). Given by
   Sir W. Gwynne-Evans, Bt

When the mythical Chinese Emperor Yao
suggested abdicating in favour of his wise
adviser Xu You (Japanese: Kyo Yū), the
latter hurried off to a waterfall in the Ying
River to wash out his ears and then
secluded himself in Mt Ji in protest. Xu
You's associate Chao Fu (Japanese: So Fu)
sought him out at the Ying River leading
an ox, but when he heard the water was
defiled in this way refused to let the ox
drink. Both men are held up as paragons of
virtue and this was a popular subject for
artists of the Kanō school painting for the
military aristocracy.

   Here Hokuba has produced a light-
hearted parody in which a smartly dressed
young woman (too smartly dressed for the
country, one feels, despite her token cotton
leggings) impersonates Xu You, washing
her ear in the waterfall, while down below
a country woman leading an ox represents
Chao Fu. Both women are Ōharame, who
brought firewood from the villages north of
Kyoto to sell in the markets of the city (see
no. 112). The blossoming cherry tree and
pine leaning over the waterfall and the red
and white azaleas in bloom on the rocky
promontory lend a touch of spring lyricism.
A similar composition with an identical
signature and seal is in the collection of the
Chiossone Museum, Genoa (UT, vol. 10
(1987), no. 30), except that there is a cliff
jutting in from the left, no pine tree and no
fardels on the back of the ox in that
version.

122

123

123

TEISAI HOKUBA

123 Moon-viewing Party on the Sumida River

Tempō era
SIGNATURE: Teisai
SEAL: Hokuba
Hanging scroll; ink, colour and gold on silk,
46.2 × 71.3 cm
PROVENANCE: William Anderson
LITERATURE: Anderson 1886, no. 1748; *UT*, vol. 1
(1987), no. 145; Tokyo 1990, no. 38
1881.12–10.01748 (Japanese Painting 1496)

The seventh month, the beginning of autumn, was the favourite time of year for moon-viewing, and in this wide, spacious composition a group of gentlemen and geishas have moored a covered pleasure-boat (*yane-bune*) off Imado on the Sumida River to hold such a party. A cook prepares dishes in the prow, while a young boy assistant leans over the edge to wash a sake cup in the river. Autumn geese fly over the full moon which is low on the horizon just above the far embankment: the

top of the stone gateway just visible above this embankment is the entrance to Mimeguri Shrine. The other small boat, rowed with a single oar at the stern, is a *choki-bune* ('boar's tusk' boat), so named after its long, curved shape, which provided a rapid ferry service for customers to and from the nearby Yoshiwara pleasure quarter.

Pleasure-boats on the Sumida River in the various seasons were a favourite subject for several large horizontal compositions by Hokuba: other scrolls show two women embarking a boat at Mimeguri in the snow (*GUDHJ*, vol. 2 (1982), no. 470), and a party viewing fireworks close to Ryōgoku Bridge in summer (Nagoya 1987, no. 28). River views with foreground figures set against a simple background of the far bank done in Kanō-style washes were the perfect composition for Hokuba, who seems to have preferred to avoid difficult middle-distance transitions whenever possible.

124

TEISAI HOKUBA

124 The Seven Gods of Good Luck at Enoshima

Tempō era
SIGNATURE: Teisai
SEAL: Hokuba gain
Hanging scroll; ink, colour and gold on silk,
   54.5 × 84.4 cm
PROVENANCE: William Anderson
LITERATURE: Anderson 1886, no. 1762; UT, vol. 1
   (1987), no. 144
1881.12–10.01762 (Japanese Painting 1497)

The shrine to Benzaiten, goddess of wealth and good fortune, on the island of Enoshima near Kamakura was consecrated in 1182 at the orders of Minamoto no Yoritomo. Together with shrines on the islands of Chikubushima and Itsukushima it is one of the three great Benzaiten shrines of Japan. The red pagoda of the shrine can be seen on Enoshima Island in the background of this painting, with Mt Fuji in the distance behind. Enoshima was a popular pilgrimage destination from Edo, particularly in the light of the growing cult of the Seven Gods of Good Luck after the middle Edo period.

Thus it is highly appropriate that Benzaiten has come out on an ox to meet the other Six Gods of Good Luck in this auspicious New Year painting. Daikoku and Ebisu with his fishing-rod lead the way, with Bishamon wearing his habitual Chinese armour carrying a treasure sack in which two Chinese boy attendants are playing with Bishamon's golden treasure tower, to his apparent annoyance. Jūrōjin kneels on the beach, while two boys put lucky treasure jewels and coral into his hat (instead of shells) and another boy scoops jewels into Hotei's sack with his Chinese fan. Last, but not least, Fukurokuju flies in on a crane to join the band. In this large painting full of delightful detail Hokuba shows us a humorous inventiveness not often seen in his other works.

124

125

125

TEISAI HOKUBA

125 Two Women Making a Snowball

Tempō era
SIGNATURE: Teisai
SEAL: Hokuba
Folding fan; ink and colour on mica-covered
   paper, 16.2 × 45.7 cm (opened)
PROVENANCE: Arthur Morrison
1913.5–1.0312 (Japanese Painting 1493). Given by
   Sir W. Gwynne-Evans, Bt

Two women have made a snowball almost
as large as themselves; one wearing a
headscarf blows her hands, while the other
adds more snow to the snowball. Shell-
white pigment (*gofun*) has been blown
through a split-reed atomiser to cover the
surface of the fan lightly in imitation of
falling snow.

Such a snow scene was presumably
meant to encourage a pleasant chill to run
down the viewer's back on the stifling
summer day when the fan would be used.
Folding fans (*sensu*) were an indispensable
accessory in the days before air-
conditioning, and of the many thousands
of fan papers decorated by Ukiyo-e painters
most must have been thrown away as they
became tattered to be replaced with the
new season's designs. One large collection
of fan paintings – many retaining their
original bamboo spines – does survive from
the Edo period, assembled by the Kōnoike
family, who were merchants in Osaka.
These are now owned by the Ōta Memorial
Museum of Art in Tokyo, and more than
100 fans painted by Ukiyo-e artists were
exhibited there in 1981.

126

126

'HOKUSAI'

126 Daikoku and Ebisu

19th century
SIGNATURE: Hokusai
SEAL: Taito
Hanging scroll; ink and colour on silk,
   90.0 × 31.0 cm
PROVENANCE: 'Kelsmcott Manor sale 1939'; Oscar
   Raphael
1939.10–14.03 (Japanese Painting ADD 143)

Paintings of the Gods of Good Luck were popularly hung at the New Year to ensure fortune and prosperity. Here smiling Daikoku, in Chinese costume with his treasure sack and mallet to confer wealth, is paired with Ebisu, sometimes said to be Daikoku's son, who carries attributes of a fishing-rod and large sea bream (*tai*) in a basket. The two were often worshipped together in household shrines.

The painting was originally ascribed to Taito II, Hokusai's pupil Toenrō Hokusen, who was ceded the name Taitō by the master in 1819. The work does not, however, correspond to any known style used by Taito II, either his close imitation of Hokusai or more personal use of broad ink strokes. Nor is Taito II known to have used the name 'Hokusai', and since this signature is done very much in imitation of Hokusai's own signature of the first two decades of the nineteenth century, it must be concluded that this is probably a deliberate forgery, or else the work of yet another amateur who used the name Hokusai (see no. 127 concerning the two main candidates for the title Hokusai II).

127

TAIGIRŌ HOKUSAI (dates unknown)

127 Fukurokuju

Mid–late 19th century
SIGNATURE: Taigirō Hokusai hitsu
SEAL: ?Hokushi no in
Hanging scroll; ink and colour on paper,
   53.0 × 25.0 cm
PROVENANCE: Arthur Morrison
1946.2–9.040 (Japanese Painting ADD 222).
   Bequeathed by Arthur Morrison

Fukurokuju, as his name implies, is the one of the Seven Gods of Good Luck who represents felicitous long life, and he is shown as a bearded old man in the dress of a scholar, with a tall, bald head, who carries a handscroll (an attribute borrowed from Jurōjin). Here his robes are painted with a variety of highly inflected 'axe-cut' brushstrokes in black ink, a highly exaggerated version of a style sometimes used by the great Katsushika Hokusai in his later years.

There are currently two candidates considered eligible by scholars for the title Hokusai II – a Suzuki Hokusai of Minami Kayaba-chō, who painted a votive panel of warriors in 1816, and a Hashimoto Hokusai of Asakusa Sanya who is mentioned in a directory of 1842 – though it is possible these are one and the same individual. At present neither of these is known to have used the *gō* Taigirō that appears on the British Museum painting. The question of identity is further complicated by the seal, which appears to read 'Hokushi' (in *hiragana*). There are at least two Katsushika pupils who used this name, Tōtei Hokushi and Reisai Hokushi (see *GUDHJ*, vol. 2 (1982), p. 126), but neither is known to have used the names Taigirō or Hokusai. A definitive identification of this minor Hokusai pupil must await further evidence.

127

Katsushika Hokuitsu
worked Bunka (1804–18)–
Bunsei (1818–30) eras

Biography unknown, but a small number
of paintings by him imitating Hokusai's
styles of the Bunka (1804–18) and Bunsei
(1818–30) eras. Used the *gō* Shikōsai,
Keikōsai, Keikōtei. A collaborative work
with Hokusai's daughter Ōi is recorded.

KATSUSHIKA HOKUITSU

128 Woman Collecting Pine Seedlings

Late Bunka–Bunsei eras
SIGNATURE: Keikōtei Hokuitsu
SEAL: Hokuitsu
Hanging scroll; ink and colour on silk,
  80.0 × 30.0 cm
PROVENANCE: Arthur Morrison
LITERATURE: *UT*, vol. 1 (1987), BW no. 34
1913.5–1.0315 (Japanese Painting 1502). Given by
  Sir W. Gwynne-Evans, Bt

One of the annual events in the calendar of
the Kyoto Imperial court was an outing to
the surrounding country on the first rat day
of the New Year to collect pine seedlings
(*ne no hi asobi* or *komatsu hiki*), and here a
woman of the court stands with a mattock
over one shoulder with which she has dug
the pine seedlings in her basket. Her robes
hang open at the front in alluring *déshabillé*,
and her long tresses of hair are allowed to
hang down free at the back.

The painting imitates all the mannerisms
of style of the beauties of Hokusai's Taito
and Iitsu periods – full face, long almond
eyes with a pink blush around them,
heavily crinkled outline to the under-robes,
and so on – but without managing to
match the level of technical
accomplishment or tautness of composition
of the master. The patterning of the robes,
for instance, is mundane in comparison
with works by Hokusai from the same
period.

128

128

129

SHUNKYOKUSAI HOKUMEI
worked Bunsei (1818–30)–Tempō (1830–44) eras

129 Tokiwa Gozen with her Sons in the Snow

Bunsei–Tempō eras
SIGNATURE: Shunkyokusai Hokumei
SEAL: Hokumei
Hanging scroll; ink and colour on silk,
   92.5 × 32.3 cm
PROVENANCE: Arthur Morrison
LITERATURE: *UT*, vol. 1 (1987), BW no. 35
1913.5–1.0316 (Japanese Painting 1503). Given by
   Sir W. Gwynne-Evans, Bt

Tokiwa Gozen, mistress of the warrior
Minamoto no Yoshitomo, fled with her
three sons after Yoshitomo's defeat in the
Heiji war of 1159. At Fushimi they were
offered refuge from a violent snowstorm by
a humble elderly couple. By the end of the
seventeenth century this touching episode
had entered the repertoire of popular ballad
singers (*sekkyō jōruri*) and was often
depicted in Ukiyo-e. Here Tokiwa rests in
the thickly falling snow, sheltering her sons
with her robes and travelling hat: the baby
nestling in the collar of her kimono is the
future warrior hero Yoshitsune.

   Shunkyokusai Hokumei was a minor
Osaka painter and printmaker, who signed
himself on an actor print of *c.* 1830 as a
pupil of Shunkōsai Hokushū (worked
1810–32), one of the principal Osaka print
designers. Hokushū in turn is known to
have assisted Hokusai in the preparation of
Hokusai gashiki, an illustrated book
published in Nagoya in 1819, following
Hokusai's artistically influential visit to
Osaka in the previous year. Thus the
present painting shows some filtered
elements of the Hokusai *bijinga* style, such
as the nervous crinkled outlines to the
drapery. No other paintings by
Shunkyokusai Hokumei are presently
known, and he should not be confused
with Hokusai's direct pupil Katsushika
Hokumei, possibly a woman with the
surname Inoue, who was given the
master's famous *kimō dasoku* ('hair on the
turtle, legs on the snake') seal in the fourth
month, 1813.

129

130

KATSUSHIKA HOKUGA
worked Bunka (1804–18)–Ka'ei (1848–54) eras

130 Sea Bream and Squid

Bunka–Ka'ei eras
SIGNATURE: Hokuga
SEAL: Hokuga
Fan painting; ink and colour on mica-covered
    paper, 17.5 × 48.6 cm
PROVENANCE: Hosomi Ryō; Ralph Harari
LITERATURE: Hillier 1970, vol. 2, no. 175
1982.7–1.017(6) (Japanese Painting ADD 702F)

Red sea bream (*tai*) and squid (*ika*) are both
auspicious fish eaten particularly at the
New Year holiday. Here they are laid out
naturalistically in the manner of a still-life
surimono print.

Katsushika Hokuga was one of the many
– almost 200, according to Nagata Seiji

(*Kobijutsu*, 82–4 (1987)) – minor pupils and
later followers of Hokusai, active in the first
half of the nineteenth century. A directory
published in Edo in 1842 gives his family
name as Yamadera Myōnosuke, *na*
Nobuyuki, *gō* Karyōsai, and says that he
lived in Ushigome Takubo. He is thought
to have first studied with the Ukiyo-e artist
Tomikawa Fusanobu, adopting the name
Ginsetsu II. His use of the *gō* Karyōsai is
said to date from *c.* 1824. He should not be
confused with the other, more famous
pupil of Hokusai called Hokuga (written
with the *ga* character meaning 'goose'), who
later used the name Hōtei Gosei and
was a prolific painter of beautiful women in
a highly individual, mannered style.

130

SŌGA (dates unknown)

131 Susano'o-no-Mikoto Making a Pact
with the Spirits of Disease

2nd month, 1860
SIGNATURE: Manjirō-mon/sessha Sōga ('Ineptly
    copied by Sōga, a pupil of Manjirō')
SEAL: (illegible)
INSCRIPTION: Hachijū-roku yowai/Manji hitsu
    ('Painted by Manji at the age of eighty-six'),
    with a copy of Hokusai's 'Mt Fuji above clouds'
    seal
Votive panel; ink, colour and gold leaf on wood,
    21.5 × 27.5 cm
PROVENANCE: William Anderson
LITERATURE: Anderson 1886, no. 2036; NU, vol. 1
    (1987), no. 151
1881.12–10.02036 (Japanese Painting 1499)

Anderson (1886, p. 401–2) attempted to
identify the spirits of disease who surround
the Shintō deity Susano'o-no-Mikoto,
brother of the Sun Goddess Amaterasu,
and are presumably being forced into a
pact of submission:

> ... One ugly being, with a horn upon his
> forehead and a mallet lying by his side
> has just stamped his inky palm upon the
> contract sheet by way of a signature,
> leaving the demon impress of a three-
> fingered hand. The representatives of
> Measles, Small-pox, Elephantiasis,
> Mumps and Itch are easily recognisable,
> but the other ghastly embodiments of
> disease are less open to identification.
> Three corpse-like starvelings, one of
> whom bears a large bundle on his
> shoulders; a hoglike creature with a half
> human half brutish head; a figure
> mottled with red blotches; and a very

131

stout, but youthful and otherwise decent-looking personage, who alone amongst the crew has black instead of red hair, are probably meant to typify respectively Fevers, Leprosy, Erysipelas, and Corpulence.

The panel is dated on the back '2nd month, Ansei 7 (1860)'. There were epidemics of measles and flu in Edo from the summer of 1859 into the spring of 1860, and one can imagine that votive plaques such as this would have been in demand from families hoping to ward off sickness.

The artist Sōga states that he is a pupil of

Manjirō, a name used by Hokusai's pupil Hokuga (Hōtei Gosei), but details of his biography are otherwise unknown. Though modest in scale, the painting has documentary value, for as stated in the inscription it is a (reduced and abbreviated) copy of a famous votive panel painted by Hokusai in his eighty-sixth year (1845). Formerly hanging in the Ushijima Shrine at Mukōjima, this grand painting was destroyed in the great Kantō earthquake of 1923 and is now known only by a poor-quality black and white photograph (see *NU*, vol. 1 (1987), p. 256).

131

132

132

Mori Gyokusen 1791–1864

Common name Umon; *gō* Kaō, Kikutei, Sodō, Sankōdō, Shisendō. Native of Nagoya. First a pupil of the Kanō painter Yoshikawa Ikkei, then the *nanga* master Nakabayashi Chikutō. Was not allowed to follow the latter to Kyoto and so studied Ukiyo-e with Maki Bokusen (1775–1824), who had studied under Hokusai when he lodged with Bokusen in Nagoya for six months in 1812 and again in 1817. In later years studied with Tosa Mitsuzane, changed his name to Kōga (Takamasa), and abandoned the Ukiyo-e style. Also designed illustrations for printed *kyōka* anthologies.

MORI GYOKUSEN

132 Two Geishas with a Maid

5th month, 1821
SIGNATURE: Gyokusen shai ('Gyokusen, painting
the intent')
SEALS: Nihonga no Minamoto ('Source of Japanese
painting'), Gyokusen
Hanging scroll; ink, colour and gold on silk,
89.6 × 38.6 cm
LITERATURE: *UT*, vol. 1 (1987), no. 168
1982.5–18.01 (Japanese Painting ADD 669)

The two extended visits by Hokusai to Nagoya in 1812 and 1817, during which he lodged with his pupil Bokusen (1775–1824), had a considerable impact on the artistic community of this thriving but culturally somewhat isolated castle town. The most famous product of these visits was, of course, the *Hokusai Manga* published by Eirakuya Tōshirō of that city, but Hokusai also developed an extended network of disciples both in Nagoya and also in the Osaka/Kyoto region when he moved on there. It is not known if Mori Gyokusen studied directly with Hokusai, and it is more likely that he learned something of the Hokusai *bijin* style through Bokusen. As with other artists with strong artistic personalities – one is reminded of Hōtei Gosei (Hokuga) – this style was radically modified into a highly mannered idiom.

Apparent, too, is the pull of the Maruyama–Shijō style of Kyoto.

Two geishas, on their way to perform at a party and accompanied by a chubby maid carrying a *shamisen*, turn together to look back in surprise at something that has caught their attention. With elongated bodies impossibly contorted, they resemble a pair of exotic but ungainly wading birds. The technique of kimono decoration is flawless, an interesting distinction being drawn between the subdued tones of the costume of the maid and the brilliant brocades of the geishas' *obi*, after the manner of Kyoto painters.

Another painting by Gyokusen in similar style, *Drunken Beauty*, with an inscription by Juppensha Ikku has recently been introduced (Kumamoto 1991, no. 72).

132 detail (opposite)

Andō Hiroshige 1797–1858

Art surname Utagawa; childhood name Tokutarō; common name Jūemon, then Tokubei; gō Ichiyūsai (with yū meaning 'bravery', c. 1818–30), Ichiyūsai (with yū meaning 'hazy', c. 1830–1), Ichiryūsai (c. 1832–42), Ryūsai (c. 1842–58), Utashige (c. late Tempō era (1830–44)). (These dates suggested by Suzuki Jūzō in GUDHJ, vol. 2 (1982), p. 84.) Son of a Bakufu fire officer, Andō Gen'emon. Lived first in the firemen's residence by the moat at Yayosu, then Oga-chō, next Tokiwa-chō and finally Nakabashi Kanō Shindō. A pupil of Utagawa Toyohiro, but also studied the Kanō style with Okajima Rinsai, nanga with Ōoka Umpō, and the Shijō style from an unknown source. First dated work an illustrated kyōka anthology, Kyōka murasaki no maki, published in 1818. During the Bunsei era (1818–30) produced prints of beauties, actors and warriors in the standard Utagawa mould, as well as surimono and illustrations for printed novels. c. 1831 designed a series, Tōto meisho, entirely in shades of blue, and the following year took a trip down the Tōkaidō Highway as part of an official envoy from the Shōgun to the Imperial court in Kyoto. Impressions from this journey were worked up into his great print series Tōkaidō gojūsan-tsugi ('Fifty-three Stations of the Tōkaidō Highway'), published by Hoeidō in 1832–3, the phenomenal success of which decided the course of his future career. The series Kisokaidō rokujūkyū-tsugi ('Sixty-nine Stations of the Kisokaidō Highway') with Eisen followed in the later 1830s, along with numerous series of views of Edo, reworkings of the Tōkaidō series and prints of birds and flowers. His later career, in terms of prints, was taken up with series of upright landscapes such as Meisho Edo hyakkei ('One Hundred Famous Views of Edo', 1856–8) and triptychs, often incorporating beauties with landscapes.

Hiroshige's earliest paintings, done during the Bunsei era (1818–30), are standing figures of women against plain backgrounds in the somewhat stiff style of his early prints. A set of eight wooden doors painted with Cherry Trees and Swallows was an important commission in 1835, or shortly after, from the abbot of the Senkokuji Temple in Yokohama. Apart from his journey along the Tōkaidō Hiroshige is known to have made many extended trips to the provinces – Kai Province (1841), Bōsō peninsula (1844), Mutsu Province (c. 1845), Shinano (1848) – making sketches along the way which were then worked up into prints and paintings. His major project in landscape painting was during the Ka'ei era (1848–54), when Hiroshige and his studio produced, it is estimated, between 100 and 200 sets of diptychs and triptychs of views of Edo and the provinces, which were 'given' by the Tendō fief of Dewa Province to their creditors in order to wipe out debts. Most of the paintings were distributed in the autumn of 1851, and it has recently been suggested that these were done during the preceding eighteen months, after Hiroshige moved to a new residence and studio in Nakabashi Kanō Shindō. A detailed chronology of Hiroshige's paintings based on the various forms of his signature and seals has yet to be established.

After Hiroshige I's death in 1858, the name Hiroshige was taken over by his pupil and adopted son Suzuki Shigenobu (1826–69) and used by him until his retirement to Yokohama in c. 1865, when he changed to the name Kisai Ryūshō. Owing to their similar styles and use of similar signatures and seals the late paintings of Hiroshige I and those of Hiroshige II have yet to be differentiated satisfactorily. Hiroshige III (?1842–94), a pupil of Hiroshige I who assumed the name upon Hiroshige II's retirement in 1865, painted in a Western-influenced manner that is more easily distinguished (see, for instance, NU, vol. 8 (1981), no. 45).

ANDŌ HIROSHIGE

133 Soga no Jūrō Taking Leave of Tora no Gozen

?Late Tempō–Kōka eras
SIGNATURE: Hiroshige hitsu
SEAL: Tōkaido
Hanging scroll; ink, colour and gold on silk, 95.8 × 33.1 cm
PROVENANCE: William Anderson
LITERATURE: Anderson 1886, no. 1756; UT, vol. 1 (1987), no. 153
1881.12–10.01756 (Japanese Painting 1552)

The revenge of the Soga brothers, Jūrō and Gorō, on their father's murderer, Kudō Suketsune, while on a hunting party led by Minamoto no Yoritomo at the base of Mt Fuji in 1193, as related in the military tale Soga monogatari, was a classic vendetta much elaborated on in later literature and drama. In the Edo period, in particular, Soga pieces were an indispensable item in the programme of plays at the Kabuki theatres each New Year. In Kabuki versions of the story much attention is given to the love affairs of the brothers – for the women Tora no Gozen and Kewaizaka no Shōshō, respectively. Tora was a courtesan of the Chōtei house at Ōiso in Sagami Province, and here she is portrayed watching from the balcony of the brothel as Jūrō rides away in the distance. Though the characters are essentially dressed in Edo-period rather than twelfth-century costume, Tora's hair is dressed in the anachronistic 'Shimada' style of the Genroku era (1688–1704), lending an historical touch. Her kimono is decorated with Jūrō's emblem of plovers.

The chronology of Hiroshige's paintings has not yet been established in detail, but the manner in which this work has been painstakingly executed so that pigment fills almost every corner of the silk is rather different from the later landscapes in which there is considerable use of atmospheric misty transitions in pale ink, perhaps indicating a relatively early date. Paintings

and prints of historical subjects are quite
rare in Hiroshige's *oeuvre*, but from 1845 to
1846 he designed a series of colour prints
entitled *Soga monogatari zue* ('Illustrations to
Tale of the Soga'), including a composition
very similar to this painting except that
Tora is seated. The painting may be close
to the print series in date. There is also a
painted version of the composition by
Hiroshige's pupil Suzuki Shigenobu
(Kanagawa Prefectural Museum), done
before he assumed the name Hiroshige II
upon Hiroshige's death in 1858.

133

133

ANDŌ HIROSHIGE

134 Ferry Boat on the Sumida River

Tempō–Ka'ei eras
SIGNATURE: Hiroshige
SEAL: Ryūsai
INSCRIPTION: Sumidagawa/watari ni fune o/
noriidete/kishi ni tsukuba no/yama mo miekeri
INSCRIPTION SIGNATURE: Hachijū-ichi nen/Reidō-ō
('Old man Reidō, in his eighty-first year')
Fan painting; ink and colour on mica-covered
paper, 13.5 × 46.7 cm
PROVENANCE: Hosomi Ryō; Ralph Harari
LITERATURE: Hillier 1970, vol. 2, no. 178
1982.7–1.017(5) (Japanese Painting ADD 702E)

A ferry boat crosses the Sumida River in
countryside on the northern fringes of Edo,
with a view of Mt Tsukuba in the distance.
The *kyōka* poem above by one Reidō
expresses the admiration of passengers for
the fine view, and plays on the phrase
watari ni fune which means both 'a boat for
crossing' and a 'stroke of luck' (in a more
proverbial sense):

> Setting out in a boat
> To cross the Sumida River,
> What good fortune –
> As we reached the bank
> Mt Tsukuba came into view.

From his earliest landscape prints of the
1830s Hiroshige designed dozens of series
celebrating well-known beauty spots in the
city of Edo, culminating in the great late
series *Meisho Edo hyakkei* ('One Hundred
Famous Places in Edo') of 1856–8. The form
of Hiroshige's signature changed little
during his later career, and ascertaining the
identity and dates of 'Reidō' would permit
a more exact dating of the painting.

ANDŌ HIROSHIGE

135 Scene on the Yodo River

Tempō–Ka'ei eras
SIGNATURE: Hiroshige
SEAL: Hiroshige
Fan painting; ink and slight colour on mica-
covered ppaer, 14.5 × 47.0 cm
1990.3–5.05 (Japanese Painting ADD 925). Given by
Jack Hillier

Hiroshige was a master of misty suggestion
in his landscapes, and this slight work
shows a scene on the Yodo River near
Osaka, with two sailboats passing in front
of Yodo Castle, beyond which are clouds
and hills in the distance. To the right a
village nestles among reeds on the shore.
The tower of Yodo Castle, with dolphin
finials at each end of the roof, was also
featured by Hokusai in the design *Moon on
the Yodo River* from his print series 'Snow,
Moon and Flowers' (*c.* 1832).

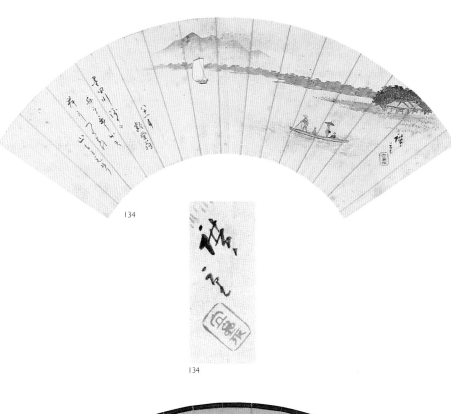

134

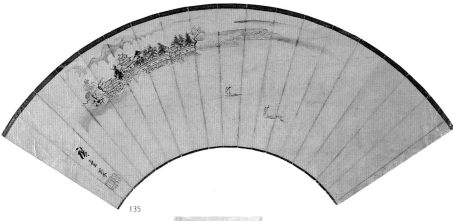

134

135

135

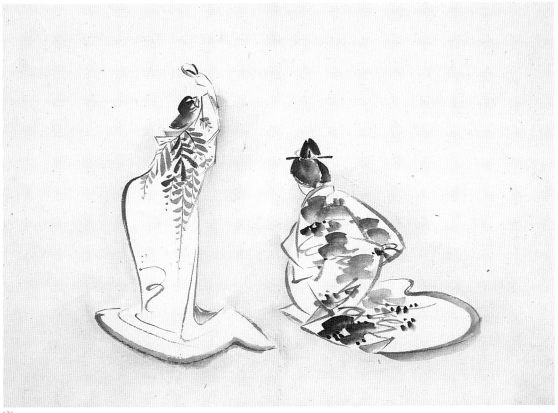

136

Attributed to
ANDŌ HIROSHIGE

136 Album of Ten Miscellaneous
Subjects

Tempō–Ansei eras
Folding album; ink and colour on paper,
  23.5 × 16.6 cm
PROVENANCE: 'Hōudō shujin' (1892); Gillet; Janette
  Ostier; Ralph Harari
LITERATURE: Hillier 1966, pls 64, 66; Hillier 1970,
  vol. 2, no. 183; Hillier 1980, no. 121
1982.7–1.06 (Japanese Painting ADD 691). Given by
  Dr and Mrs Michael Harari

The postscript to the album by one 'Hōudō
shujin', dated October 1892, explains that
his father had been fond of painting and
had studied with Hiroshige and that he
had found these sheets of paintings by the
master preserved at the bottom of a chest
and had them bound into an album.
Though unsigned, the ten abbreviated
sketches are certainly in Hiroshige's most
convivial style, and other versions of
several of the compositions bearing a
Hiroshige seal are in the collections of the
Freer Gallery of Art, Washington, DC

(Freer Gallery of Art (eds), *The Freer Gallery
of Art II: Japan*, Tokyo, Kodansha, n.d.
(?1972), no. 66) and Library of Congress
(Lee 1984, vol. II, pls 4, 11, 19), confirming
the attribution. It was customary for
teachers to make copies, often unsigned, of
previously worked-out compositions for
pupils to use as study material (*tehon*). The
ten subjects in the album are:
1 *Sambasō* dancer.
2 Man dreaming of pleasure quarters.
3 (?)Chinese with an elephant in a
   procession.
4 Iwafuji striking Onoe with the sandal,
   from the Kabuki play *Kagamiyama kokyō
   no nishiki-e* (illustrated).
5 Shintō priest dancing.
6 Woman with a parcel walking past a
   large lantern in the street. (?)Ohatsu,
   the faithful maid.
7 Sukeroku with his umbrella, seen from
   behind.
8 Blossoming cherry trees on riverbank.
9 The Third Princess's cat running out
   from under a blind.
10 Bust portrait of a courtesan as Daruma.

137

137

ANDŌ HIROSHIGE

137 Woman Composing a Poem Looking at Mt Fuji

?Late Tempō era
SIGNATURE: Hiroshige hitsu
SEAL: Ichiryūsai
INSCRIPTION: Ōju nana fu no yose zu ('A set of seven pictures of women by special request')
Hanging scroll; ink and colour on silk, 36.5 × 55.3 cm
PROVENANCE: Arthur Morrison
LITERATURE: *UT*, vol. 1 (1987), BW no. 42
1946.2–9.044 (Japanese Painting ADD 226).
Bequeathed by Arthur Morrison

As the inscription next to the signature says, this is one from a set of seven paintings of women, and one wonders what the other subjects might have been. The woman stands in front of clumps of cotton rose (*fuyō*) and the so-called courtesan flower (*ominaeshi*), with its crests of small golden blooms; both are flowers of autumn. She looks back at the already snow-covered graceful peak of Mt Fuji and is about to compose a poem describing the scene, and there may be a reference here to famous poets of the past who composed poems to the sacred mountain, such as Ariwara no Narihira in *Tales of Ise* or the itinerant monk-poet Saigyō Hōshi. The shape of the eight protrusions on the peak of Mt Fuji was sometimes likened to the shape of an open cotton rose flower.

The form of signature and seals is similar to that in the well-known painting *Courtesan Takao* (Freer Gallery of Art), dated by Narazaki (*US*, vol. 16 (1981), no. 57) to the late Tempō era (1830–44).

138

ANDŌ HIROSHIGE

138 Standing Beauty

?Ka'ei era
SIGNATURE: Ryūsai hitsu
SEAL: Hiroshige
Hanging scroll; ink and colour on paper,
  91.5 × 27.4 cm
PROVENANCE: Arthur Morrison
LITERATURE: *UT*, vol. 1 (1987), BW no. 52
1913.5–1.0297 (Japanese Painting 1551). Given by
  Sir W. Gwynne Evans, Bt

The woman, soberly dressed in a black-checked kimono and plain brown *obi* tied in a large diagonal knot across her back, is probably a restaurant waitress or tradesman's wife. She stands with her arms drawn into her sleeves. Though quickly executed, the dry outlines have been surely placed and the washes of ink on the kimono skilfully modulated to suggest the sheen of the fabric. The alert, smiling face is softened by pale brown rather than grey outlines, and the oiled hairstyle neatly codified with a variety of deft grey and glossy black brushstrokes.

The combination of a 'Ryūsai' signature and this particular 'Hiroshige' seal is characteristic of the more than 100 sets of landscape paintings thought to have been done by Hiroshige in the eighteen months prior to the autumn of Ka'ei 4 (1851) for distribution by the Tendō fief to their creditors, though the 'sai' character of the signature on the Tendō paintings generally has a long, trailing stroke down the right-hand side. The British Museum painting may be close to these in date.

138

ANDŌ HIROSHIGE

139 Views of Edo
(preparatory sketches)

(?)Ka'ei–Ansei eras
SIGNATURE: Hiroshige
SEALS: Ichiryūsai
Folding album; ink and colour on paper,
 30.0 × 18.0 cm (cover)
PROVENANCE: Arthur Morrison
LITERATURE: Strange 1925, p. 122
1913.5–1.0290 (Japanese Painting 1544). Given by
 Sir W. Gwynne-Evans, Bt

139

Edward Strange (*The Colour Prints of
Hiroshige*, London, Cassell, 1925, p. 122)
suggests that these are preparatory
drawings for prints and that they must date
from Hiroshige's lastest period. The
squarish proportions of the drawings (30.0
× 36.0 cm) with a title written in a border
down the right-hand side do not suggest
the dimensions of a horizontal *ōban* print,
however; nor is the size of the figures
relative to the composition normal for
Hiroshige's prints. It seems more likely that
they were intended as preparatory sketches
for an album of paintings. Many drawings
have small *pentimenti* added to make
corrections to individual figures and a few
touches of wash. Only the last drawing is
completely coloured. The settings are all
famous places in Edo:

1 The plum garden at Kameido (*Kameido
  Umeyashiki*).
2 Winter [should be autumn?] – maple
  viewing on the Ōji road (*Fuyu Ōji-michi
  momiji-mi*).
3 Viewing cherry blossoms at Mukōjima
  (*Mukōjima hanami*).

139

4 View of the Tanabata Festival
  throughout the city (*Shichū tanabata
  matsuri no kei*).
5 Spring – view of Imado from Mukōjima
  (*Haru Mukōjima yori Imado no kei*).
6 Village . . . [at the Tama River?] (*. . . no
  sato*). (Paper damaged.)
7 Winter – ferry at Hashiba (*Fuyu Hashiba
  no watashi*).
8 Autumn – moonlit night at Yanagibashi
  (*Aki Yanagibashi no tsukiyo*).
9 Autumn – Shinagawa, the cape in the
  moonlight (*Aki Shinagawa tsuki no
  misaki*).
10 Winter – snow falling on the Sumida
  River seen from Imado, from a set of
  famous places (*Fuyu meisho no uchi
  Imado yori Sumidagawa no yukifuri*).

140

ANDŌ HIROSHIGE

140 Landscape at Mt Kanō in Kazusa Province

140

(?)Ka'ei–Ansei eras
SIGNATURE: Hiroshige
SEAL: Ichiryūsai
Hanging scroll; ink and colour on silk;
    44.7 × 60.5 cm
PROVENANCE: William Anderson
LITERATURE: Anderson 1886, no. 1895; *UT*, vol. 1
    (1987), no. 154
1881.12–10.01895 (Japanese Painting 1565)

All Hiroshige's landscapes are based on actual places, and the straight flight of stone steps climbing steeply through the pines and cypress trees in the background of this painting are also seen, as Yokoto Yōichi has pointed out (*UT*, vol. 1 (1987), no. 154), in the view of *Mt Kanō in Kazusa Province* from Hiroshige's late series *Sankai mitate sumō* ('Parodies of Sumō by Mountain and Sea'), published in 1858. The composition of the painting is very different, however, with the two landscape

elements pushed daringly to diagonally opposite corners and separated by a chasm of mysterious, atmospheric mist. It was the combination of this sensitive use of ink washes to suggest deep space with views of particular beauty spots known and loved by many travellers from Edo that was Hiroshige's particular contribution to landscape painting. Here the foreshortened winding path that leads from the foreground and the gradually reducing scale of the tiny pilgrims on the path open up a sense of that deep space and suggest the enormity of scale of the natural features. The stone steps lead up to Jinyaji Temple and Shiratori Shrine with a spectacular view of the 'ninety-nine valleys' (Kujūku Tani) from the top.

As with nos 141–3 the top corners of the painting appear at one time to have been covered by a gabled frame which has left stains and discolorations on the silk. This shape is used particularly for votive plaques presented to shrines.

141

142

(?)ANDŌ HIROSHIGE I

141 Coastal Landscape

(?)Ansei era
SIGNATURE: Hiroshige
SEAL: Ryūsai
Hanging scroll; ink and colour on silk,
44.1 × 60.2 cm
PROVENANCE: William Anderson
LITERATURE: Anderson 1886, no. 1896
1881.12–10.01896 (Japanese Painting 1562)

Though well composed to give a sense of
deep space to this coastal panorama, the
rough and somewhat rudimentary level of
technique – seen, for instance, in the
scrubby dotting to suggest vegetation on
the distant hills – raises doubts as to
whether this work was actually painted by
Hiroshige I. It bears a damaged, but
apparently authentic signature, and the seal
is found on at least one fine *bijin* painting
(*Kobijutsu*, suppl. vol. 3 (March 1983),
painting no. 3), so it must be concluded
that Hiroshige I has 'authorised' the work
of a pupil, possibly Hiroshige II
(nos 143–5).

Like nos 140, 142 and 143 the painting
must have originally been intended for a
frame with a gabled top. The location of
the view has not been identified.

141

SHIGETOSHI

142 Landscape

(?)Ansei era
SIGNATURE: Shigetoshi
SEAL: Shigetoshi
Hanging scroll; ink and colour on silk,
44.7 × 60.0 cm
PROVENANCE: William Anderson
LITERATURE: Anderson 1886, no. 1897
1881.12–10.01897 (Japanese Painting 1680)

The location of this view of a bridge over a
river, with buildings amid trees to the left
and distant mountains, has not been
identified. The technique and style,
however, follow Hiroshige I (though not
quite matching his level of accomplishment)
in the convincing depiction of deep space
and the atmospheric combination of soft
washes and dark accents for the trees; the
pine trees, in particular, are drawn with the
characteristic mannerism of piling up
rounded horizontal strokes.

Though recorded as a pupil of
Hiroshige I, nothing else is known
concerning the biography of Shigetoshi.

142

143

SUZUKI HIROSHIGE II (1826–69)

143 Mt Fuji Seen Through a Mountain Pass

1865–9
SIGNATURE: Kisai Ryūshō hitsu
SEAL: (?)Ryūsai
Hanging scroll; ink and colour on silk,
44.4 × 59.8 cm
PROVENANCE: William Anderson
LITERATURE: Anderson 1886, no. 1898
1881.12–10.01898 (Japanese Painting 1563)

In this cursory work Mt Fuji appears on the horizon at the end of a gently sloping valley with figures climbing a path in the foreground. The view does not relate to any of the designs in Hiroshige I's last print series, *Fuji sanjū-rokkei* ('Thirty-six Views of Mt Fuji', 1858), and it has not been possible to locate the scene.

The painting has all the hallmarks of hasty and rather careless execution: the broad washes of pale *sumi* and green that form the hills have none of the sensitivity of works by Hiroshige I (no. 140), and the minimal number of stick figures and occasional clumps of trees are perfunctory. One can imagine such works were produced in large numbers to sell to tourists, Japanese perhaps, but more likely foreigners, since Hiroshige II was living in Yokohama at this time.

143

144 (1555)

144 (1554)

144 (1555)

144 (1554)

145

SUZUKI HIROSHIGE II

144 Two Views of Mt Fuji from the Sumida River

c. 1859–65
SIGNATURE: Hiroshige hitsu
SEAL: Nise Ichiryūsai Hiroshige gain ('Painting seal of the second-generation Ichiryūsai Hiroshige')
Pair of hanging scrolls; ink and colour on silk, each 88.8 × 29.8 cm (approx.)
PROVENANCE: Arthur Morrison
LITERATURE: *UT*, vol. 1 (1987), nos 165, 166; Smith 1990, no. 202; Tokyo 1990, no. 39
1913.5–1.0298, 0299 (Japanese Painting 1554/5). Given by Sir W. Gwynne-Evans, Bt

The Sumida River passed through the neighbourhoods where the merchants and artisans lived, the 'low city' (*shitamachi*), as distinct from the more elevated Yamanote districts inhabited by the feudal aristocracy and samurai classes. Apart from a few riverside villas and government buildings such as boat-houses and granaries, the river was given over for the enjoyment of commoners and samurai alike. In this pair of views of the river in spring and early summer geishas are shown enjoying the blossoming cherry trees which clustered along the embankment near Mimeguri Shrine (right) and preparing for a trip with a client in a covered boat at a landing stage near Ryōgoku Bridge, under the fresh green hanging branches of a willow tree (left).

The accomplished technique of the painting – soft wash landscapes with accents of stronger colour for the figures – is a faithful continuation of the style of Hiroshige I, and in fact the compositions are copied from two designs of Hiroshige's last print series, *Fuji sanjū-rokkei* ('Thirty-six Views of Mt Fuji'), with slight modifications being made to suit the hanging-scroll format. In addition, Hiroshige I is known to have done a painted version of the cherry-viewing composition, albeit with the figures and trees in a slightly different configuration (formerly Takeoka Toyota collection; see Hoshino 1927, pls not numbered). Though the size of Mt Fuji has been exaggerated for artistic effect, the sacred peak could often be seen from the city of Edo.

(?)SUZUKI HIROSHIGE II

145 Miscellaneous Landscape and Figure Subjects

c. 1859–65
SEAL: Shige
Paintings in various shapes; ink and colour on paper, various sizes
1983.11–11.01 (1–25) (Japanese Paintings ADD 743–767)

145

Various landscapes (mainly around Edo) and figure subjects (some historical, some genre) are painted on circular, fan-, kidney- and octagon-shaped papers and were probably originally stuck scattered over folding screens or sliding doors as interior decoration. The diamond-shaped seal of the stylised character 'shige' was used by both Hiroshige I and Hiroshige II, but the broad, large figure style and jaunty colouring with accents of brilliant blue and green suggest Hiroshige II, working during the period after Hiroshige I's death, before he moved to Yokohama (*c.* 1859–65). The subjects are drawn from the standard Hiroshige repertoire and the paintings briskly but pleasingly done. Each is inscribed by the artist with a title, listed as follows:

1 Arakawa [River] – fan.
2 Sakurada-jō – fan.
3 Tonegawa [River] – circle.
4 The historical site and carp pool at the Yatsuhashi Bridge (*Ike rifu Yatsuhashi koseki*) – circle.
5 Gojō no hashi [Bridge] – circle.
6 Ferry at Ichikawa (*Ichikawa no watashi*) – circle.
7 Kasuga – circle.
8 The Ataka Barrier, Kaga Province (*Kaga Ataka no seki*) – circle.
9 Teppōzu – circle.
10 Ōmori – circle.
11 Tsukudajima [Island] – kidney.
12 Fudō Shrine at Meguro (*Meguro Fudō*) – circle.
13 Cherry trees in the mountains (*Sanchū sakura*) – kidney.
14 Ryōgoku [Bridge] – kidney.
15 The base of the hill at Dōkanyama (*Dōkanyama shita*) – kidney.
16 Yakushi Temple at Arai (*Arai Yakushi*) – kidney.
17 The cutting at Yanaka (*Yanaka Kiridōshi*) – kidney.
18 The Bay at Miho (*Miho no ura*) – kidney.
19 Susaki [Point] – octagon.
20 Ducks in a pond (*Ike no naka no oshidori*) – octagon.
21 Nagato Shimonoseki – octagon.
22 Meguro Chiyogaoka [Hill] – octagon.
23 The ferry at (?)Sakaoi (*?Sakaoi no watashi*) – octagon.
24 The ferry at Fujikawa [River] (*Fujikawa funawatashi*) – octagon.
25 Noda in Ōmi Province (*Ōmi Noda*) – octagon.

Illustrated here is no. 14, a geisha standing in the prow of a covered boat moored under Ryōgoku Bridge (ADD 746).

146

147

Kikukawa Eizan 1787–1867

Na Toshinobu; common name Mangorō, in
Edo hōgaku-wake, his name given as
Sabanaya Mankichi; *gō* Chōkyūsai,
Kodamaya Eizan. The son of a maker of
artificial flowers, with a shop named Ōmiya
in Ichigaya. Later addresses given as
Yotsuya Tansu-machi, then Kōjimachi
rokuchōme. In later years lodged with his
pupil Uegiya Magohachi in Takada village;
and finally from 1862 lived with his
daughter Toyo and her husband's family at
Fujioka-chō in Kōzuke Province. Studied
first with his father, then the Shijō artist
Suzuki Nanrei, and also said to have been
acquainted with Hokkei. A few early prints
of actors from the beginning of the Bunka
era (1804–18), but his main output was
prints of beauties taking over from the late
Utamaro style which he produced regularly
until the late Bunsei era (1818–30). Also
known for a small number of paintings of
beauties, with their characteristic large oval
faces, with long straight noses, pouting
mouths and large eyes with heavy
eyelashes and pupils placed in the centre.
Continued to paint long after he had
abandoned print designing, and a six-fold
screen of *Courtiers in a Boat Admiring Cherry
Blossom* bears the signature 'painted by the
old man of seventy-seven years, Kikugawa
Eizan Toshinobu', and so must have been
done in 1863 (*NU*, vol. 6 (1981), no. 64).

146

KIKUKAWA EIZAN

146 Geisha Seated on a Balcony Overlooking the Sumida River

Bunka–early Bunsei eras, before 1823
SIGNATURE: Kikukawa Eizan hitsu
SEALS: (illegible)
INSCRIPTION: Eizame no/kokoro mo tsuki no/ensaki
ni/kaze no kaketaru/hitoemono kana
INSCRIPTION SIGNATURE: Shokusanjin
INSCRIPTION SEAL: Shokusan
Fan painting; ink and colour on mica-covered
paper, 16.3 × 45.6 cm
PROVENANCE: Hosomi Ryō; Ralph Harari
LITERATURE: Hillier 1970, vol. 1, no. 88
1982.7–1.017(4) (Japanese Painting ADD 702D)

Though rubbed and soiled from heavy use,
the basic composition of this fan painting
can, nevertheless, be made out: a geisha
seated on a balcony toys with a hairpin as
she looks out over the moonlit Sumida
River (with probably Ryōgoku Bridge in the
distance). The *kyōka* poem inscribed by Ōta
Nampo (1749–1823) suggests that she has
left a drinking party to come and take the
air and settle confused, wine-fuelled
emotions:

> Sobering up,
> Her feelings become clear
> On the moonlit balcony,
> As the wind flutters
> Her thin summer robe.

Scenes of 'taking the cool evening air' (*yū-
suzumi*) near the river were popular and
appropriate subjects for summer fans. Here
the curve of Ryōgoku Bridge effectively
echoes the shape of the paper.

148

147

KIKUKAWA EIZAN

147 The Sumida River at Mimeguri Shrine

Mid Bunka–Bunsei eras
SIGNATURE: Eizan Toshinobu hitsu
SEAL: Kikukawa
Hanging scroll; ink and colour on silk,
    39.4 × 56.0 cm
PROVENANCE: Arthur Morrison
1913.5–1.0411 (Japanese Painting 1448). Given by
    Sir W. Gwynne-Evans, Bt

Mimeguri Shrine was on the upper reaches of the Sumida River on the northern outskirts of the city and a popular place for outings, particularly in spring when the cherry trees along the embankment were in bloom, and in autumn when boats would moor on the river for moon-viewing parties (no. 123). The stone gateway to the shrine that could be seen over the top of the embankment was a famous landmark.

Here, however, there is no hint of such pleasurable pastimes, and the scene is shown as a peaceful, somewhat desolate, rural idyll, with workmen punting a log raft and a solitary ferry boat being rowed across to Imado. Views of the Sumida were a common subject for Edo–Kanō painters and Kanō-trained Ukiyo-e painters such as Hosoda Eishi, with their distinctive blue, green and gold wash technique; but this rare example of Eizan's pure landscape style is somewhat different and provides good evidence for his having studied the Kyōto-Shijō style with Suzuki Nanrei (1775–1844), as maintained in Saitō Gesshin's

manuscript of the *Ukiyo-e ruikō* (Yura Tetsuji (ed.), *Zōhō ukiyo-e ruikō*, Gabundō, Tokyo, 1979, p. 195). The composition and treatment of foliage and washes on the riverbank are very close to a view of Mimeguri in a handscroll of *Views of Famous Places* by Nanrei in the British Museum collection (Japanese Painting ADD 944).

KIKUKAWA EIZAN

148 Woman Adjusting her Hairpins

Mid Bunka–Bunsei eras
SIGNATURE: Eizan hitsu
SEALS: Kikukawa, Toshinobu
Hanging scroll; ink and colour on paper,
    128.0 × 29.0 cm
PROVENANCE: Arthur Morrison
1913.5–1.0412 (Japanese Painting 1449). Given by
    Sir W. Gwynne-Evans, Bt

To judge from her shaved eyebrows this is a married woman, and she is shown from behind with arched back adjusting a hairpin with one hand while rearranging the bow of her *obi* with the other. The rapid outline and wash technique with angular outlines to the drapery is Eizan's most abbreviated style, displayed more extensively in an album of *Fourteen Types of Women* in the collection of the Japan Ukiyo-e Museum (Matsumoto 1985, nos 218–23). The abbreviated style was an option used by almost all Ukiyo-e painters, but these works have in the past been considered of inferior quality to more meticulously detailed paintings on silk and are rarely reproduced.

148

Keisai Eisen 1790–1848

Family name Ikeda; *na* Yoshinobu (at one period Shigeyoshi); *azana* Konsei; common name Zenjirō; *gō* Keisai, Kokushunrō (1816), Koizumi; *gesaku-gō* Ippitsuan Kakō, Fūsen Ichiin, Mumei'ō; *ingō* Insai Hakusui, Inransai. Also said to have used the names Hokutei and Hokkatei, but these are unconfirmed. Born at Hoshigaoka in Edo, his father a samurai, Ikeda Masahei Shigeharu, a talented calligrapher. Lived in Owari-chō; Hamamatsu-chō; Nezu Shichiken-chō; Shitaya Ikenohata; and Nihombashi Sakamoto-chō nichōme. After his parents died forced to become a *rōnin* to support his younger sisters. At one time a Kabuki playwright using the name Chiyoda Saishi, and about this time lodged with the family of Kikukawa Eizan and studied painting with Eizan's father, Eiji. Also worked as a brothel owner and seller of face powder. In later years a prolific author of popular literature and also in 1833 compiled the manuscript *Mumei'ō zuihitsu* (*Zoku ukiyo-e ruikō*), a reworking of the biographies of Ukiyo-e artists. Studied with the minor Kanō painter Hakkeisai and with Kikukawa Eizan.

From the late Bunka era (1804–18) onwards many illustrations for the various genres of popular literature as well as *surimono* and a large output of single-sheet prints of women, including some fine bust portraits, exploring the world of the unlicensed pleasure quarters of Edo in his own rich, seductive style. Also many illustrations to erotic works. Contributed twenty-four designs in a Kanō-influenced style to the landscape series *Kisokaidō rokujūkyū-tsugi* ('Sixty-nine Stations of the Kisokaidō Highway', late 1830s) designed with Hiroshige. Eisen painted a relatively large number of hanging scrolls of beauties, sometimes with particularly large (half life-size) figures drawn so that they appear to get larger the higher up the body they are viewed, giving them very vivid presence. The eyes are set wide apart with particularly luxuriant lashes and the pupils always glancing off to one side, but otherwise the faces are not unlike those painted by Eizan.

149

149 Beauty Arranging her Hair

Bunsei era
SIGNATURE: Eisen sha
SEALS: Keisai, Eisen no in
Hanging scroll; ink, colour and gold on silk, 85.1 × 34.0 cm
PROVENANCE: Douglas Wright; Ralph Harari
LITERATURE: Hillier 1970, vol. 1, no. 90; *UT*, vol. 1 (1987), no. 139; Smith 1990, no. 201
1982.7–1.018 (Japanese Painting ADD 703)

A young woman, probably the daughter of a well-to-do merchant family, is seated looking into her pocket mirror to arrange her hair, and the paper tissue held in her teeth suggests she has corrected her makeup as well. Her knees are crossed in her lap in the ungainly manner of a still-awkward teenage girl.

Eisen's treatment of her costume is a *tour de force* of dark rapid ink outlines and rich, gaudy patterning. Particularly impressive is the handling of the transparent gauze over-kimono painted with flowering pinks, through which can be seen the scarlet under-robe decorated with a more stylised design of cherry blossoms against a wicker fence. The broad *obi* is of a bold blue and white floral brocade, with gold threads worked into the background.

The rich, almost overripe style of nineteenth-century Ukiyo-e paintings and prints has often in the past been dismissed as 'decadent'. Certainly many nineteenth-century images of women have little of the quiet restraint of, say, a Harunobu print of the late 1760s, confronting the viewer in a more directly passionate way. They are representative products of the last and most highly wrought phase of Edo culture.

The careful way in which the signature is written with neat, square characters suggests a relatively early date in Eisen's *oeuvre*, perhaps the early–mid Bunsei era (1818–30).

149

Kitagawa Tsukimaro
worked *c.* 1794–1836

Family name Ogawa; *na* Jun; *azana* Shitatsu (should be Shisen(?); see below); common name Sensuke (or Rokusaburō); *gō* Kikumaro, Tsukimaro, Kansetsu, Kansetsusai, Bokutei, Yūsai. In the Bunka era (1804–18) lived at Kodemma-chō sanchōme Umaya Shindō, where he worked as a watchman. Pupil of Utamaro. Began by designing prints of women and *kibyōshi* using the name Kikumaro. From 1802 changed the way the characters with which this was written from 'chrysanthemum' to 'joy eternal'. From 1804 changed his name to Tsukimaro. From *c.* 1820 ceased to design prints, painting instead hanging scrolls of beauties in a style influenced by the Maruyama–Shijō school, which he signed 'Kansetsu'. His last dated work is an illustration for a *kyōka* anthology published in 1836.

KITAGAWA TSUKIMARO

150 Geishas

Bunsei era
SIGNATURE: Kansetsu sha
SEALS: Kansetsu no in, Shisen-uji
Pair of hanging scrolls; ink-colour and gold on silk, 118.7 × 53.3 (right), 126.4 × 54.8 mm (left)
PROVENANCE: William Anderson
LITERATURE: Anderson 1886, nos 2311, 2312; *UT*, vol. 1 (1987), nos 121, 122; Smith 1990, no. 200
1881.12–10.02311/02312 (Japanese Paintings 2632/3)

Though originally mounted with different brocade surrounds and of slightly different sizes, these two hanging scrolls seem, nevertheless, to form a pair of scenes of geishas indoors and out. This is further borne out by the complementary poses – the two standing figures leaning in towards one another and the two seated women facing outwards in *contrapposto*. The colour schemes of the two paintings are similar, too, each with kimonos of plain purple and green set off by florid accessories, sashes and undergarments in the characteristic fashions of geishas of the Bunsei era (1818–30). In the indoor scene the standing woman carries a finely worked metal sake kettle on a stand, while her seated companion leans on a similarly elaborate metal tobacco pipe. In the outdoor scroll the young geisha is seated on a garden bench, and both women have fans, suggesting summer. This standing woman has shaved eyebrows and blackened teeth, indicating that she is married.

Early in his career Tsukimaro designed woodblock prints in the manner of Utamaro, but from *c.* 1820 onwards he concentrated on large, finely executed paintings of amply proportioned beauties in a style showing the influence of the Kyoto Maruyama–Shijō school. These bear the signature Kansetsu.

150 (2633)   150 (2632)

150 (2633)

150 (2632)

151

151

Utagawa Toyokuni II ?1802–?35

Common name (according to *Ukiyo-eshi Utagawa retsuden*) Genzō; *gō* Toyoshige, Ichiryūsai, Toyokuni segare Toyoshige ('Toyokuni's son Toyoshige', *c.* 1824–5), Toyokuni II (*c.* 1825–34), Ichiesai (*c.* 1828), Ichiyōsai (*c.* 1828–9), Gosotei (*c.* 1828–34), Mansuian. Lived in Hongō Haruki-chō (*c.* 1828). Pupil of Toyokuni I, adopted by him in the New Year of 1824, or before. Earliest works *c.* 1823. Known for prints of actors and *bijin* and illustrations for *gōkan*. In 1825 assumed the name Toyokuni II on the death of Toyokuni I. In early 1830s designed some fine landscape prints and did a few paintings. No works known after *c.* 1835 and is assumed to have died or given up painting. Said to have run a pottery business, but this is not proven.

UTAGAWA TOYOKUNI II

151 Carp

c. 1828–34
SIGNATURE: Gosotei Toyokuni hitsu
SEAL: Toyokuni
(?)Album leaf (mounted in board); ink, slight colour and gold on silk, 29.4 × 44.5 cm
PROVENANCE: William Anderson
LITERATURE: Anderson 1886, no. 1826
1881.12–10.01826 (Japanese Painting 1446)

A carp is seen through ripples on the surface of the water, flicking its tail lazily. There is a slight pink tinge to the flesh and gold pigment used in the eye, but otherwise the painting is entirely executed in shades of *sumi*, after the manner used by artists of both the Kanō and Maruyama–Shijō schools. Carp were a common subject for decorative paintings, and it cannot be said that Toyokuni II has come up with a particularly novel or inspiring composition in this case.

The remains of a vertical fold are visible in the centre of the painting and it may have originally been mounted in an album. The large round red seal with the characters 'Toyokuni' in white reserve was one used regularly by Toyokuni I on his paintings. After 1844 the same seal (by now with a nick out of the circumference at the eleven-o'clock position) was taken over in turn by Kunisada (nos 154–5), who proclaimed himself Toyokuni II, even though Toyoshige had used that name during the decade *c.* 1823–34. Kunisada is therefore referred to by historians as Toyokuni III.

152

UTAGAWA TOYONAGA (dates unknown)

152 Chinese Beauty

(?)First half of 19th century
SIGNATURE: Utagawa Toyonaga ga
SEALS: ('Toshidama' ring), Toyonaga Kiyotaka
Hanging scroll; ink and colour on silk,
   76.7 × 31.5 cm
1985.6–15.03 (Japanese Painting ADD 811)

A Chinese beauty, probably Yang Guifei
(see no. 72), her face partly seen through
the transparent gauze of a fan, stands
behind a vase of large peonies on a red
lacquer stand. Nothing is known of the
artist Utagawa Toyonaga. Elements of the
style – particularly the face – are
reminiscent of the Maruyama–Shijō school
of Kyoto, though overall the work is thinly
painted and the line is not particularly
steady. The artist's name suggests, of
course, that he is a pupil of Toyokuni. For
the time being he should simply be
classified as a minor Utagawa pupil,
probably working in the Kansai region. The
seal implies that his *na* (official name) was
Kiyotaka.

152

Utagawa Kuninaga d. 1827

Common name Kayanosuke; *gō* Ichiunsai.
Born in Edo and lived in Mita, later
Shimbashi Kinroku-chō. The most senior
pupil of Toyokuni I after Kunimasa. Active
after 1806 doing actor prints, perspective
prints, paintings for lanterns and a small
number of hanging scrolls of beauties.

UTAGAWA KUNINAGA

153 Woman in a Black Kimono

Bunka era
SIGNATURE: Kuninaga ga
SEALS: Kuni, Naga
Hanging scroll; ink and colour on paper,
  80.1 × 26.5 cm
PROVENANCE: Arthur Morrison
LITERATURE: *UT*, vol. 1 (1987), no. 167
1913.5–1.0354 (Japanese Painting 1570). Given by
  Sir W. Gwynne-Evans, Bt

With her fierce frown and treble chin this
formidable matron is perhaps a courtesan,
working in one of the unlicensed pleasure
quarters in Edo, who had a reputation for
toughness. In appearance, however, there
was often little to distinguish illicit
prostitutes from ordinary women and she
may equally be a perfectly respectable
geisha or other entertainer. The crest of
three flying plovers on the sleeve of her
black kimono – a pattern repeated on the
pale blue 'middle robe' (*aigi*) – may
ultimately provide the clue to a more
certain identification.

Though the few other paintings by
Kuninaga so far introduced suggest that he
basically followed the styles of his teacher
Toyokuni I (Matsumoto 1985, nos 255–8),
the strongly characterised expression of the
woman in this case gives evidence also of a
certain artistic independence, as well as
confirming just how calm and acquiescent
is the image of women normally portrayed
to us in Ukiyo-e paintings.

153

153

Utagawa Kunisada 1786–1864

Family name Sumida; common name Shōzō (changed the characters used to write this upon taking lay religious vows in 1844); *gō* Kunisada (1807–43), Ichiyūsai (?1812), Gototei (?1811–43), Gepparō (1811), Kinraisha (1813), Kōchōrō (?1827–c. 1850), Toyokuni II (actually III, 1844–64), Ichiyōsai (1844–), Hanabusa Ittai, Kunisada Sha Toyokuni, Hokubaiko, Fuchō Sanjin, Fuchōan, Sūshi Toyokuni, Kiō (1862–); *ingō* Bukiyō Matabei (these dates as given by Suzuki Jūzō in *GUDHJ*, vol. 2 (1982), p. 32). Son of the proprietor of the Fifth Ferry at Honjo Itsutsume; also lived in front of the Kameido Tenjin Shrine and later at Yanagishima. Earliest dated work illustrations for a *gōkan* by Bakin, *Oisenu kado keshō wakamizu*, published in 1807. Colour prints from 1809 in the style of Toyokuni I, though quickly establishing an energetic personal tone in both prints of actors and beauties, notably the set of seven mica-ground bust portraits of actors, *Ōatari kyōgen* (c. 1815), and the series of customs of beauties, *Hoshi no shimo tōsei fūzoku* (c. 1819). Became the most prolific Ukiyo-e artist ever, particularly subsequent to assuming the name Toyokuni (III) in 1844, after which time he led an atelier of some twenty-eight pupils in producing ever-larger series of actor portraits and prints of beauties, of increasingly technical complexity. Prolific illustrator of *gōkan*, notably the *Nise Murasaki inaka Genji* ('Fake Murasaki and a Rustic Genji'), produced with Ryūtei Tanehiko in 1829–42 (and after with his pupils) – which led to hundreds of spin-off series of colour prints relating to the Genji parody in the 1850s.

In 1825 Kunisada painted a votive plaque of Ichikawa Danjūrō VII in the *Arrow Sharpening Gorō* role which was presented to the Narita Fudō Shrine (*NU*, vol. 8 (1981), no. 47), but it would appear that it was not until he studied with the Hanabusa-school painter Ikkei, taking the name Hanabusa Ittai and adopting the *gō* Kōchōrō (after 1828), that he began to paint with any regularity. A scroll showing *King Emma Looking in his Jade Mirror*, a collaboration between Kunisada and Ikkei, is thought to have been painted in 1830 (*NU*, vol 8 (1981), no. 48). After this Kunisada painted mainly beauties in his own highly polished, rich and seductive style, though there is an album of *Scenes of Kabuki and the Yoshiwara* of c. 1834 in the collection of the Seikadō Foundation, Tokyo.

154

UTAGAWA KUNISADA

154 Ichikawa Danjūrō VII in 'Shibaraku'

Mid-Bunka era
SIGNATURE: Kunisada ga
SEALS: Kuni, Sada
INSCRIPTION: Harusame no/kakaru tokoro e/hitokoe no/ne o uguisu no/ume ni shibaraku
INSCRIPTION SIGNATURE: Tatekawa Danshūrō Emba
Hanging scroll; ink and colour on paper, 46.0 × 35.0 cm
PROVENANCE: Ralph Harari
LITERATURE: Hillier 1966a, pl. 55; Hillier 1970, vol. 1, no. 93; Hillier 1980, no. 119
1982.7-1.019 (Japanese Painting ADD 704)

This loose, impressionistic lightning sketch, with lines that seem to explode out from the centre, captures brilliantly the energy of the *Shibaraku!* ('Stop one moment!') role, as performed here by Ichikawa Danjūrō VII (1791–1859). The wildness of both painting and inscription suggests that they may have been done while artist and poet were drunk at some party in support of the actor. *Shibaraku* is the heavily stylised showpiece of the Ichikawa family, in which with cries of 'Stop one moment!' from the back of the theatre a hero enters down the raised walkway (*hanamichi*) to rescue some hapless victim about to be done to death.

The voluminous persimmon-coloured robes emblazoned with a huge 'triple rice measure' (*mimasu*) crest of the Ichikawa family, paper 'strength' decorations in the hair and massive curved sword of the role are all clearly discernible.

The form of Kunisada's signature, if compared with those on woodblock prints, suggests a date in the mid-Bunka era (1804–18), early in Kunisada's career, when Danjūrō VII, too, had just turned twenty. The inscription is by the carpenter turned raconteur Utei (Tatekawa) Emba (1743–1822), who had loyally supported the Ichikawa Danjūrō actors since the generation of Danjūrō IV in the 1760s and who led the Mimasu poetry group that regularly put out *surimono* prints of Danjūrō VII designed by Kunisada. The poem likens the auspicious call of the spring warbler perched on a flowering plum branch to Danjūrō's shout of *Shibaraku!* and encourages him to stay:

Where the spring rain
Beats down
A single cry
Of the warbler on the plum –
'Tarry awhile!'

155

155

UTAGAWA KUNISADA

155 Kumagai and Atsumori at the
Battle of Ichinotani

Early–mid-Tempō era
SIGNATURE: Kōchōrō Kunisada ga
SEALS: Kō, Chō
Hanging scroll; ink, colour and gold on silk,
    36.4 × 54.0 cm
PROVENANCE: Mrs W. Bateson
LITERATURE: *UT*, vol. 1 (1987), BW no. 56
1926.4–10.031 (Japanese Painting ADD 34).
    Presented by Mrs W. Bateson

One of the most poignant episodes in the
warrior epic *Heike monogatari* ('Tales of the
Heike') is the story of the death of the
young warrior Taira no Atsumori at the
hands of Kumagai Jirō Naozane at the
Battle of Ichinotani in 1184. The scene
depicted here shows Atsumori returning to
the shore when challenged to combat by
Kumagai, by whom he was quickly
overcome. It was not until Kumagai
removed the helmet of his opponent that
he discovered him to be no more than a
teenage boy – the same age as his own son
– and was inclined to spare him. Other
warriors were hurrying to the scene,
however, and so, tearfully, he was forced
to take Atsumori's life. In a brocade bag
Atsumori was carrying he discovered the
bamboo flute, the mournful sound of which
had moved both armies on the eve of the
battle, and reflected on the cultivated lives
the Taira courtier-warriors had led before
the war. After this Kumagai decided to take
holy orders.

Following the success of Kuniyoshi's
print series of Chinese warriors from the
novel *Shuihu zhuan* (Japanese: *Suikoden*) in
the late 1820s, there was a vogue for prints
of both Chinese and Japanese warriors
which Kunisada quickly joined. The
signature on this painting suggests a date
in the early–mid-Tempō era (1830–44), and
one can imagine this was a special
commission following that fashion.

Utagawa Kuniyoshi 1797–1861

Childhood name Yoshisaburō; common name Magosaburō; *gō* Ichiyūsai (from *c.* 1818), Saihōsha (mid-1820s), Chōōrō (from mid-1830s), Sekkoku, Senshin; *kyōka-gō* Ryūen; *ingō* Ichimyōkai Hodoyoshi. Later used the family name Ikusa. Son of Yanagiya Kichiemon, a dyer of Nihombashi, Hongin-chō itchōme. Lived first at Mukōjima, later at Shin Izumi-chō, Genya-dana. Pupil of Utagawa Toyokuni I, also said to have studied with Tsutsumi Tōrin III, Shibata Zeshin and Katsukawa Shuntei. First dated publication an illustrated book of 1814, *Mibuji chūshingura*, and actor prints from 1815. First major success the series of *Suikoden* Chinese warrior portraits for the publisher Kagaya Kichibei in 1827. During the Tempō era (1830–44) large numbers of warrior, *bijin*, comic prints and erotica, as well as landscapes in Western-influenced style. During the Kōka (1844–8)–Ka'ei (1848–54) eras many triptychs of warrior and historical subjects characterised by a unique sense of fantasy and strong creative imagination.

Aside from his many preparatory drawings for woodblock prints that survive, in which the forms take shape out of a swirl of free and fluid lines, Kuniyoshi's paintings are generally more tame and dominated by scrolls of beauties. Other subjects include Gods of Good Luck done in Kanō ink style. He is also known to have painted a large votive plaque of *Firemen* that was presented in 1833 to the Fudō Temple at Narita; and a large votive plaque, *Old Hag of Hitotsuya*, painted to the commission of the owner of the Okamotoya brothel in 1855, is still at the Asakusa Kannon Temple today.

UTAGAWA KUNIYOSHI

156 Woman Carrying a Potted Morning Glory

c. Ka'ei era
SIGNATURE: Ichiyūsai Kuniyoshi
SEAL: Kuniyoshi
Hanging scroll; ink, colour and gold on silk, 84.0 × 29.0 cm
PROVENANCE: Arthur Morrison
LITERATURE: Morrison 1911, vol. II, pl. XXXIII; *UT*, vol. 1 (1987), BW no. 53
1913.5–1.0358 (Japanese Painting 1567). Given by Sir W. Gwynne-Evans, Bt

To judge from her wide hairstyle, kimono with long, hanging sleeves and *obi* tied high at the back this is a lady's maid (*oku jochū*) from one of the *daimyō* or Bakufu households, carrying a flowering pink morning glory in a large porcelain planter ceremoniously out in front of her, as if she will present it to her mistress. The outlines have been quickly sketched in with a fairly dry brush – much in the manner of Kuniyoshi's preparatory drawings on paper – and then the patterns on the robes added in simple washes of colour, with a design of stone breakwaters beside a winding river around the hem of the kimono. Such paintings must have been rapidly executed to order, requiring little time and effort from a draughtsman of Kuniyoshi's capabilities.

156

156

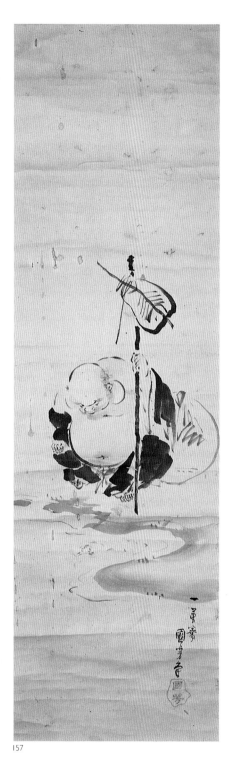

157

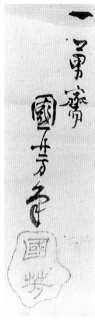

157

UTAGAWA KUNIYOSHI

157 Hotei Looking at his Reflection

c. Ka'ei era
SIGNATURE: Ichiyūsai Kuniyoshi hitsu
SEAL: Kuniyoshi
Hanging scroll; ink on paper, 90.5 × 27.0 cm
PROVENANCE: Arthur Morrison
LITERATURE: Robinson 1961, no. 97; *UT*, vol. 1 (1987),
  BW no. 55
1913.5–1.0359 (Japanese Painting 1568). Given by
  Sir W. Gwynne-Evans, Bt

Hotei, numbered as one of the Seven Gods
of Good Luck (*shichifukujin*) in the Edo
period, is generally portrayed as a
laughing, pot-bellied Chinese monk,
carrying a staff, Chinese fan and linen bag
(from which he derives his name), in which
he stows lucky treasures. Paintings of the
Gods of Good Luck were always hung at
the New Year holiday, and prints of them
arriving in a lucky treasure ship were
placed under the pillow at night to ensure
good fortune during the coming year.

   Hotei was a common subject for Zen ink
painters during the Muromachi period and
he is variously shown in carefree attitudes
riding an ox, gazing at the moon, fording a
river, and so on, but this composition of
him gazing at his reflection in a stream
seems to be unusual. Perhaps the idea was
simply to poke fun at how difficult it must
have been to see his reflection over such an
enormous belly.

   The technique is a loose version of the
Kanō ink style (ultimately derived from Zen
monk painters) habitually adopted by
artists of all schools for paintings of the
Lucky Gods.

UTAGAWA KUNIYOSHI

158 The Arhat Handaka

c. Ka'ei era
SIGNATURE: Ichiyūsai Kuniyoshi
SEAL: Kuniyoshi
Hanging scroll; ink and slight colour on paper,
  125.0 × 51.2 cm
PROVENANCE: Arthur Morrison
LITERATURE: Robinson 1961, no. 98
1913.5–1.0360 (Japanese Painting 1569). Given by
  Sir W. Gwynne-Evans, Bt

158

Handaka Sonja (Sanskrit: Panthaka) is one
of the sixteen *arhats*, or disciples of the
Buddha Sakyamuni, beings credited with
supernatural powers who practise and
protect the faith between the time of his
death and the coming of of Maitreya, the
Buddha of the future. All of the *arhats* wear
similar monastic robes and are depicted as
old men with shaven heads and large
earrings, but Handaka's particular attribute
is a bowl from which emerges a dragon or
rain cloud. Paintings from as far back as
the end of the Heian period (twelfth
century) show him with a fierce
countenance seated on a rock holding a
sacred jewel and with a dragon curled
around his feet trying to get the jewel.

As might be expected from an artist of
Kuniyoshi's playful temperament, the
subject is given a somewhat irreverent
treatment: the scowling monk pokes with
his finger the equally ferocious little dragon
that has just emanated from his begging
bowl in the middle of the rain cloud, and
the two attempt to stare each other down.
The monk's emaciated shoulder echoes the
shape of the bony protrusion on his head,
and the drapery of his robes is formed into
eccentric coils. Though large and quickly
painted, the figure combines freely
executed strokes in a wide variety of ink
tones with a sure grasp of form.

158

159

Life comes to imitate art, however, when she becomes pregnant and is tortured to induce a miscarriage by a sinister woman referred to simply as 'the jealous wife'. When this fails, Okume is forced to commit suicide by ritual disembowelment and the hag stabs the unborn child. Her body is then shown in various stages of decomposition.

A taste for sadism and bloody murder is apparent in quite a significant segment of late Edo fiction, popular imagery and theatre, starting perhaps with the *yomihon* of Bakin and Hokusai. Kuniyoshi's prints of the Hag of Hitotsuya and his pupils Yoshitoshi and Yoshiiku's series of 1867 on twenty-eight famous murders, *Eimei nijū-hachi shuku*, must be among some of the most horrific, if aestheticised, images ever produced. Most societies have a taste for such brutality, and the Ukiyo-e artists' exploration of such areas, though undoubtedly following that public taste, also had the concomitant result of extending the expressive range of their work.

159

TACHIBANA SEI'EI
worked Ka'ei (1848–54)–Bunkyū (1861–4) eras

159 Scenes in the Life of a Travelling Actress (after Kuniyoshi)

1849–62
SIGNATURE: Amano kudai Tachibana Sei'ei ('Amano, ninth-generation Tachibana Sei'ei')
Handscroll; ink, colour and gold on paper, 31.7 × 1655.0 cm
PROVENANCE: William Anderson
LITERATURE: Anderson 1886, no. 1767; UT, vol. 1 (1987), BW nos 57–62
1881.12–10.01767 (Japanese Painting 1595)

The artist of this scroll, one 'Amano, ninth-generation Tachibana Sei'ei' of whom nothing else can be ascertained at present, explains that this is an old story of a jealous woman, which has been reworked in modern fashion by Kuniyoshi and then copied by himself, with a few additions to the text, over a period of almost fourteen years from 1849 to 1862 while living in Honjo. Certainly in several scenes the painting of the face of the woman protagonist is very close to Kuniyoshi's style of drawing beauties.

The eighteen painted scenes and minutely written text tell a story of increasing horror concerning the life and grisly death of a travelling actress, Okume. She specialises in roles of male heroes and is often called upon to act gorily realistic scenes of suicide and death, involving extensive use of fake blood in her makeup.

Utagawa Kunihisa
worked Kyōwa (1801–4)–Bunka (1804–18) eras

Gō Ichigyosai. According to one account a woman artist, though this may refer to Kunihisa's daughter. Apparently a senior pupil of Toyokuni I, known by a few colour prints but mainly for a group of accomplished paintings of beauties showing the influence of Toyokuni and Utamaro, datable to the Kyōwa (1801–4) and Bunka (1804–18) eras. These include several large scrolls such as *Party of Actors* based on a composition by Toyokuni from *Yakusha sangai kyō* (1801), and a pair of screens of *Pleasure-boats in Summer* and *Snow-viewing in Winter* (Idemitsu 1988, no. 162).

UTAGAWA KUNIHISA
160 Party of Geishas

Kyōwa–Bunka eras
SIGNATURE: Utagawa Kunihisa ga
SEALS: Uta, ?Kuni
Hanging scroll; ink, colour and gold on silk, 80.4 × 94.6 cm
OA+0374 (Japanese Painting 3584)

In this large composition a group of five geishas and a young attendant are shown playing their musical instruments and preparing for a party. Two women strum *shamisen*, while a third balances a *kokyū*, played with a bow, on her knee. Another figure seated on the other side of a red

160

160

lacquer table loaded with dishes of raw fish offers a cup of sake, and the fifth woman stands holding a round fan and a long metal pipe. The fan and the thin gauze garments indicate that the weather is still warm, but this must be the seventh or eighth month, for the vase in the *tokonoma* is filled with early chrysanthemums and the fan decorated with flowering bushclover, another plant of autumn. The party room is luxuriously appointed, its *tokonoma* filled with shelves painted in black lacquer and gold on which are placed coloured porcelains and tea-jars. The cupboard doors are all painted with ink landscapes (some on gold backgrounds) in Kanō style – showing off the fact that this style, too, was part of Kunihisa's repertoire – and a scroll of a courtier admiring a waterfall hangs behind the vase of chrysanthemums. The room opens on to a pine tree in the garden, behind which

seagoing fishing-boats are moored, suggesting that this is one of the unlicensed pleasure quarters facing on to Edo Bay in Shinagawa, Tsukuda Island or Susaki in Fukagawa.

The figures have the same idiosyncratic style seen in other paintings by Kunihisa, showing a certain degree of influence from his (or her) teacher Toyokuni mixed with the predominant late style of Utamaro. Outlines are strong and angular, and the faces all have open, pouting mouths with iridescent green lipstick painted on the lower lips. Kunihisa demonstrates considerable technical skill in the way he (or she) handles the transparency of the summer gauze kimono and pays a great deal of attention to the complex brocade patterns, including much use of gold lines, on the *obi*. He (or she) should be considered one of the most accomplished of the later Utagawa school painters.

161   161

Utagawa Kunitsuru 1807–78

Family name Wada; *na* Yasugorō; *gō* Ichijusai, Toyoshige II. Born in Tsukuji, Edo. During the Tempō era (1830–44) lived and worked for a while in Osaka, before returning to Edo. Residences listed as Asakusa Hanakawado; a *nagaya* in Tozawa; lodging with Niikado Shingorō; Shitaya Kōtoku-ji Yokochō (after the earthquake of 1855); moved to Yokohama some time in the 1860s to Hon-mura; then Basha-dō; after the Yokohama fire to Okina-machi; *c.* 1877 ran a bookstore in Yoshida-chō. Pupil of Utagawa Toyokuni II (Toyoshige). Known by an Osaka actor print of 1835. Otherwise actor prints in Utagawa style and Yokohama-e; also designs for kimono embroideries, votive plaques, picture lanterns and tattoos.

UTAGAWA KUNITSURU

161   Scenes of Edo Life

c. Ansei–Keiō eras
SIGNATURE: Kunitsuru (on painting no. 7)
Eight paintings mounted as a handscroll; ink and
   slight colour on silk, each 27.8 × 23.4 cm
   (approx.)
PROVENANCE: Exhibited at the Exposition
   Universelle, Paris, 1867, no. 4100; Sir A. W.
   Franks
LITERATURE: *UT*, vol. 1 (1987), BW nos 74, 75
1902.6–6.025 (Japanese Painting 1592). Bequeathed
   by Sir A. W. Franks

Though mounted as a handscroll, the eight paintings are of the shape one would normally expect to find in an album. The hard, unyielding line and generally flat patterning suggest that they may have been painted in imitation of woodblock prints, and the colouring is entirely in shades of *sumi* with a pale pink used just on areas of flesh. The figure style is derived from Kunisada's later period, when he used the name Toyokuni (III). The subjects are as follows:

1 Two *bugaku* (court dance) performers.
2 Procession of a Yoshiwara courtesan.
3 Woman, girl and dandy in the street.
4 Nobleman's daughter, maid and
    retainer in the interior of a mansion.

5 Man dancing with fans, watched by
    two geishas.
6 Two Yoshiwara geishas dressed for the
    Niwaka Festival.
7 Girl dancing with fan and two geishas
    playing flute and *shamisen.*
8 Prince Mitsuuji (from the parody of
    Tale of Genji) and maid.

When exhibited at the Exposition Universelle in Paris in 1867, the paintings would have been examples of contemporary art and may, indeed, have been produced for this purpose to show Edo manners and customs of the time to a foreign audience. A French title written on the mount of the scroll, *Scènes d'intérieur de Daimios,* is presumably derived from the subject of painting no. 4.

Utagawa Kuniaki

worked Kōka (1844–8)–Keiō (1865–8) eras

Family name Hirazawa; *gō* Ippōsai, Ichiōsai. His father, Tatsunosuke, a minor samurai in the fourteenth division of castle guards. Pupil of Kunisada. Produced actor and genre prints and paintings of beauties during the late Edo period. Also did Yokohama prints.

UTAGAWA KUNIAKI

162   Courtesan and Kamuro

Kōka–Bunkyū eras
SIGNATURE: Toyokuni monjin/Ichiōsai Kuniaki ga
   ('Painted by Ichiōsai Kuniaki, pupil of Toyokuni
   [Kunisada]')
SEAL: Kuniaki
Hanging scroll; ink, colour and gold on silk,
   120.0 × 56.2 cm
PROVENANCE: William Anderson
LITERATURE: Anderson 1886, no. 1755; *UT*, vol. 1
   (1987), no. 63
1881.12–10.01755 (Japanese Painting 1590)

Courtesans' fashions of the late Edo period grew evermore extravagant. In order to walk in the high lacquer clogs she wears here the woman had to perform a slow, waddling 'figure of eight' (*hachimonji*) manoeuvre, lifting each foot out and round to the side before placing it down, and this became a feature of courtesans' processions in the quarter. The robes are very sumptuous, with a design of dragons coiling amid storm clouds and lightning over the sea on the *uchikake*, in life, one suspects, painted directly in ink on the fabric. An amusing contrast is drawn between the courtesan looking down kindly at the little *kamuro* attendant wearing the cloth cap and the principal dragon on the courtesan's robe glowering down fiercely at the smaller dragon on the attendant's robe. Also the claws of this creature are painted where one would expect to find the girl's hand, while on the sleeve of the second attendant, almost hidden behind the courtesan, is the tail of another dragon equally hard to spot. The courtesan's wide gold sash tied floridly at the front has yet more stylised dragons woven in blue-green into the brocade.

In this and the few other scrolls by Kuniaki so far published he gives evidence of considerable technical skill and should be considered on a par with other major pupils of Kunisada such as Kunichika (1835–1900). Though the composition is presumably learnt from his teacher, there is a particular expression about the face – a kind of wide-eyed surprise – that is uniquely Kuniaki's own.

162

162

211

UTAGAWA SCHOOL

163 Courtesan

Kōka–Keiō eras
SIGNATURE: Utagawa
SEAL: 'Toshidama' (handwritten)
Hanging scroll; ink, colour and gold on paper,
  76.0 × 37.0 cm
PROVENANCE: Arthur Morrison
LITERATURE: Morrison 1911, vol. II, pl. XXXII;
  UT, vol. 1 (1987), BW no. 64
1913.5–1.0355 (Japanese Painting 1566). Given by
  Sir W. Gwynne-Evans, Bt

The courtesan wears a costume with
patterns associated with autumn – red
maple leaves and court gong (from the
'Momiji no ga' chapter of *Tale of Genji*) on
her *uchikake*, bamboo on the kimono and
florid chrysanthemum heads on the *obi*,
one end of which is tossed over her arm.

The Utagawa signature and Toshidama
handwritten seal hidden in the folds of the
robe near her feet confirm what can be
surmised stylistically – that this is the work
of a minor Utagawa pupil who is
competent enough to claim affiliation with
the school but not accomplished enough to
have received an independent art name.
Though the patterning is impressive
enough on the surface, the general line
quality is in fact weak and hesitant, and the
form bulky and lacking in finesse. A
comparison with no. 162 by Kuniaki shows
the work of an altogether more talented
contemporary working in a similar Utagawa
idiom.

163

163

164

ANON. (Utagawa school)

164 Sexual Grotesques

c. Ka'ei–Keiō eras
Handscroll; ink, colour and gold on paper,
  29.7 × 369.0 cm
OA+0138 (Japanese Painting ADD 531)

In three separate fragments from a handscroll, now remounted together, a workman displays his sexual prowess and the gigantic size of his member in a variety of challenging situations. The text is generally crude and jocular ('mine's the biggest in all Japan!'). The scene depicted shows him piercing a stack of (?)roof tiles ('Ow! Let's show you I can stick it through these'); and otherwise he is seen making love five times a night to a voracious woman, with his phallus resting on a festival cart pulled by two naked women, shattering a metal cauldron, and with a child swinging on Uncle's 'thing'.

Phallic worship was an ancient and important part of Shintō and folk belief, and there are comic works from the Edo period in this tradition (Suntory Museum of Art (eds), *Nihon no giga*, exh. cat., Tokyo, 1986, nos 101, 102). The style here suggests a pupil of Utagawa Kuniyoshi, who regularly designed erotic works.

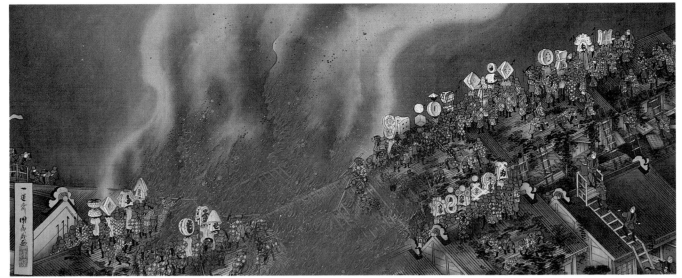

165 (1571)

165 (1572)

165 (1571)

165 (1572)

Utagawa Kunitoshi
worked early Meiji era (1868–1912)

?Art surname Hara; *gō* Ichiunsai. A pupil of
Utagawa Kunisada (Toyokuni III), though
at one time thought to be a pupil of
Kunitsugu. Known by *surimono* and a few
paintings of beauties. The three paintings
in the British Museum collection
considerably extend his known range of
subjects and styles.

UTAGAWA KUNITOSHI

165   Scenes Before and After a Fire

?1868–72
SIGNATURE: Ichiunsai Kunitoshi giga ('Painted for
   amusement by Ichiunsai Kunitoshi')
SEAL: Ichiunsai
Pair of handscrolls; ink and colour on silk, each
   36.7 × 94.0 cm (approx.)
PROVENANCE: Arthur Morrison
LITERATURE: *UT*, vol. 1 (1987), nos 176, 177; Tokyo
   1990, no. 13
1913.5–1.0356/0357 (Japanese Paintings 1571/2).
   Given by Sir W. Gwynne-Evans, Bt

As explained in the detailed commentary
on these two handscrolls by Ikegami
Akihiko (*UT*, vol. 1 (1987), nos 176, 177),
paintings of actual fires done with this
degree of realism would have been illegal
during the Edo period, bearing in mind the
censorship of the reporting of
contemporary events, so it is most natural
to place these works at the very beginning

166

of the Meiji era. On the other hand, they must date before Meiji 5 (1872) when the fire service was reconstituted and the design of their 'standards' changed.

During the Edo period firemen were grouped into neighbourhood squads named after the forty-seven syllables of the writing system and the numbers one to sixteen, and they were often called into action to fight the massive conflagrations (the 'flowers of Edo', as they were ironically named) that regularly swept through the largely wooden buildings of the city. The main technique was to try to destroy buildings in the path of the fire to starve it, and the small amounts of water sprayed from the hand-pumps was used, as shown in these paintings, to douse the firemen rather than the fire. Thick-walled storehouses had their doors and windows sealed up with wet mud and generally escaped severe damage. It is not known which specific fire is recorded here, but it must have been of a considerable scale because the bands of firemen can be identified as coming from all over Edo.

The style is generally meticulous and accurate, with architectural lines clearly drawn with a ruler; a more freehand version is given by Kunitoshi in the longer handscroll of fire scenes (no. 166). The scene in the background of the scroll of the aftermath of the fire, in which silhouetted figures are shown raking through the smouldering ashes, is an interesting stylistic precursor to Kobayashi Kiyochika's colour prints of the great Tokyo fires of 1881.

UTAGAWA KUNITOSHI

166 Scenes at a Fire

?1868–72
SIGNATURE: Ichiunsai giga ('Painted for amusement by Ichiunsai')
SEAL: Kunitoshi
Handscroll; ink, colour and gold on paper, 26.7 × 406.0 cm
PROVENANCE: Sir A. W. Franks
LITERATURE: *UT*, vol. 1 (1987), BW nos 65–7
1902.6–6.026 (Japanese Painting 1591). Bequeathed by Sir A. W. Franks

Though the technique on paper is more spontaneous than Kunitoshi's fire scenes on silk (no. 165), it seems likely that this handscroll depicts the aftermath of the same fire in the early Meiji era. Here firemen are seen dousing down the last small pockets of flames and helping citizens to salvage what they can from the ruins of their homes. The thick-walled storehouses, however, seem to have escaped largely unscathed, and at the end of the scroll, auspiciously, can be seen the beginning of a row of undamaged houses the firemen have managed to save.

Assuming that the dating of *c.* 1868–72 suggested by Ikegami Akihiko is correct, then it suggests that artists were very quick to exercise new freedoms after the downfall of the Tokugawa Shōgunate in 1868 and the concomitant demise of the laws restricting the reporting of contemporary events. Alongside the decorative virtuosity of the treatment of the flames (using cut gold leaf no less), which might be seen as a more purely traditional element, Kunitoshi adapts old techniques in a new way to convey a keen impression of the confusion of muddy debris that is altogether more reportorial in character than paintings of the Edo period.

166

167

167

UTAGAWA KUNITOSHI

167 Killing the Nue

Early Meiji era
SIGNATURE: Ōju Hara Kunitoshi ('Hara Kunitoshi, by special request')
SEAL: Kunitoshi
Theatre signboard; ink, colour and gold on ?hemp, 139.0 × 3710.0 cm
PROVENANCE: William Anderson
LITERATURE: Anderson 1886, no. 1771
1881.12–10.01771 (Japanese Painting 1573)

The warrior chronicles *Heike monogatari* and *Gempei seisuiki* both relate how in the fourth month, 1153, the Emperor was disturbed every night by the cries of a bird-like creature and terrible dreams, and the warrior Minamoto no Yorimasa was commanded to discover the cause. As he waited at night with his henchman I no Hayata, a black cloud appeared from the forest at Higashi Sanjō and, praying to Hachiman, Yorimasa let fly an arrow from his great bow. A creature fell out of the sky – and was promptly finished off by I no Hayata with his dagger – the like of which had never been seen before – head of a monkey, body of a badger, tail of a serpent and legs of a tiger. Its cry was like the fabulous monster of the night, the Nue, and so it was identified as such.

The story of the killing of the Nue (*Nue taiji*) was adapted as the Nō play *Nue* and incorporated by Danjūrō II into the Kabuki play *Yorimasa sambasō* as early as 1708,

subsequently performed in many versions. The present painting was clearly intended as a large signboard to advertise such a Kabuki performance, but it has not been possible to link it to a specific performance in the early Meiji era. Since the actors are not identified with crests and the painting was done on cloth rather than paper (to last longer), it was perhaps meant to be used by a travelling company for a number of performances. The faces of the actors are done very much in the style used by the Ukiyo-e print artist Toyohara Kunichika (1835–1900) during the 1860s and 70s, and it may be that the use here by Kunitoshi of the otherwise unrecorded art surname Hara in his signature expresses a pupil relationship with Kunichika. The background of the Shishinden Palace is painted with the exaggerated sense of perspective habitually used in theatre backdrops. William Anderson must have acquired the painting as virtually new during his time in Japan from 1873 to 1880.

168

OSAKA SCHOOL

168 Atsumori and Kumagai
on Gojō Bridge

Early Meiji era
Theatre signboard; ink, colour and gold on paper,
    130.5 × 206.0 cm
PROVENANCE: C. H. Hindley
1921.6–14.010 (Japanese Painting ADD 16A)

The death of the young Taira warrior
Atsumori at the hands of Kumagai Jirō
Naozane at the battle of Ichinotani has
already been described (no. 155).
Encounters between the two became
elements of many Kabuki plays, including
Suma no Miyako Gempei tsutsuji (also known
as *Ōgiya Kumagai*) in which the plot was

transferred to Kyoto. In 1832 the scene
depicted on this large theatre signboard,
the encounter at Gojō Bridge, was added to
be performed by the great Nakamura
Utaemon III and has been an integral part
of the play ever since. The fight between
the handsome young Atsumori and
Kumagai, with his fierce red makeup, was
a reworking of the encounter between
Ushiwaka-maru (the young Minamoto no
Yoshitsune) and the warrior-monk Benkei
at the same spot, a story well known to all.

The style of the paintings – reminiscent
of artists such as Ichiyōtei Yoshitaki (1841–
99) – points to Osaka in the early Meiji era
(1868–1912), but since the faces are not
portraits of particular actors and the

costumes do not bear personal crests, it has
not been possible to identify the theatre or
performance where the signboard might
have been used. It may equally well have
been done for a minor theatre or travelling
company. The actors stand in tense *mie*,
bravura poses struck at moments of
theatrical climax, Atsumori crouched low
and wide holding a scroll in his
outstretched hand, and Kumagai towering
over him in fury, with his heels brought
together and war fan brandished in the air.
The shadowy span of Gojō Bridge curves
into the night behind them, serving as an
admirable backdrop for the brilliantly
painted figures, much in the style of the
painted scenery actually used onstage.

169

OSAKA SCHOOL

169 Scenes from the play 'Hana Fubuki Uta no Nadokoro'

Early Meiji era
Theatre signboard; ink and colour on paper,
142.0 × 197.0 cm
OA+0480

Matsudaira Susumu has kindly identified the scenes on this signboard as coming from the play *Hana fubuki uta no nadokoro*, a version of the ever-popular drama *Shin usuyuki monogatari* concerning the love of Princess Usuyuki for the young samurai Sonobe Saemon. The tragic plot culminates in the enforced suicide of both lovers' fathers, the Governor of Iga and Sonobe Hyōe, to clear the young couple from implication in a plot to kill the Shōgun.

   This is the only one of the four signboards in the British Museum collection which actually includes the crests of the actors on some of the costumes, and all are minor Osaka players. Professor Matsudaira suggests that the young woman brandishing the axe in the top left corner is Omitsu (played by an actor of the Kataoka family), who threatens Usuyuki-hime (played by an actor of the Arashi family, possibly Arashi Rikō), dressed in the standard princess's costume of red kimono with long, hanging sleeves and silver hair ornaments. The male servant with the white body makeup standing in the centre with his ankles together, fighting off the ruffians, may be Tsumahei (?Asao Sekijūrō), and the only other actor identifiable is the man in the green kimono standing in the top right corner, who, from his crest, may be Asao Daikichi. It has not been possible to link the depiction to any particular performance described in Kabuki records.

OSAKA SCHOOL

170 Scenes from a Kabuki Play

Early Meiji era
Theatre signboard; ink, colour and gold on paper,
133.0 × 202.0 cm
PROVENANCE: C. H. Hindley
1921.6–14.011 (Japanese Painting ADD 16B)

It has not yet been possible to identify the
Kabuki play to which this signboard
relates, but the three scenes depicted seem
to be the standard fare of Osaka domestic
dramas (*sewamono*): from left to right, a
fight between a ruffian, two men and a
courtesan crouching with a drawn dagger
at the foot of a bridge surrounded by
autumn maples; a courtesan being reunited
with a child who has a travelling hat and
talisman, with a ghost standing in the
doorway behind; and a courtesan
protecting a man from abuse by two
bullying characters in a brothel.

The technique of combining several
highlights in the drama – each in their own
pocket of space representing a different
setting – into a single composition was
common to signboards, advertising
handbills (*tsuji banzuke*) and illustrated
programmes (*ehon banzuke*) for the theatres.
The signboards were hung in frames above
the entrance to the theatre and generally
seem to have been discarded after the

170

performance. The oldest examples to have
survived date from the middle of the
eighteenth century, and remain only
because they were painted on wooden
panels which were subsequently presented
to shrines as votive plaques.

170 detail (*opposite*)

Tsukioka Yoshitoshi 1839–92

Family name Yoshioka; common name
Yonejirō. Later adopted by his cousin
Kyōya Shikisaburō. Finally succeeded to
the art surname Tsukioka from Tsukioka
Sessai. *Gō* Gyokuō, Gyokuōrō, Kaisai,
Ikkaisai, Taiso (from 1873), Sokatei
(according to *Ukiyo-eshi den*). Residences as
follows: Nakabashi (1865); Tachibana-chō
nichōme (1866); Oke-chō, then Hiyoshi-chō
(early years of Meiji era, 1868–1912);
Minami Kinroku-chō (1876); Maruya-chō
(1878); Minami Kinroku-chō (1879); Nezu
Miyanaga-chō (1883); Asakusa Suga-chō
(1885); temporary lodgings at Honjo
Fujishiro-chō in his last years (these dates
given by Suzuki Jūzō in *GUDHJ*, vol. 2
(1982), p. 103). Pupil of Utagawa
Kuniyoshi; also studied the style of Kikuchi
Yōsai.

Yoshitoshi is said to have entered
Kuniyoshi's studio in 1850, and his earliest
work appears to be a triptych of *Heike
Warriors Falling into the Sea* published in
1853. In the last years of the Edo period
many prints of warriors, beauties and
actors; some notable works in the sadistic,
blood-drenched taste then prevalent.
During 1872–3 suffered from a mental
illness which would trouble him again in
his last years. From *c.* 1873 influenced by
the style of Kikuchi Yōsai, combining this
with elements derived from European art
into a personal idiom, illustrating
mainly historical subjects. From 1874
illustrations for colour woodblock
'newspapers' and an ever-increasing
number of illustrations for novels. Major
print series include *Shinsen azuma nishiki-e*
(1885–6), *Fūzoku sanjūni-sō* (1888) and *Tsuki
hyakushi* (1885–91), as well as vertical
diptychs of historical subjects in a strong,
dynamic style full of fantasy and invention.

Yoshitoshi's preparatory drawings, of
which the British Museum has recently
acquired a group of fifty-two (1990.6–14.01),
demonstrate this strength and power of
invention vividly: ideas are first sketched in
in red ink and then the final, more definite
outlines for the woodblock print drawn
over this in black, much in the same
manner as Kuniyoshi, though with a highly
individual nervous and energetic line. The
few paintings by Yoshitoshi so far
introduced include a scene from the *Battle
of Shizugadake* painted on a hemp curtain
nine metres long for a festival in Kōfu in
1865; a set of twelve hanging scrolls on
subjects taken from the *Tsuki hyakushi* ('One
Hundred Phases of the Moon') series; and
several impressive votive plaques presented
to shrines and temples.

171

171

TSUKIOKA YOSHITOSHI

171 Courtesan Undressing

c. Keiō era
SIGNATURE: Yoshitoshi hitsu
SEAL: Yoshitoshi no in
Hanging scroll; ink and colour on silk,
 96.0 × 30.0 cm
PROVENANCE: William Anderson
LITERATURE: Anderson 1886, no. 1754; *UT*, vol. 1
 (1987), no. 182; Smith 1990, no. 203; Tokyo
 1990, no. 34
1881.12–10.01754 (Japanese Painting 1588)

In this erotically charged work Yoshitoshi
shows a courtesan kneeling on a thin
summer quilt, holding a pillow on a black
lacquer stand in her lap. She has already
untied the long scarlet crepe silk sash,
which lies scattered around her, and is
pulling her arm from the sleeve of her tie-
dyed blue and white robe. With flushed
face and a few stray strands of hair trailing
from an otherwise stiff arrangement, no
doubt it is the customer on whom she fixes
her gaze.

Even compared with the sensuality of
Kunisada and Eisen (no. 149) Yoshitoshi's
painting is remarkably candid. A sense of
arrested movement is conveyed in the
informality of the pose and the piercing
glance, and a nervous visual excitement
created by the vivid blue dots of the robe
and the black diamond weave of the quilt.
The characteristic drawing of the face with
a long aquiline nose and jutting lower lip
and jaw is found in works by all artists of
the Utagawa school, including Yoshitoshi's
teacher Kuniyoshi.

Utagawa Yoshiteru 1808–91

Family name Tanaka; *na* Yoshisaburō; *gō*
Hokunen, Itchinsai, Gansuisha. Second son
of Yoneyama Genjirō, later adopted by the
Tanaka family who ran an inn at Takazaki.
Pupil of Tani Bunchō from the age of
fifteen or sixteen, using the name
Hokunen, then studied with Kuniyoshi
from the age of about twenty-five or
twenty-six.

UTAGAWA YOSHITERU

172 Princess Sotōri and the Spider

1867
SIGNATURE: Rokujū-ō Itchinsai Yoshiteru hitsu
 ('Painted by Itchinsai Yoshiteru, old man of
 sixty')
SEAL: Yoshiteru gain
Hanging scroll; ink, colour and gold on silk,
 111.9 × 52.1 cm
PROVENANCE: Arthur Morrison
LITERATURE: *UT*, vol. 1 (1987), no. 181
1913.5–1.0413 (Japanese Painting 1574). Given by
 Sir W. Gwynne-Evans, Bt

Princess Sotōri was the concubine of the
Emperor Ingyō (reigned AD 412–53), so
named for the beauty of her skin which
seemed to radiate through her robes. Later
accounts associated her with the deity
Tamatsushima Myōjin, enshrined at
Wakanoura in Kii Province, and venerated
her as one of the three gods of poetry
together with Kakimoto no Hitomaro and
Yamabe no Akahito. In the preface to the
Kokin waka shū Imperial poetry anthology of
the early tenth century it is claimed that the
famed eighth-century poetess and beauty
Ono no Komachi followed the poetry
lineage of Princess Sotōri.

According to one account in the chronicle
Nihon shoki, Princess Sotōri lived in
seclusion in the Fujiwara Shrine out of
deference to the Empress. The Emperor
decided to visit her there in secret, but
even before he arrived the Princess had
divined that he was coming by noticing a
spider building its web in the roots of a
dwarf bamboo plant. In the present
painting, however, Sotōri-hime is seated
indoors dressed in gorgeous court robes,
leaning on a padded arm-rest, and the
spider is hanging from a thread attached to
the tassel of the hanging curtain behind
her.

The brilliant saturated colours and highly
polished, even brittle, style is typical of the

172

172

works by Utagawa artists of the end of the
Edo period. A pair of hanging scrolls by
Yoshiteru of a similar historical subject,
Empress Jingū and Takenouchi no Sukune,
painted in 1871 when he was sixty-four,
have recently been introduced (Kumamoto
1991, no. 92).

173

173

Utagawa Yoshiume 1819–79

Family name Nakajima; *na* Tōsuke; *gō* Ichiōsai, Yabairō. Native of Osaka, lived at Horie. Pupil of Kuniyoshi. Earliest datable work an *ōban* actor print relating to a performance at the New Year, 1841. Designed prints of actors in the small *chūban* format, landscapes and genre subjects and illustrated books. One of the leading Osaka Ukiyo-e artists of his day, with many pupils.

UTAGAWA YOSHIUME

173 Common Sayings Made into Pictures

Ka'ei–Ansei eras
SIGNATURE: Yoshiume giga ('Painted for amusement by Yoshiume')
SEAL: Rakuze Yūkyo
Album; ink and colour on paper,
23.0 × 16.4 cm (cover)
1979.1–29.03 (Japanese Painting ADD 587)

In this album of fifty paintings Yoshiume devises literal pictorial renditions of the homilies and other common sayings written above the pictures. The results are generally bizarre as human bodies are distorted or dismembered, and the treatment comic, cruel and even

scatological. In the page illustrated, for instance, a large face looks up to the heavens and grimaces in pain as it is set upon by four lilliputian figures who are acting out four common sayings. A woman stands on his shoulder with one hand resting on his lip and tweaking a nose hair (*hanage o yomu*, literally 'read a nose hair', meaning a man twists the woman who loves him round his little finger). Another figure straddles his neck threatening to choke him (*nodo no shita e hairu*, 'get under someone's throat', meaning to fawn on someone). A second woman comes out of his collar (*shiri ni tsuku jorō*, 'woman who sticks to his backside', meaning trailing after someone like a dog). Finally, a man who looks like a thief with a swag bag and stolen clothes clambers over his side (*kasuri o toru*, 'to take pattern-dyed fabric', meaning to get a kickback).

There was a tradition of clever visual puns and comic distortions of reality in the illustrations to printed comic novels of the eighteenth and nineteenth centuries, but to find them in paintings such as these is a late Edo phenomenon. Though he worked in Osaka, Yoshiume is said to have been a pupil of Kuniyoshi, and one recalls Kuniyoshi's famous prints in which groups of small writhing figures come together to look like faces in various moods.

Ichiyōtei Yoshitaki 1841–99

Family name Nakai (for a period *c.* 1874–5 succeeded to the family name Sasaki); *na* Tsunejirō; *gō* Ichiyōsai, Ichiyōtei, Yōsui, Satonoya, Ittensai (1861), Hōgyoku, Jueidō, Handen Shakyo, Noriya. Born at Unagidani in Osaka. Lived at Minami Hommachi nichōme; later moved to Kyoto, then Sakai, where he died at Kai-chō. The son of a paste merchant. Pupil of Nakajima Yoshiume. Earliest work *c.* 1854. With Hirosada, one of the two leading designers of *chūban* actor prints in Osaka during the 1860s and 70s. Also known for paintings of beauties in an Utagawa-influenced, but recognisably Osaka, style.

ICHIYŌTEI YOSHITAKI

174 Standing Beauty

c. 1860s–early 70s
SIGNATURE: Naniwa Yoshitaki hitsu ('Painted by Yoshitaki of Osaka')
SEAL: Yoshitaki
Hanging scroll; ink and colour on paper,
100.0 × 21.8 cm
PROVENANCE: William Anderson
LITERATURE: Anderson 1886, no. 1753; UT, vol. 1 (1987), no. 183
1881.12–10.01753 (Japanese Painting 1589)

The season is early summer to judge from the design on the woman's kimono of swallows flying among the hanging branches of a willow tree. Holding a case for paper tissues with both hands, she looks up into the air to one side. The bare feet, red undergarments and iridescent green lipstick all suggest that she is an Osaka courtesan or entertainer of some kind.

Though the overall impression is not dissimilar from an Edo, Utagawa-style painting of a beauty, the certain flatness of the facial features and particular rounded fluidity of the lines of the drapery are uniquely Yoshitaki's own and represent a distinctly Osaka variant of the Ukiyo-e idiom. The painting is signed 'by Yoshitaki of Osaka', so must have been done during a visit elsewhere, perhaps to Edo. Once again this must have been purchased as an example of contemporary painting by William Anderson during his time in Japan from 1873 to 1880.

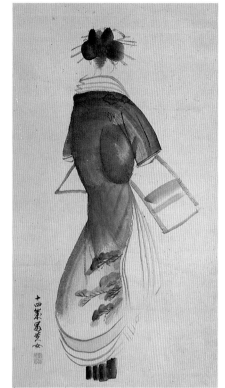

175

174

174

FUKI (dates unknown)

**175 Processing Courtesan
          Seen from Behind**

Mid-19th century
SIGNATURE: Jūyon-sai Fuki jo ('Fourteen-year-old
     woman, Fuki')
SEAL: Fuki jo ('The woman Fuki')
Hanging scroll; ink and slight colour on paper,
     49.9 × 28.0 cm
PROVENANCE: Arthur Morrison
1913.5–1.0278 (Japanese Painting 1580). Given by
     Sir W. Gwynne-Evans, Bt

A courtesan is seen from behind
processing, her tall, elongated form
accentuated by high black clogs. The
uchikake is decorated around the hem with a
design of pine trees, and the broad wash
style in which this is painted suggests the
Shijō school of Kyoto rather than the
Ukiyo-e style in Edo. Perhaps the young
woman who signs herself 'Fourteen-year-
old woman, Fuki' was an apprentice
courtesan in the Kyoto Shimabara pleasure
quarter.

175

176

Kobayashi Eitaku 1843–90

Na Tokusen; common name Hidejirō
(Shūjirō); *gō* Sensai, Issensai, Kadō, Mugyo.
The third son of Miura Kichisaburō, a
fishmonger at Nihombashi Uogashi. Died
in lodgings at Mukōjima Koumemura.
About the age of twelve or thirteen became
a pupil of Kanō Eitoku Tatsunobu (1814–91)
and a few years later was employed by Ii
Naosuke, Lord of Hakone, as an official
painter and given *samurai* status. In 1860,
when his lord was assassinated, Eitaku
resigned his position and began travels
throughout Japan, finally returning to settle
in Nihombashi. Influenced by various
styles, including Ming and Western-style
painting. Studied briefly with Yoshitoshi
and did colour prints in Ukiyo-e style after
c. 1870, colour-print illustrations for the
Yokohama mainichi shimbun newspaper and
also picture-books such as *Bambutsu
hinagata gafu* and *Sensai Eitaku gafu*. His
paintings combine Kanō, Ukiyo-e and
Western-style elements.

KOBAYASHI EITAKU

176 Seated Courtesan

1870s
SIGNATURE: Ōju Issensai Eitaku sha ('Painted by
   Issensai Eitaku at special request')
SEAL: three fish in a jar
Hanging scroll; ink and colour on silk,
   85.0 × 41.0 cm
PROVENANCE: William Anderson
LITERATURE: Anderson 1886, no. 1765
1881.12–10.01765 (Japanese Painting 1601)

The early years of the Meiji era (1868–1912)
witnessed many hybrid styles as old
schools such as the Kanō lost their
privileged status, allegiances were
realigned, and artists experimented with
elements of Western-style painting. Though
trained in the Kanō style, Eitaku seems to
have left this behind even before the end of
the Edo period to incorporate elements of
Ukiyo-e and Western-style depiction.

   Here the courtesan sits with one arm
behind her leaning slightly backwards,
fingering the mouthpiece of a long silver
pipe with the other hand. The outlines are
nervous and highly modulated in a manner
which no longer has the old Kanō
slickness, and Eitaku experiments too with
a slight use of modelling in the face and
hands. He feels he must foreshorten the
knees in a manner more prosaic than the
elegant, ballooning sweeps of drapery seen
in paintings by Utamaro (no. 69) and Eisen
(no. 149). In short, the old idealisation has
disappeared leaving a work which although
refreshingly candid and bravely searching

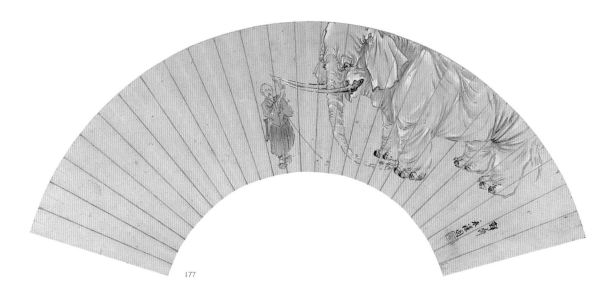

177

for a new idiom is still tentative in its sense of what that new beauty will be. One can also perhaps detect qualms about how a *bijin* (a 'beautiful woman' in the traditional sense) should be presented in the new age of civilisation and enlightenment.

Eitaku is known to have changed the character 'Ei' with which he wrote his name from one using the 'leg' radical (as here) to one using the 'water' radical, commonly encountered in his printed books. Once the date of this transition has been established, it should be possible to date this painting more accurately.

176

KOBAYASHI EITAKU

177 Blind Man Feeling an Elephant

Meiji era, before 1890
SIGNATURE: Sensai Eitaku zu
SEAL: ?Kadō
Fan painting; ink and colour on mica-covered
    paper, 12.1 × 48.4 cm
PROVENANCE: Hosomi Ryō; Ralph Harari
LITERATURE: Hillier 1970, vol. 3, no. 217
1982.7–1.017(8) (Japanese Painting ADD 702H)

Henry Joly (*Legend in Japanese Art*, London, John Lane, 1908, p. 25) gives a concise explanation of the subject of this painting:

Blind men feeling an elephant is a
common subject, and there is a story that
once an Indian elephant having been
brought to Japan, a party of blind people
went to feel it, and could not agree in
their opinions of the nature of the
monster, finding it like a dagger, a
snake, the trunk of a tree as they
touched the tusks, the trunk or the legs
of the animal. And a moral is deduced
therefrom, not to judge of anything on
the impression caused by the parts only,
instead of the whole.

The placing of the tiny blind man as if he were lost in the centre of the composition cleverly suggests his disorientation, with the massive elephant pushed over to one side and half cut off by the edge of the fan paper. The combination of traditional Kano-style ink and wash painting techniques with newer Western-derived elements, such as the foreshortened stance of the beast and the sense of modelling of his leathery skin, reflects the mixed influences to which painters such as Eitaku working in the early Meiji era were subject.

177

Hashimoto Chikanobu 1838–1912

Na Naoyoshi; *gō* Ikkakusai, Yoshitsuru II, Yōshū. Born in Echigo Province, a minor Bakufu retainer. Lived in Ueno Kita Ōmon-chō (1877–80); Yushima Tenjin-chō sanchōme (1884–91). Pupil of both Kuniyoshi and Kunisada; then became the leading pupil of Toyohara Kunichika, from whom he took the art surname Toyohara. First dated work a collaboration with Kunichika in 1867. Prolific artist of triptych prints showing new sights of Tokyo during the 1870s, publicising the activities and changing appearance of the Imperial family; and later, in the 1890s, of historical works showing the customs of the Shōgunal harem in Edo Castle (series such as *Chiyoda no ōoku*, 1896). Also half-length portraits of beauties in the series *Shin bijin* (1897) and many actor prints. The few paintings by him so far introduced – all idealised images of *bijin* – display a highly accomplished technique.

HASHIMOTO CHIKANOBU

178 Woman Tying her Obi
(Parody of the Third Princess)

178

1890s
SIGNATURE: Yōshū
SEAL: Chikanobu
Hanging scroll; ink, colour and gold on silk,
 114.9 × 44.2 cm
PROVENANCE: Arthur Morrison
LITERATURE: *UT*, vol. 1 (1987), no. 184
1913.5–1.0284 (Japanese Painting 1578). Given by
 Sir W. Gwynne-Evans, Bt

The many Ukiyo-e paintings showing a cat playing in the skirts of a woman's robes refer to the famous scene in the 'Young Herbs: Part One' (*Wakana jō*) chapter of *Tale of Genji*, in which the pet cat belonging to Onna Sannomiya (the Third Princess) escapes out on to the balcony, and Kashiwagi, who is playing court football outside, catches a glimpse of the princess through the gap in the curtain and falls in love with her. Here the woman has clearly just come from her bath, with long combed-out hair hanging loose down her back and wearing a diaphanous gauze robe through which can be seen her breasts and one delicate arm. Since she wears a wedding ring it can be assumed she is a young wife. The cat plays in the end of the *obi* that she winds around her waist, and Chikanobu has sensitively modulated the ink to give a sense of the sheen on the black silk fabric. The colour scheme is extremely muted, adding to the overall sense of freshness.

While on the one hand the beauty still has the impassive, idealised features associated with the Ukiyo-e tradition, the very three-dimensional depiction of the voluptuous body beneath the diaphanous robe is new and informed by a much keener sense of anatomical accuracy than in the past (compare, for instance, with no. 25 by Eishun). Though dismissed unfairly as weak and vapid by critics in the past, Meiji-era painters such as Chikanobu were clearly capable – as in this instance – of matching the achievements of many earlier masters and served as an important link between Ukiyo-e and the *bijin* paintings of later Nihonga masters such as Uemura Shōen (1875–1949).

The form of the signature is similar to that found on late print series such as *Shin bijin* (1897).

HASHIMOTO CHIKANOBU

179 Two Women by a River

1890s
SIGNATURE: Yōshū
SEAL: Chikanobu
Hanging scroll; ink, colour and gold on silk,
   111.3 × 41.5 cm
PROVENANCE: Arthur Morrison
LITERATURE: *UT*, vol. 1 (1987), no. 185
1913.5–1.0285 (Japanese Painting 1579). Given by
   Sir W. Gwynne-Evans, Bt

179

A girl crouches on a landing stage holding a fishing-rod and -line and turns to face the young woman who has stepped up beside her. Everything about the painting suggests midsummer: on the embankment faced with stone behind them a silk tree (*nemu no ki*) displays its pink fronded blossoms and, as with the previous painting, the standing woman has her long hair combed out loosely to dry after washing. She wears a thin transparent kimono decorated with flying swallows and carries a round fan painted with a calling cuckoo. A somewhat bizarre and intrusive detail is provided by two crabs climbing up the wall.

Chikanobu was the most talented pupil of Toyohara Kunichika and as such represented the main line of the Utagawa school that had begun with Toyoharu in the 1760s. The long aquiline nose and slightly cross-eyed expression were the hallmarks of Utagawa painters since the Bunsei era (1818–30), but Chikanobu softens the effect by using a crimson outline. Bringing the posts of the breakwater to the very foreground of the image and fading the rippling water away into the distance create a sense of spatial recession that is new.

179

180

Miyagawa Shuntei 1873–1914

Family name Watanabe; *na* Moriyoshi; *gō* Gyoshi. Born in Aichi Prefecture, lived in Edo. Pupil first of Watanabe Shōka, later Tomioka Eisen. Known for prints of women, children and genre subjects, as well as illustrations for newspapers and magazines.

180

MIYAGAWA SHUNTEI

180 Woman Painting

c. 1890s
SEAL: Shuntei
Album leaf; ink and colour on silk, 24.7 × 32.4 cm
PROVENANCE: Arthur Morrison
1913.5–1.0389 (Japanese Painting 1594). Given by
Sir W. Gwynne-Evans, Bt

A woman artist is seated with a frame stretched with silk on her lap, painting a branch of flowering plum blossom. She uses the twin brushes, one for *sumi* and the other for colour, that were employed by painters of traditional schools, and beside her is a pot of brushes, an ink-stone and a ceramic dish for mixing colours. The scene differs little from the illustration of Moronobu's granddaughter Osan painting included by Okumura Masanobu in his picture-book *Ehon fūga nana Komachi*, published in the 1740s (Introduction, fig. 5). The figure style here is reminiscent of the colour prints of genre subjects by Shuntei issued in the 1890s.

Kaburagi Kiyokata 1878–1973

Na Ken'ichi. Born in Kanda Sakuma-chō, the son of Jōno Saigiku and Kaburagi Fumi. His father was an important writer of popular fiction using the name Sansantei Arindo, who founded two newspapers – the *Tokyo nichinichi shimbun* (1872) and *Yamato shimbun* (1886). In 1891, while living in Kanda Higashi Konya-chō, became a pupil of Mizuno Toshikata (a pupil of Yoshitoshi), from whom he received the name Kiyokata in 1893. For the rest of the 1890s and until 1907 active as an illustrator of newspapers, literary journals and, from 1900, *Kabuki* magazine. During the decade leading up to World War I contributed colour-printed frontispieces and cover designs to novels by Izumi Kyōka, Shimazaki Tōson and other leading authors.

Began to exhibit paintings from 1897 onwards, forming in 1901 the Ugōkai group which sought to revive genre painting in a contemporary manner. Sometimes these had nostalgic literary associations, such as *Ichiyō joshi no haka* ('The Grave of Higuchi Ichiyō', 1902). In addition to exhibition pictures of beauties in his neo-Ukiyo-e style, such as the prize-winning *Tsukiji Akashi-chō*, shown at the eighth Teiten in 1927, he began a series of imaginative literary portraits such as that of the *rakugo* performer *San'yūtei Enchō* (1930). From *c.* 1927 revived genre painting in the album and handscroll formats which he referred to as 'table-top art' (*takujō geijutsu*). Kiyokata had ambivalent feelings about being called an Ukiyo-e painter since, particularly early in his career, the lowly social status of Ukiyo-e artists might have hindered his acceptance by the Meiji art establishment. Once his position as a leading Nihonga painter was secure, however, he felt able to refer to himself as 'Kiyokata, last painter in the Ukiyo-e line' ('Ukiyo-e matsuryū Kiyokata') in an inscription on the box of a copy he made of one of Shunshō's great series, 'Manners and Customs of Women in the Twelve Months'. It was about this time, in 1935, that he did his own tribute to Shunshō, a series called 'Manners and Customs of the Twelve Months in the Meiji Era'.

181

181

KABURAGI KIYOKATA

181 Interior of a Brothel

Late 1890s–early 1900s
SEAL: Kiyokata
INSCRIPTION: Motome ni yorite ('By special
  request')
Hanging scroll (mounted in board); ink and
  colour on silk, 26.8 × 44.9 cm
PROVENANCE: Arthur Morrison
1913.5–1.0351 (Japanese Painting 1577). Given by
  Sir W. Gwynne-Evans, Bt

The scene is the first floor of a brothel,
with party rooms leading off a gallery
around a central courtyard. The courtesan

seems to be hurrying expectantly into the
room towards us, the suddenness of her
action stressed by the calm manner in
which another courtesan and attendant are
proceeding along the verandah in the
background. The hanging gas-lamp
provides a discreetly modern touch.

The inscription 'By special request'
suggests a commission and we can
conjecture that this, like no. 182, may be a
painted version of the printed frontispiece
to a novel done for a particular patron. The
novel has yet to be identified.

182

182

KABURAGI KIYOKATA

182 Woman and Plantain

Late 1890s–early 1900s
SIGNATURE: Kiyokata
SEAL: ?Kiyokata
Album leaf (or hanging scroll?); ink, colour and
  gold on silk, 26.2 × 35.2 cm
PROVENANCE: Arthur Morrison
1913.5–1.0350 (Japanese Painting 1576). Given by
  Sir W. Gwynne-Evans, Bt

A woman is seated on a bench beneath the
spreading leaves of a plantain under a full
moon. Apparently lost deep in thought,
she toys idly with a stem of lily, and there
is a round fan painted with an egret on the
bench beside her. The banana plant is
sketched in velvety wet tones of ink which
strike a sophisticated contrast with the
polished, flowing lines of the drapery, the
lilac and blue of her costume given a pale,
cold hue to suggest the moonlight.

The mood is sentimental, without being
cloying, and one can imagine that this, as
in the previous example (no. 181), is a
character from some Meiji novel. The new
psychological depth permitted heroines in
late Meiji literature in turn prompted artists
such as Kiyokata occasionally to turn away
from the sunny depictions of women
traditionally found in Ukiyo-e and
experiment with new formulas for
suggesting introspection. The head shown
in profile but with half-closed eyes works
well here to that effect.

APPENDIX
FAKES

It is difficult to draw a clear distinction between 'genuine' and 'fake' Ukiyo-e paintings. The problem is exacerbated at present by the lack of monograph studies on even the most important artists and also – as with any field of connoisseurship – by issues of school pieces, revivalist styles and so forth. Relegated to this section, therefore, are only those works about which there is likely to be general agreement that they are fakes. Any doubts about paintings in the main body of the catalogue will be found in the commentaries pertaining to each. As our knowledge of Ukiyo-e painting improves, the various versions of particular compositions are compared, and detailed analysis is undertaken of signatures and seals, then undoubtedly some of the paintings presently accepted as genuine will be called into question. Such matters are best left not entirely to the all-too-fallible judgement of one individual, and comments from colleagues concerning the division would be welcome.

183

183 Fan Dancer

(?)One leaf of a six-fold screen; ink, colour, gold and gold leaf on paper, 123.5 × 57.2 cm
PROVENANCE: Yamanaka & Co.
1926.7–14.08 (Japanese Painting ADD 44)

A woman wearing a black kimono decorated with a pattern of dragonflies hovering over autumn plants and grasses dances holding an open fan painted with an ink design of a dragon over waves. This looks to be a nineteenth-century pastiche in the style of the early seventeenth-century genre painters (no. 1). The face is too 'modern', not impassive in the manner of the earlier masters.

184 Blind Man and Fox

Hanging scroll; ink, colour and gold on silk, 25.5 × 40.8 cm
PROVENANCE: William Anderson
LITERATURE: Anderson 1886, no. 1706
1881.12–10.01706 (Japanese Painting 1394)

Two women standing at a gateway beneath cherry blossom laugh as a blind man is led off holding on to the tail of a mischievous fox. The style of the women, in particular, is copied from genre paintings of the early seventeenth century, but the colouring and brushwork look to be much later – almost certainly nineteenth century.

184

185

185

'MORONOBU'

185 Pleasure Party

SIGNATURE: Nihon-e Hishikawa Moronobu zu
('Japanese picture painted by Hishikawa
Moronobu')
SEAL: Moronobu
Hanging scroll; ink, colour and gold on silk,
31.3 × 44.7 cm
PROVENANCE: Arthur Morrison
1913.5–1.0370 (Japanese Painting 1369). Given by
Sir W. Gwynne-Evans, Bt

This is a painted copy of a famous print by
Moronobu, from the series *Yoshiwara no tei*
(reproduced, for instance, in Tokyo
Kokuritsu Hakubutsukan (eds), *Ukiyo-e*,
1984, no. 30–10). A tree has been removed
from the right-hand side of the print and
the decoration on the screen changed from
calligraphy to a painting of a willow tree;
otherwise the figures are in virtually the
same configuration. The painting looks to
have been done on silk that was already
'aged', and the faces are not in true
Moronobu style.

'MORONOBU'

186 Woman Walking

SIGNATURE: Bōkoku Hishikawa Moronobu zu
('Painted by Hishikawa Moronobu of Awa
Province')
Hanging scroll; ink and colour on silk,
69.0 × 26.7 cm
PROVENANCE: Arthur Morrison
1946.2–9.033 (Japanese Painting ADD 190).
Bequeathed by Arthur Morrison

Though the hairstyle and fashions are of
the Genroku era (1688–1704), the figure of
the walking woman is too large and
inelegant and the signature too crudely
done to be from Moronobu's hand.

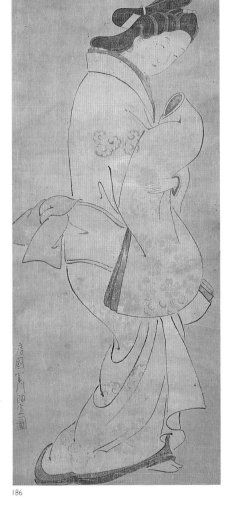

186

186

'MORONOBU'

187 Courtesan with Woman Playing
the Shamisen

SIGNATURE: Hishikawa Kichibei Moronobu zu
SEALS: Moronobu, Hishikawa-uji
Hanging scroll; ink, colour and gold on silk,
97.5 × 33.0 cm
PROVENANCE: William Anderson
LITERATURE: Anderson 1886, no. 1704
1881.12–10.01704 (Japanese Painting 1377)

The signature here is written with the
character 'nobu' meaning 'truth' rather than
the one meaning 'to say' or 'announce'
with which the great Hishikawa Moronobu
(d. 1694) signed his name. Asano Shūgō
(*GUDHJ*, vol. 2 (1982), p. 131) notes that the
dictionary of painters *Gajō yōryaku* (1832)
seems to have made a similar mistake
about Moronobu, and it may be that this
mistake about the name was common at
the time this forgery was made. At best it
can be regarded as a feeble nineteenth-
century pastiche in archaistic style.

187

189

189

187

'MORONOBU'

188 Ushiwaka-maru Visits Princess Jōruri

SEALS: Hishikawa, Moronobu
Hanging scroll; ink, colour and gold on silk,
39.2 × 61.0 cm
PROVENANCE: William Anderson
LITERATURE: Anderson 1886, no. 1702
1881.12–10.01702 (Japanese Painting 1376)

The silk of the painting is completely
unblemished and looks as if it would have
been almost brand new when the scroll
was purchased by Anderson in the 1870s.
The design of Ushiwaka (the future
Minamoto no Yoshitsune) visiting Princess
Jōruri is taken from a famous print now
attributed to Sugimura Jihei (reproduced,
for instance, in *Ukiyo-e taikei*, vol. 1 (1974),
no. 9). The colour combinations and effects
of 'shading' are not at all characteristic of a
late seventeenth-century painting.

'KAIGETSUDŌ ANDO'

189 Woman Dressing the Hair of a
Young Man

SIGNATURE: Nihon giga Kaigetsudō Ando kore [o]
zu [su] ('Light-hearted painting in Japanese
style, this picture was done by Kaigetsudō
Ando')
SEALS: (unread), Ando
Hanging scroll; ink, colour and gold on silk,
49.5 × 34.5 cm
PROVENANCE: Arthur Morrison
LITERATURE: Fujikake 1943, no. 113; Lane 1959,
pl. 33
1913.5–1.0347 (Japanese Painting 1386). Given by
Sir W. Gwynne-Evans, Bt

The scene of a woman combing the hair of
a young man is a reference to the famous
episode in Kabuki 'Soga' plays in which the
courtesan Tora of Ōiso combs the hair of
her lover, Soga no Jūrō. The signature
follows the general mannerisms of Ando
but is weak, and the seal is not quite like
those impressed on works taken to be
authentic: the characters are carved in a
slightly different cursive form and the
space between the square and circle is too
wide. Certain colours stand out as strange
– notably the plum on the man's robe and
the acid blue on the courtesan's robe.
Though the general line quality is not too
confident, the overall composition is
convincing, and it is likely this is a copy of
a now-lost authentic work by Ando.

188

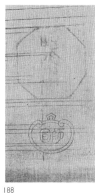

188

190

191

'SHIGENAGA'

190 Women in a Boat

SIGNATURE: Gakō Nishimura Shigenaga hitsu ('Painted by the artist Nishimura Shigenaga')
SEAL: Shigenaga no in
Hanging scroll; ink, colour and gold on silk, 36.8 × 59.8 cm
PROVENANCE: James Tregaskis
LITERATURE: *NU*, vol. 1 (1987), no. 114
1925.11–18.02 (Japanese Painting ADD 31)

Shigenaga was a prolific artist of hand-coloured prints (*beni-e*) and prints with two and three printed colours (*benizuri-e*) in the middle of the eighteenth century but is not otherwise known to have done any paintings. The line quality of this painting is poor, the colours flat, new-looking and not well applied, and the overall impression that of a late nineteenth-century pastiche. The figure style does not relate to that of Shigenaga's prints, and the feeble painting of the willow tree inconceivable from an artist who did such fine bird and flower prints in Kanō style.

'SETTEI'

191 Two Women

SIGNATURE: Tsukioka Settei Masa
SEAL: Sei Genji Kida na Masanobu azana Daikei gō Settei betsugō Tsukioka jishō Shinten'ō ('Clan name Genji Kida; *na* Masanobu; *azana* Daikei; *gō* Settei; *betsugō* Tsukioka; common name Shinten'ō')
Hanging scroll; ink, colour and gold on silk, 90.4 × 28.1 cm
PROVENANCE: Arthur Morrison
1913.5–1.0381 (Japanese Painting 1415). Given by Sir W. Gwynne-Evans, Bt

The line quality is poor, the colours not properly applied to the silk, and the figures look lost in an otherwise empty composition. The signature is crooked and badly written, and the seal definitely a forged version of the famous seal in which Settei lists all his names and titles.

190

191

192

STYLE OF TOYOHARU

192 Processing Courtesan

Hanging scroll; ink, colour and gold on silk,
89.0 × 30.2 cm
PROVENANCE: Arthur Morrison
LITERATURE: *NU*, vol. 1 (1987), no. 132
1913.5–1.0396 (Japanese Painting 1436). Given by
Sir W. Gwynne-Evans, Bt

Though unsigned, this is very much a
pastiche in the style of Utagawa Toyoharu
(nos 56–8) and clearly is intended to be
attributed to him. The closest among
authentic paintings by Toyoharu presently
known is reproduced in Matsumoto 1985,
no. 236, a composition which also has the
figure of the *kamuro* attendant in front,
facing away from the viewer. A comparison
with this painting will make clear the
weaknesses of the British Museum work:
the face is too 'modern' with long
narrowed eyes, and the ice-blue pigment
(never found in the Edo period) used for
the 'linked hemp-leaf' (*asa no ha*) pattern on
her kimono is painted directly on to the silk
rather than over carefully layered pigments.
The *kamuro*'s hairstyle, too, is too 'thinly'
painted.

'EISHI'

193 Courtesan Looking in a Mirror

SIGNATURE: Kitagawa Utamaro ga
SEALS: Kitagawa-uji, Utamaro
Hanging scroll (mounted on a panel); ink, colour
and gold on silk, 100.5 × 34.5 cm
1962.5–12.01 (Japanese Painting ADD 373)

A courtesan stands *en déshabillé*, pulling her
kimono around her body and looking at
her reflection in a mirror held at her feet by
a crouching *kamuro*. The style is closest to
Eishi of the later 1790s, even imitating a
common Eishi colour scheme with the blue
plovers on a light blue robe and gold
drapery lines on the red undergarment.
The face, however, is not quite as long as
those painted by Eishi and is more similar
in shape to examples in Utamaro's
woodblock prints. For this reason, perhaps,
rather than the signature of Eishi, the
forger elected to add the more marketable
signature of Utamaro, though in neat
square characters not otherwise seen on
any genuine Utamaro painting.

193

193

194

194

'EISHI'

194 Women under Cherry Blossom

SIGNATURE: Chōbunsai Eishi hitsu
SEAL: Eishi
Hanging scroll; ink, colour and gold on silk,
    117.0 × 49.0 cm
PROVENANCE: Arthur Morrison
1913.5–1.0409 (Japanese Painting 1428). Given by
    Sir W. Gwynne-Evans, Bt

A group of women and a young girl stand
under the blossoms of a cherry tree, one
attaching a poem slip to the branch above.
The first disconcerting fact is that the
colours are dull and seem to imitate the
effect of a faded woodblock print. The
figures are over-elongated, even for Eishi,
and the faces considerably distorted from
his style. The cut-off 'stump' of the tree in
the bottom left corner is feeble for an artist
who trained with the leading Kanō painter
of the times. The signature and seal are,
needless to say, both forged. Several
versions of this composition are in
circulation, but none appear genuine to the
present writer.

'HOKUSAI'

195 Seller of Tea Whisks

SIGNATURE: Hokusai ga
SEAL: handwritten cipher (kaō)
Hanging scroll; ink and slight colour on paper,
    79.7 × 24.5 cm
PROVENANCE: James Martin White
LITERATURE: Tokyo 1901, no. 38; Gray 1948, no. 16
1950.11–11.015 (Japanese Painting ADD 335). Given
    by the Trustees of the late James Martin White

An old man in tattered black robes carries a
pole to which have been attached Tea
Ceremony whisks for sale. In the sky a
flock of birds passes in front of the moon.
Writing in the catalogue of the Hokusai
exhibition held in Tokyo in 1900, Ernest
Fenollosa comments '... the utmost
breadth and free beauty ... are realised in
this rapid but masterly study'. To the
present writer, however, the various rapid
strokes that make up the limbs and robes
do not coalesce to give any sense of volume
or anatomical structure to the figure – a
carelessness of which Hokusai was never
guilty – and the birds and moon are
similarly flaccidly done. It is true that
Hokusai uses a similar signature and
handwritten red cipher (kaō) on several
genuine paintings of the early Bunka era
(1804–18), such as the hanging scroll
Chinese Warrior Leaning on an Axe, but in
this case neither signature nor seal is
written with any strength or conviction.

195

195

196

'HOKUSAI'

196 Kokusempū Riki with an Axe

SEAL: Katsushika
Hanging scroll; ink and colour on paper,
41.3 × 24.9 cm
PROVENANCE: Arthur Morrison
1913.5–1.0319 (Japanese Painting 1452). Given by
Sir W. Gwynne-Evans, Bt

An inferior copy of an illustration by
Hokusai of this Chinese hero in the
woodblock-printed *Ehon suikoden* (p. 17
recto), published in 1829. Though there are
at least two genuine versions of the
'Katsushika' seal (see no. 101), this is not
one of them and is so distorted as to be
almost illegible.

196

'HOKUSAI'

197 White Snake Coiled around a Biwa

SIGNATURE: Kōka ni kinoto mi nen/shōgatsu gantan
yowai hachijū-roku sai/Manji hitsu ('From the
brush of Manji, aged eighty-six on New Year's
day, Kōka 2 (1845)')
SEAL: Katsushika
Hanging scroll; ink and colour on silk,
39.5 × 54.0 cm
PROVENANCE: James Martin White
LITERATURE: Gray 1948, no. 173
1950.11–11.017 (Japanese Painting ADD 337). Given
by the Trustees of the late James Martin White

A white snake is coiled around a *biwa* (a
kind of lute-like musical instrument struck
with a plectrum) wrapped in a brocade bag.
Though several versions of this
composition are known – ostensibly done
for the Year of the Snake (1845) – none
appear to be genuine. Presumably the
original, if there ever was one, has been
lost. In this case the signature is
painstaking and lifeless, as is the execution
of the painting. Colours are applied too
thinly and flatly, and whereas in the
genuine version one imagines Hokusai
would have made great play of painting
each scale of the snake in different tones
and with outlines of different character,
here they are uniform and dull.

197

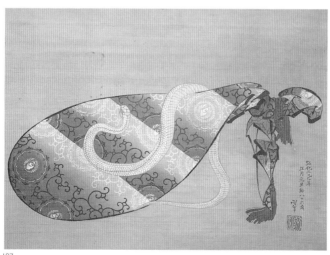

197

198

199

200

'HIROSHIGE'

198 View at Kanagawa

SIGNATURE: Hiroshige hitsu
SEAL: Hiroshige
Hanging scroll; ink and colour on paper,
  37.6 × 46.5 cm
PROVENANCE: Arthur Morrison
LITERATURE: Morrison 1911, vol. II, pl. XXXIV
1913.5–1.0295 (Japanese Painting 1549). Given by
  Sir W. Gwynne-Evans, Bt

The ascribed title is 'View at Kanagawa',
and travellers are shown pausing to rest at
a roadside stall in a valley lined with
maples displaying brilliant autumn foliage.
The forger has taken the style of
Hiroshige's pocket sketch-books and blown
the composition up into hanging-scroll size,
something Hiroshige himself never did.
The forms of the figures are in any case too
spindly and not accurately rendered.
Neither signature nor seal corresponds with
those on genuine paintings.

198

'HIROSHIGE'

199 Waterfall

SIGNATURE: Hiroshige ga
SEAL: Ichiryūsai
Hanging scroll; ink on silk, 49.5 × 67.3 cm
PROVENANCE: Arthur Morrison
1913.5–1.0296 (Japanese Painting 1550). Given by
  Sir W. Gwynne-Evans, Bt

The work is not in a style used by
Hiroshige, and the signature 'Hiroshige ga'
was used almost exclusively on his
woodblock prints, never on paintings of
any but his earliest period of activity. The
seal (which is impressed crooked) is not
otherwise recorded.

199

'HIROSHIGE'

200 Iris Pool

SIGNATURE: Hiroshige hitsu
SEAL: Tōbu ikke ('A lineage of the East' (i.e., Edo))
Hanging scroll; ink and colour on silk,
  59.0 × 36.5 cm
PROVENANCE: William Anderson
LITERATURE: Anderson 1886, no. 1757
1881.12–10.01757 (Japanese Painting 1553)

The only other use of this seal presently
recorded is on the famous triptych of
woodblock prints *The Whirlpools at Awa*,
published in 1857, the year before
Hiroshige's death. The signature is thin
and weak and the painting so perfunctorily
done – the dots of grass on the hill are
particularly mechanical – as to be
inconceivable as a genuine work by either
Hiroshige I or Hiroshige II.

200

BIBLIOGRAPHY

Listed here are works cited in abbreviated form elsewhere in the catalogue. Many of these refer particularly to the British Museum Japanese collections, though not necessarily exclusively to Ukiyo-e paintings. Also included are abbreviations for multi-volume series on Ukiyo-e published in Japan.

AIC 1955. Gunsaulus, Helen C., *The Clarence Buckingham Collection of Japanese Prints: The Primitives*. Chicago, Art Institute, 1955

Anderson 1886. Anderson, William, *Descriptive and Historical Catalogue of Japanese and Chinese Paintings in the British Museum*. London, Trustees of the British Museum, 1886

Anderson 1886a. Anderson, William, *The Pictorial Arts of Japan*. London, Sampson Low, 1886

Binyon and Sexton 1923. Binyon, Laurence, and Sexton, J. J. O'Brien, *Japanese Colour Prints*. London, Ernest Benn, 1923

Forrer and Goncourt 1988. Forrer, Matthi, and Goncourt, Edmond de, *Hokusai*. New York, Rizzoli, 1988

Gray 1948. Gray, Basil, *The Work of Hokusai – Woodcuts, Illustrated Books, Drawings and Paintings: A Catalogue of an Exhibition held on the Occasion of the Centenary of his Death*. London, British Museum, 1948

GUDHJ 1980–2. *Genshoku ukiyo-e daihyakka jiten* ('Ukiyo-e Encyclopaedia'). 11 vols, Tokyo, Taishūkan, 1980–2

Hillier 1955. Hillier, Jack, *Hokusai: Paintings, Drawings and Woodcuts*. London, Phaidon, 1955

Hillier 1970. Hillier, Jack, *The Harari Collection of Japanese Paintings and Prints*. 3 vols, London, Lund Humphries, 1970–3

Morrison 1911. Morrison, Arthur, *The Painters of Japan*. 2 vols, London, 1911

NU 1980–2. *Nikuhitsu ukiyo-e*, ed. Narazaki Muneshige. 10 vols, Tokyo, Shūeisha, 1980–2

Robinson 1961. Robinson, Basil, *Kuniyoshi*. London, HMSO, 1961

Smith 1988. Smith, Lawrence (ed.), *Ukiyo-e: Images of Unknown Japan*. London, British Museum Publications, 1988

Smith 1990. Smith, Lawrence, *Japanese Art: Masterpieces in the British Museum*, with Victor Harris and Timothy Clark. London, British Museum Publications, 1990

Strange 1925. Strange, Edward, *The Colour Prints of Hiroshige*. London, Cassell, 1925

TNM 1987. Tokyo National Museum (eds), *Daiei Hakubutsukan shozō Nihon Chūgoku bijutsu meihin ten* ('Masterpieces of Japanese and Chinese Art from the British Museum'). Exh. cat., 28 Apr.–7 June 1987

Tokyo 1990. Tokyo-to Bijutsukan (eds), *Daiei Hakubutsukan hizō Edo bijutsu ten*. Exh. cat., 9 Aug.–24 Sept. 1990

Ueno 1985. Tokyo, Ueno no Mori Bijutsukan, *Daiei Hakubutsukan shozō ukiyo-e meisaku ten* ('Masterpieces of Ukiyo-e from the British Museum'). Exh. cat., 29 March–12 Apr. 1985

US 1980–5. *Ukiyo-e shūka*. 18 vols, Tokyo, Shōgakkan, 1980–5

UT 1987–90. *(Hizō) Ukiyo-e taikan* ('Ukiyo-e Masterpieces in European Collections'), ed. Narazaki Muneshige. 13 vols, Tokyo, Kōdansha, 1987–90

Annotated bibliography for Ukiyo-e painting studies

This, like any bibliography, cannot hope to be an exhaustive collection of sources relating to the study of Ukiyo-e painting. It will be found particularly deficient in auction and dealers' catalogues and magazine articles. Wherever possible, it has been noted whether or not collectors' names appear in catalogues, to encourage the study of the provenance of Ukiyo-e paintings. It would have been impossible to make detailed remarks about the authenticity of paintings published in these sources; this is a matter best debated elsewhere. In the case of items which were hard to come by some library shelf-marks are included where known. The abbreviations used are as follows:

BK   Bunkazai Kenkyūjo. Tokyo National Research Institute for the Study of Cultural Properties. 東京国立文化財研究所.

FR   Freer Gallery. Library of the Freer Gallery of Art, Smithsonian Institution, Washington, DC

HYC   Harvard Yenching Library, Harvard University, Cambridge, Mass.

KT   Kokkai Toshokan. National Diet Library, Tokyo. 東京国立国会図書館.

LC   Library of Congress, Washington, DC

RL   Rubel Library, Sackler Museum, Harvard University, Cambridge, Mass.

SP   Spinks. The Manrakudō Library of Dr Charles Nelson Spinks, The American University Library, Washington, DC

TNM   Tokyo National Museum. 東京国立博物館.

UBM   *Ukiyo-e bunken mokuroku*. Harigaya Shōkichi *et al.* (eds), *Ukiyo-e bunken mokuroku*. 浮世絵文献目録. Tokyo, Mito shooku, 1972

1886

Anderson, William. *Descriptive and Historical Catalogue of a Collection of Japanese and Chinese Paintings in the British Museum.* London, Trustees of the British Museum, 1886

Anderson was a surgeon working for the Meiji government in Japan from 1873 to 1880. Upon his return to London in 1881 he sold his collection of 3,299 Japanese and Chinese paintings and studies to the British Museum and was commissioned by the Trustees to write this catalogue. The chapter 'Popular School, or, Ukiyo-ye Riu' (pp. 328–403) lists 330 items, some of which will be found in the present catalogue, though many have since been reclassified into other schools.

Anderson, William. *The Pictorial Arts of Japan.* London, Sampson Low, 1886

This pioneering work is divided into sections: 'General History', 'Applications of Pictorial Art', 'Technique', 'Characteristics', 'Chinese and Korean Pictorial Art'. A few Ukiyo-e paintings from Anderson's own collection are used to illustrate the text.

1888

London, Dowdeswell & Dowdeswell. *Catalogue of a Collection of Japanese Kakemonos.* London, 1888

Sales exhibition of 488 paintings from the H. Ahrens collection held at Dowdeswell's, 160 New Bond Street, in May 1888. Lists sixty-seven Ukiyo-e paintings described as being by Moronobu, Hokusai, Itchō, *et al.*

1892

Kobayashi Bunshichi. *Ukiyo-e tenrankai himmoku,* 小林文七　浮世絵展覧会品目. Tokyo, Kobayashi Bunshichi, 1892

Catalogue of what must have been one of the earliest public exhibitions of Ukiyo-e, organised by Kobayashi Bunshichi at Shōgenrō Restaurant in Ueno on 12 and 13 November 1892. 119 Ukiyo-e paintings; thirty-four prints. Many collectors' names given. Preface by Hayashi Tadamasa.

1893

Fenollosa, Ernest Francisco. *Special Exhibitions of the Pictorial Art of Japan and China, No. 1: Hokusai, and His School.* Boston, Museum of Fine Arts, 1893

No illustrations. Catalogue of 172 Boston Museum prints and paintings by Hokusai and pupils, '5 screens, some 65 other signed paintings, about 100 unsigned studies...'. Fenollosa wrote in the introduction, 'In fact, the true history of the course of changes in Hokusai's style must be founded primarily upon a study of his paintings rather than of his prints', and 'Even of the paintings and drawings available not more than half could be here shown'.

1896

Fenollosa, Ernest Francisco. *The Masters of Ukiyo-e. A Complete Historical Description of Japanese Prints and Color Prints of the Genre School as Shown in Exhibition at the Fine Arts Building.* New York, 1896

No illustrations. The first major general exhibition of Ukiyo-e paintings and prints in the USA, in which Fenollosa sets forth his canonical views: concerning Kiyonaga, 'We must now consider the work of a man [Kiyonaga] who, all things considered, is to be regarded as the central figure of Ukiyoe. All up to his central date is a rising curve; all afterward the gradual descent of decay'. It is logical to assume that the source of these works was the dealer Kobayashi Bunshichi; certainly he was the source of a second consignment brought over by Fenollosa in November 1896. The ownership of the second shipment (and perhaps the first too) was disputed in a legal case, Kobayashi v. Ketcham (Feb.–March 1898). Charles Freer purchased about thirty paintings from the 1896 catalogue when they were in the custody of the New York lawyer E. S. Hull in 1898. They are now in the Freer Gallery of Art, Washington, DC.

Goncourt, Edmond de. *Hokousaï.* Paris, Bibliothèque Charpentier, 1896

On pp. 268–325 Goncourt lists (but does not illustrate) all the Hokusai paintings and drawings known to him in Europe, the USA and Japan. Collectors' names given.

New York, American Art Association. *Rare lacquers, paintings, prints, etc. ... Messrs. Yamanaka & Co.* Auction cat., 12–14 March 1896.

1898

Fenollosa, Ernest Francisco. *Catalogue of the Exhibition of Ukiyo-e Paintings and prints, held at Ikao Onsen, Uyeno Shinzaka from April 15–May 15, 1898.* Tokyo, Kobayashi Bunshichi, 1898

Kobayashi Bunshichi. *Ukiyo-e tenrankai mokuroku,* 小林文七　浮世絵展覧会目録. Tokyo, 4/1898 (Japanese trans. of above, BK 20604/366/C3)

No illustrations. 241 paintings and prints. Fenollosa writes in the introduction, 'Last year Mr. Kobayashi Bunshichi held a public exhibition of Ukiyoe paintings, only, at the rooms of the Bijitsu Kiokwai at Uyeno' (no catalogue known); also, 'The difference between the New York exhibition [1896] and this one consists chiefly in the present far larger proportion of paintings'.

1901

Fenollosa, Ernest Francisco. *Catalogue of the Exhibition of Paintings of Hokusai held at the Japan Fine Art Association, Ueno Park from 13th to 30th January, 1900.* Tokyo, Kobayashi Bunshichi, 1901

Fifty illustrations. About 300 paintings and drawings by Hokusai and pupils (including some forgeries and works which should be reassigned to pupils). The nucleus of the exhibition was the Kobayashi and Homma Collections, the latter family being descendants of Hokusai's pupil Hokuyō, 北曜. At least twenty of these works were purchased by Freer.

1902

New York, American Art Association. *Rare old Japanese screens, Ukiyo-paintings, water colors, illustrated books ... Bunshichi Kobayashi, Tokyo.* Auction cat., 7–8 Jan. 1902

No illustrations. Includes '50 different sketches and drawings ... from a private collection of one of the pupils of the late Hokusai' and about 100 lots of Ukiyo-e paintings (including screens) with artists' names and brief title of each work.

1903

Paris, Hotel Drouot. *Collection Hayashi – objets d'art, deuxième partie.* Auction cat., 16–21 Feb. 1903

Several illustrations. 207 lots of Ukiyo-e paintings, including eighty-one by Hokusai and pupils. This is the sale at which Freer purchased the huge Utamaro painting of the brothel at Shinagawa.

1904

Paris, Galerie Durand-Ruel. *Collection Gillot – Objets d'art et peintures d'Exrême-Orient.* Auction cat., 8–13 Feb. 1904

Several illustrations. About fifty lots of Ukiyo-e paintings.

1906

Ikeda Seisuke. *The Ikeda Seisuke collection of kakemonos and screens,* Kyoto, 1906 (FR)

Sixty illustrations, many of Ukiyo-e paintings. Catalogue of 210 paintings, perhaps half Ukiyo-e.

Tajima, Shiichi (ed.). *Masterpieces Selected from the Ukiyoye School.* 5 vols, Tokyo, Shimbi shoin, 1906–9

Many colour woodcuts and collotypes, including Ukiyo-e paintings. Collectors' names given. At least one Japanese edition was issued: Shimbi shoin (eds), *Ukiyoe-ha gashū,* 審美書院編　浮世絵派画集. 5 vols, Tokyo, 2/1929–9/1930.

1908

New York, Yamanaka. *Catalogue of the exhibition of Ukiyo-e paintings and prints at Yamanaka Galleries,* by E. F. Fenollosa. Exh. cat., 27 Feb.–14 March 1908

No illustrations. Sales exhibition to celebrate the opening of the new Yamanaka galleries in New York. 156 Ukiyo-e paintings and prints described by Fenollosa.

Shimbi shoin (eds). *Tōyō bijutsu taikan,* 審美書院編　東洋美術大観. Tokyo, 8/1908–2/1912 (BK 790/1515/B2)

Colour woodblock or collotype illustrations. Ch. 5 of sect. 7 of vol. 6, 'Ukiyo-e' (1909), includes sixteen important Ukiyo-e paintings.

1910

Tajima Shiichi (ed.). *An Illustrated Catalogue of Japanese Old Fine Arts displayed at the Japan–British Exhibition, London 1910.* Tokyo, Shimbi shoin, 1910

Fifty-six illustrations of genre and Ukiyo-e paintings; 174 brief descriptions of genre and Ukiyo-e paintings. Collectors' names given: Fukuba Tōru, Homma Shichisō *et al.* Very major loan exhibition sponsored by the Japanese government. See Kuwabara Yōjirō (1911) below.

1911

Morrison, Arthur. *The Painters of Japan.* 2 vols, London, 1911

Illustrations of Ukiyo-e paintings now in the British Museum.

Conder, Josiah. *Paintings and Studies of Kawanabe Kyōsai.* Tokyo, Maruzen, 1911

Highly important not only for its many collotype illustrations but also for its eyewitness descriptions of Kyōsai's working methods.

Kuwabara Yōjirō (Fukuba Tōru). *Catalogue of Kuwabara's Collection of One Hundred Ukiyo-e Paintings.* London, 1911

One hundred small illustrations, with descriptions and dates. Kuwabara's collection was originally sent as part of the Japan–British Exhibition held at Shepherd's Bush in 1910. It then toured Stockholm (Royal Academy of Fine Arts, 15 Jan.–15 Feb. 1911) and Paris (Louvre, 24 Feb.–19 March 1911), and Swedish and French editions of the catalogue are known. Some copies include prices, suggesting it was a sales exhibition. However, most of the paintings seem to have returned to Japan and were photographed, together with others from this major early collection, at the Tokyo National Institute for Research into Cultural Properties (Kokuritsu Bunkazai Kenkyūjo) in Sept. 1933. In the short preface Kuwabara champions Ukiyo-e paintings and warns, 'Very few of these old paintings are exported, and frequently those sent abroad are counterfeits'.

Tanaka Masuzō (ed.). *Ukiyo-e gashū,* 田中増蔵 浮世絵画集. 3 vols, Tokyo, Shūseidō, 1911–13; repr. (2 vols) Tokyo, Yabuki Kōshōdō, 矢吹高尚堂, 11/1919

About 280 illustrations of genre and Ukiyo-e paintings (collectors' names given) based on an exhibition of women's fashions of the Edo period, *Tokugawa jidai fujin fūzoku,* 徳川時代婦人風俗, held at the Tokyo Imperial Museum in 1911.

Kyoto, Yamato-e Kyōkai (eds). *Dai-ikkai nikuhitsu hanga tenran mokuroku,* 京都大和絵協会 第一回肉筆版画展覧目録. Kyoto, Geisōdō, 7/1911

Fifty Ukiyo-e paintings (illustrated, collectors' names given) and 112 prints (some illustrated). First exhibition of works belonging to Kansai collectors organised by the Kyoto Yamato-e Kyōkai, 15–17 Apr. 1911, in the Kyoto Municipal Library. The preface promises that a second exhibition will be held.

1912

Kyoto, Yamato-e Kyōkai (eds). *Dai-nikai nikuhitsu hanga tenrankai mokuroku,* 京都大和絵協会

第二回肉筆版画展覧会目録. 1912

Listed in UBM.

1914

Kawasaki Hōtarō (ed.). *Chōshunkaku kanshō,* 川崎芳太郎 長春閣鑑賞. 6 vols, Tokyo, Kokkasha, 12/1914 (BK 2650/B7)

Includes illustrations of some important Ukiyo-e paintings. No collectors' names given.

1916

Kyoto Hakubutsukan (eds). *Kobijutsuhin zuroku,* 京都博物館 古美術品図録. 5 vols, Kyoto, Benridō, 4/1916

Vol. 3 (of 5) includes illustrations of fifteen Ukiyo-e paintings and lists a total of forty-two. Collectors' names given, mainly Kansai. Apparently the catalogue of a major exposition held at the Kyoto Imperial Museum, some editions having the title *Kyoto hakurankai chinretsuhin sōmoku.*

1917

Kitamura Suzuna (ed.). *Kodai fūzoku gashū,* 北村鈴菜 古代風俗画集. Kyoto, Geisōdō, 7/1917 (KT 147/181)

Illustrations of ninety-two Ukiyo-e paintings. Collectors' names given: Takeoka Toyota *et al.* Exhibition held at Osaka, Mitsukoshi Department Store, in Jan. 1917. Includes the nine drawings of *sumō* wrestlers by Sharaku, owned by Kobayashi Bunshichi, which were subsequently lost in the great Tokyo earthquake.

Kusano Morindo (ed.). *(Kokusui) Ukiyo-e kessaku shū,* 草野守人 国粋浮世絵傑作集. Tokyo, Kokusuisha, 9/1917 (KT411/53)

About 120 illustrations of Ukiyo-e paintings. No collectors' names given; some now TNM. Some of dubious quality/authenticity.

Tokyo, Bijutsu Kurabu. *Itō Daihachi,* 東京美術倶楽部 伊藤大八. Auction cat., 29 Nov. 1917

Lot nos 57–64, 211–45 are Ukiyo-e paintings.

1918

Takeoka Toyota ihin ten, 武岡豊太遺品展. Kobe, 1918, sales exh.

Listed in UBM.

1919

Takeoka Toyota (ed.). *Yamato-e,* 武岡豊太 やまとゑ. Kyoto, Gabundō, 1919 (HYC J6285/4224)

About 120 Ukiyo-e paintings (seventy-eight illustrated). Collectors' names given. Exhibited at Ōta Shinjirō's 太田新次郎 (?)shop in Kobe, Motomachi, on 8–9 March 1919, as the twelfth meeting of the Kobe Yamato-e Kyōkai, of which Takeoka Toyota was chairman.

Yoshikawa Kambō (ed.) *Nikuhitsu ukiyo-e kankōkai gashū,* 吉川観方 肉筆浮世絵刊行会画集. 1919

Listed in UBM.

Yuasa Hangetsu. *Shoga gambutsu katari,* 湯浅半月 書画贋物語. Nishōdō, 2/1919

Listed in UBM.

Saitō Ryūzō (ed.). *Shinko gasui,* 斉藤隆三 新古画粋. 15 vols, Tokyo, Shinko Gasuisha, 12/1919 (KT 421/1; BK T.8.12/20563/C3)

Issue no. 10 of this magazine includes photographs of ten Ukiyo-e paintings. Collectors' names given.

1921

Iwasaki (eds). *Seikadō kanshō,* 岩崎家 静嘉堂鑑賞. 5 vols, 1921 (BK 3101/B7)

Includes illustrations of the Ukiyo-e paintings in Baron Iwasaki's collection, now in the Seikado Foundation, Tokyo.

Kyoto, Yamato-e Kyōkai. *Dai-sankai nikuhitsu hanga tenrankai mokuroku,* 京都大和絵協会 第三回肉筆版画展覧会目録. 1921

Listed in UBM.

1922

Loewenstein, Fritz E. *Die Handzeichnungen der Japanischen Holzschnittmeister.* Plauen im Vogtland, C. F. Schulz & Co., 1922

Pioneering study of preparatory drawings for Ukiyo-e woodblock prints. Thirty illustrations. Collectors' names given.

1923

Gookin, F. W. 'Japanese paintings and prints', Art Institute of Chicago *Bulletin,* XVII (1923), 53–5

Kyoto, Teishitsu Hakubutsukan. *Ukiyo-e shūei,* 京都帝室博物館 浮世絵聚英. Kyoto, Benridō, 4/1923 (RL AA109.1/K.m.)

Illustrations of seventy Ukiyo-e paintings, selected from the 100 from the collection of Takeoka Toyota, 武岡豊太, exhibited at the Kyoto Imperial Museum in Apr. 1923. Very fine paintings from one of the largest Kansai collections of the time.

1924

Yoshida Kitarō (ed.). *Nikuhitsu ukiyo-e (Kishida Ryūsei-shi hizō hin),* 吉田喜太郎 肉筆浮世絵 岸田劉生氏秘蔵品. 2 vols, Kyoto, Higashiyama shobō, 8/1924 (KT 333/90)

Albums pasted with photographs of about twenty early genre paintings which belonged to Kishida Ryūsei.

1926

Nihon Bijutsu Kyōkai (eds). *Keichō/Kan'ei fūzoku gashū,* 日本美術協会 慶長・寛永風俗画集. Tokyo, Gahōsha, 1926.

1927

Hoshino ?Seki (ed.). *Sesshoku ukiyo-e hyaku-sugata, zempen,* 星野錫 設色浮世絵百姿・前編. Tokyo, Gahōsha, 4/1927

Includes illustrations of about fifty Ukiyo-e paintings in colour. Collectors' names given. Preface by Fujikake Shizuya, 藤懸静也.

243

1928

Yoshioka Hanrei (ed.). *Shingi hyōka shoga kantei shishin*, 吉岡班嶺　真偽評価書画鑑定指針. Tokyo, Teikoku Kaiga Kyōkai, 1928
A series of thirty guides to auction prices fetched by various categories of works of art at the Tokyo Bijutsu Kurabu during Taishō. The volume for Ukiyo-e painting includes facsimile seal impressions; details about the major paintings by each artist sold at the Tokyo Bijutsu Kurabu during Taishō (including vendors' names); photographs of about fifty selected paintings.

Gookin, F. W. 'Two ukiyo-e paintings', Art Institute of Chicago *Bulletin* (Jan. 1928), 4–6
Short article about two *bijin* paintings by Eishi and Shunshō in the Buckingham Collection.

Tanaka Kisaku (ed.). *Shoki ukiyo-e senshū*, 田中喜作　初期浮世絵選集. Tokyo, Shurakusha, 4/1928
Large folio with collotypes of twenty-one genre screens (with details). Limited edition of 100 copies.

Hōchi Shimbunsha (eds). *Tokugawa jidai kakuha meisaku: ukiyo-e gashū*, 報知新聞社　徳川時代各派名作・浮世絵画集. n.p., Kōgeisha, 6/1928 (BK 1213/C3; KT 333/116; TC)
Includes photographs of about sixty-five Ukiyo-e paintings. Collectors' names given. This exhibition, held at the Tokyo-fu Bijutsukan, 6–25 June 1928, was reviewed in English in the *Yearbook of Japanese Art* (1928), pp. 58–64.

1929

Maeda Seison (ed.). *Nihon fūzokuga taisei 4: Toyotomi jidai*, 前田青邨　日本風俗画大成 4　豊臣時代. Tokyo, Chūō Bijutsusha, 3/1929
Sixty-four examples of Momoyama genre painting. Collectors' names given.

Kikuchi Keigetsu (ed.). *Nihon fūzokuga taisei 5: Tokugawa jidai shoki*, 菊地契月　日本風俗画大成 5　徳川時代初期. Tokyo, Chūō Bijutsusha, 4/1929
Sixty-five genre and Ukiyo-e paintings to *c*. Kambun (1660s). Collectors' names given.

Kaburagi Kiyokata (ed.). *Nihon fūzokuga taisei 6: Tokugawa jidai chūki*, 鏑木清方　日本風俗画大成 6　徳川時代中期. Tokyo, Chūō Bijutsusha, 8/1929
Sixty-four Ukiyo-e paintings of the period Itchō–Toyohiro. Collectors' names given.

Hirafuku Hyakusui. *Nihon fūzokuga taisei 7: Tokugawa jidai kōki*, 平福百穂　日本風俗画大成 7　徳川時代後期. Tokyo, Chūō Bijutsusha, 7/1929
Sixty-two Ukiyo-e paintings of the period Utamaro–Eizan. Collectors' names given.

1930

Yoshida Teruji (ed.). *Ukiyo-e taisei*, 吉田暎二　浮世絵大成. 12 vols, Tokyo, Tōhō shoin, 1930–1
Each volume includes a few illustrations of Ukiyo-e paintings; but mainly prints. No collectors' names given.

Tokyo, Teishitsu Hakubutsukan (eds). *Ukiyo-e tenrankai zuroku*, 帝室博物館　浮世絵展覧会図録. Tokyo, Ōtsuka Kōgeisha, 9/1930 (BK 1475/3021/4301/C3; KT 424/59)
Illustrations of seventy-five Ukiyo-e paintings. Collectors' names given. Text by Fujikake Shizuya. Strong on early eighteenth century, particularly Kaigetsudō.

1931

Ukiyo-e taika shūsei, 浮世絵大家集成. 20 vols, Tokyo, Ōhōkaku shobō, 1931–2

Ukiyo-e Kenkyūkai (eds). *Ukiyo-e gashū*, 浮世絵研究会　浮世絵画集. Tokyo, Ohōkaku, 3/1931 (KT 424/78)
Ukiyo-e prints and paintings and genre paintings. No collectors' names given.

1932

Iizuka Beiu. *Nihonga taisei 18: Fūzokuga*, 飯塚米雨　日本画大成18　風俗画. Tokyo, Tōhō shoin, 8/1932
132 genre paintings. Some collectors' names given.

Uemura and Takamizawa Tadao (eds). *Kinsei Nihonga taikan 4: shoki fūzokuga*, 近世日本画大観 4　初期風俗画. Tokyo, Takamizawa Mokuhan Sha, 8/1932

Kyoto, Hakubutsukan (eds). *Nikuhitsu ukiyo-e shū*, 京都博物館　肉筆浮世絵聚. Kyoto, Geisōdō, 1932 (KT 430/59)
Illustrations of forty-three Ukiyo-e and genre paintings. Collectors' names given.

Hōchi Shimbunsha (eds). *Nikuhitsu ukiyo-e senshū*, 報知新聞社　肉筆浮世絵選集. Tokyo, Kōgeisha, 1932 (SP ND/1052/.N45; KT 245/56)
167 illustrations of Ukiyo-e paintings. Collectors' names given. Many Kaigetsudō paintings.

Kyoto, Hakubutsukan (eds). *Nikuhitsu ukiyo-e tenrankai mokuroku*, 京都博物館　肉筆浮世絵展覧会目録. 1932
Listed in UBM.

Shimizu Gensendō (ed.). *Ukiyo-e nikuhitsu Ōtsu-e chinretsu tenrankai mokuroku*, 清水源泉堂　浮世絵肉筆大津絵陳列展覧会目録. 1932
Listed in UBM.

Tokyo, Ukiyo-e Kyōkai. *Ukiyo-e sōgōten zuroku*, 浮世絵協会　浮世絵総合展図録. Tokyo, Shichijō Shoin, 5/1932 (BK)
Illustrations of forty Ukiyo-e paintings, including several Yata-esque fakes, and thirty prints. Collectors' names given. Edited by Kaneko Fusui, 金子孚水.

1933

Kyoto Hakubutsukan. *Nikuhitsu ukiyo-e taikan*, 京都博物館　肉筆浮世絵大観. Kyoto, Benridō, 1/1933 (BK 2786/C3; LC f7 NE1310/K9; BM 1935–6–5–01)
Sixty-six illustrations of Ukiyo-e paintings exhibited at the Kyoto Museum. Collectors' names given.

Iizuka Beiu. *Nihonga taisei 40: Nikuhitsu ukiyo-e I*, 飯塚米雨　日本画大成40　肉筆浮世絵 1. Tokyo, Tōhō shoin, 8/1933
167 Ukiyo-e paintings (Moronobu–Masanobu). Some collectors' names given.

Kyoto Hakubutsukan. *Semmen gafu: Kōnoike Danshaku-ke zō*, 京都博物館　扇面画譜　鴻池男爵家蔵. Kyoto, Geisōdō, 8/1933 (BK 19752/C3)
Includes illustrations of twenty Ukiyo-e fan paintings from the Kōnoike Collection (see also Tokyo, Ōta Kinen Bijutsukan 1981).

Tokyo, Nihon Bijutsu Kyōkai. *Jidai byōbu ukiyo-e rimpa tenrankai*, 日本美術協会　時代屏風浮世絵琳派展覧会. 12/1933
Exhibition of 100 lots of Ukiyo-e paintings (eighteen illustrated) and 144 lots of ex-Bigelow Ukiyo-e paintings (thirty-three illustrated) owned by Yamanaka & Co. at the Nihon Bijutsu Kyōkai, Tokyo, 1–5 Dec. 1933.

Tokyo, Bijutsu Kurabu. *Ko-Bigerō-shi iaihin ukiyo-e oyobi Shijō-ha gafuku nyūsatsu*, 東京美術倶楽部　故ビゲロー氏遺愛品浮世絵及四條派画幅入札. Auction cat., 11 Dec. 1933
192 lots of Ukiyo-e paintings (seventy illustrated) formerly in the Bigelow Collection, de-accessioned from the Museum of Fine Arts, Boston.

1934

Iizuka Beiu. *Nihonga taisei 41: nikuhitsu ukiyo-e II*, 飯塚米雨　日本画大成41　肉筆浮世絵 2. Tokyo, Tōhō shoin, 2/1934
Illustrations of 161 Ukiyo-e paintings from the period of Kaigetsudō–Masayoshi, including Shunshō, Utamaro *et al.* Some collectors' names given.

Tokyo Bijutsu Kurabu. *Shumpōan jūshū ukiyo-e kane bō-ke shizōhin tenkan nyūsatsu zuroku*, 東京美術倶楽部　春峯庵什襲浮世絵并某家斯蔵品展観入札図録. Auction cat., 12–14 May 1934
Twenty-two lots of forged Ukiyo-e paintings produced by the Yata family and offered for sale in conspiracy with the scholar Kaneko Fusui and the dealer Shimizu Naoji. The family also produced many more forgeries which are not included in this catalogue. The scandal cast a long shadow over the study of Ukiyo-e painting for many decades.

Sasakawa Rimpū. *Shumpōan kahōshū*, 笹川臨風　春峯庵華宝集. Tokyo, Kokindō, 5/1934 (KT 425/112)
A de luxe edition of the Shumpōan auction catalogue of forged Ukiyo-e paintings, with accompanying essays by the scholar Sasakawa Rimpū.

1936

Osaka Bijutsu Kurabu. *Jidai kinshū kodai ningyō maki-e mono nikuhitsu ukiyo-e tenrankai*, 大阪美術倶楽部 時代綿繍古代人形蒔絵物肉筆浮世絵展覧会 Sales exh., Yamanaka & Co., 12–14 May 1936
114 lots of Ukiyo-e paintings (fourteen illustrated), including some dubious-looking examples.

1938

Osaka Shiritsu Bijutsukan. *Nikuhitsu ukiyo-e senshū*, 大阪市立美術館 肉筆浮世絵選集 Kyoto, Geisōdō, 1938 (KT 755/3)
Album of thirty plates of Ukiyo-e paintings from an exhibition held 12–27 March 1938. No collectors' names given.

1939

Hirano Chie. *Kiyonaga: A Study of his Life and Works*. 2 vols, Cambridge, Mass., Harvard University Press, 1939
A *catalogue raisonné* of Kiyonaga's works, including thirty-two paintings.

1943

Fujikake Shizuya. *Ukiyo-e no kenkyū*, 藤懸静也 浮世絵の研究. 3 vols, Tokyo, Yūzankaku, 1943
A classic, integrated study of Ukiyo-e, illustrating some paintings. Collectors' names given.

1948

Kokusuisha (eds). *Genshoku nikuhitsu ukiyo-e shū*, 国粋社 原色肉筆浮世絵集. Tokyo, Kokusuisha, 1948 (SP ND/1052/G4)
About fifty illustrations of Ukiyo-e paintings. Collectors' names given.

1957

Tokyo Kokuritsu Hakubutsukan. *Catalogue of an Exhibition of Early Genre Paintings held at the Tokyo National Museum*. Tokyo, 1957
Seventy-eight important early genre paintings (forty-four illustrated).

Yata Michio. 'Shinsetsu shumpōan gisaku jiken', 矢田三千男 真説春峯庵偽作事件. *Geijutsu shinchō*, 芸術新潮. Vol. 8, no. 12
An account by one of the principal figures involved in the Shumpōan forged Ukiyo-e painting scandal of 1934.

1958

Stern, Harold P. 'Ukiyo-e Painting: Selected Problems', Ph.D. dissertation, University of Michigan, 1958
Stern's approach is to discuss in chronological order selected paintings from the collection of the Freer Gallery of Art.

1959

Lane, Richard. *Kaigetsudō* (Kodansha Library of Japanese Art, vol. 13). Tokyo and Rutland, Vermont, Charles E. Tuttle, 1959
Useful survey of the work of the Kaigetsudō atelier, including forty-one small plates, mainly of paintings. Collectors' names given.

1960

Endō Kintarō. *Hiroshige e-nikki I*, 遠藤金太郎 広重絵日記 1. Tokyo, Bijutsu Shuppansha, 1960
Forged sketchbooks purporting to have been done by Hiroshige during trips along the Tōkaidō and Kisokaidō Highways.

1961

Kirby, John B. 'A painting by the Japanese print artist Shunshō', Worcester Art Museum *Annual*, vol. IX (1961), 29–31.

Kondō Ichitarō. *Japanese Genre Painting: The Lively Art of Renaissance Japan*. Rutland, Vermont and Tokyo, Tuttle, 1961
Account of early genre painting; 119 illustrations.

1962

Tokyo, Nihombashi Mitsukoshi. *Ukiyo-e nikuhitsu meisaku ten*, 東京日本橋三越 浮世絵肉筆名作展. Tokyo, Mainichi Shimbunsha, 1962
Exhibition of seventy-three fine Ukiyo-e paintings (all illustrated) from the former Kanda Raizō, 神田雷蔵, collection which then passed into the possession of Ōtani Takayoshi, 大谷孝吉. (see 3/1980).

Nihon Ukiyo-e Kyōkai (eds). *Ukiyo-e geijutsu*, 日本浮世絵協会篇 浮世絵芸術. Vols 1–present; Tokyo, 1962–present
Journal of the Japan Ukiyo-e Society, which has not traditionally included many articles on Ukiyo-e painting, though more since issue 84, when the editorship was taken over by Asano Shūgō.

Yoshida Teruji and Kaneko Fusui (eds). *Kikan ukiyo-e* ('The Ukiyo-e Quarterly'), 吉田暎二 金子孚水 季刊浮世絵, 100 issues, Tokyo, Rokuen Shobō, then Gabundō, 1962–85
Frequent articles on Ukiyo-e painting, often of the erotic subjects particularly featured by this journal. From no. 1 to no. 5 Kaneko Fusui ran a series 'Shimbutsu to nisemono' ('Genuine and Fake') in which he tried to show genuine and forged versions of paintings. His assumption seemed to be that there was only one version of each, and the 'genuine' paintings he introduced sometimes appear dubious. From issue 38 to issue 88 Richard Lane ran a series of twenty-three articles, 'A Gallery of Ukiyo-e Paintings [Abroad]'.

Nagasaki Shiritsu Hakubutsukan. *Ukiyo-e nikuhitsu meisaku ten*, 長崎市立博物館 浮世絵肉筆名作展. Exh. cat., 11/10–19/10 1962
Selection of seventy-five paintings made by Kaneko Fusui. Collectors' names not given but includes works belonging to Yawata Yōtarō and Ujiie Takeo.

Narazaki Muneshige and Kikuchi Sadao. *Nikuhitsu ukiyo-e*, 楢崎宗重 菊地貞夫 肉筆浮世絵. 2 vols, Tokyo, Kōdansha, 1962–3
Major study, reproducing 119 genre and Ukiyo-e paintings (vol. 1) and 106 colour and 110 black and white Ukiyo-e paintings (vol. 2). Some collectors' names given.

1963

Palm Beach, Society of the Four Arts. *Japanese Paintings from the Frank E. Hart Collection*. Exh. cat., 2–24 Feb. 1963
Lists seventy-eight Ukiyo-e paintings, of which eighteen are illustrated.

1964

Kaneko Fusui. *Ukiyo-e nikuhitsu gashū*, 金子孚水 浮世絵肉筆画集. 3 vols, Tokyo, Rokuen shobō, 1964
Vol. 1 has not been examined; vol. 2 reproduces sixty-two Ukiyo-e paintings, with details of signatures and seals; vol. 3 ninety-six paintings. Some of the works, particularly those of the Hokusai school, appear of dubious authenticity.

Tokyo Shinjuku Isetan. *Nikuhitsu ukiyo-e meisaku ten*. 東京新宿伊勢丹 肉筆浮世絵名作展. Tokyo, 1964
139 Ukiyo-e paintings, mostly illustrated. Collectors' names given. Exhibition held to mark the Tokyo Olympics, 8–18 Oct. 1964.

Bowie, Theodore. *The Drawings of Hokusai*, Bloomington, Indiana University Press, 1964

1965

Shirasaki Hideo. 'Shumpōan jiken' in *Shingan*, 白崎秀雄 春峯庵事件 真贋. Tokyo, Kōdansha, 1965
Investigative account of the 1934 Shumpōan forged Ukiyo-e painting incident.

1966

Kanazawa, Ishikawa Kenritsu Bijutsukan. *Ukiyo-e bijinga ten*, 石川県立美術館 浮世絵美人画展. Exh. cat., 5–27 March 1966
Fifty-five Ukiyo-e paintings mostly illustrated. Some collectors' names given, including examples from the ex-Sugawara and Tokyo National Museum collections. Introduced by Kikuchi Sadao.

Ithaca, White Art Museum, Cornell University. *Japanese Painters of the Floating World*. Exh. cat., April–June 1966
Eighty-two important Ukiyo-e paintings (mostly illustrated) from USA museum and private collections (excluding Freer Gallery and Boston Museum of Fine Arts). Collectors' names given. Notes and commentary by Martie W. Young and Robert J. Smith. See review by Richard Lane (1968) below.

Paris, Musée du Louvre. *Images du Temps qui Passe*. Exh. cat., 1 June–30 Oct. 1966
See review by Richard Lane (1968) below.

Hillier, Jack. *Hokusai Drawings*. London, Phaidon, 1966
110 drawings and paintings by Hokusai and his school. Collectors' names given.

Hillier, Jack (1966a). *Japanese Drawings from the 17th through the 19th Century*. Boston, Little, Brown and Co., 1966
About half the small paintings and preparatory drawings are by Ukiyo-e artists. Collectors' names given.

1967

'т'. 'Shumpōan jiken zuroku: shōkai to bunseki', 春峯庵事件図録紹介と分析. *Ukiyo-e*, 浮世絵 30 (1967), 57–67
An introduction to the Shumpōan forged Ukiyo-e painting catalogue (see 12–14 May 1934 above) showing how the forgers copied or combined existing Ukiyo-e paintings and prints to devise many of their compositions. The identity of the author 'т' is not known to me.

1968

Narazaki Muneshige, 'Kabu yūen zu', 楢崎宗重 歌舞遊宴図. *Kokka*, 国華 912 (March 1968), 28.

Lane, Richard. 'Ukiyo-e paintings abroad', *Monumenta Nipponica*. Vol. xxiii, nos 1–2 (1968), 190–207
Highly significant review article and essay in which the author discusses recent exhibitions and catalogues on Ukiyo-e painting, with particular emphasis on issues of attribution and forgery.

Narazaki Muneshige. *Masterworks of Ukiyo-e: Early Paintings*. Tokyo, Kōdansha International, 1968
Fifty-nine important genre and early Ukiyo-e paintings reproduced in colour with commentaries and a short introduction by Narazaki Muneshige.

1969

Nagoya Meitetsu Hyakkaten. *Ukiyo-e nikuhitsu meisaku ten*, 名古屋名鉄 浮世絵肉筆名作展. Exh. cat., 3–8 Oct. 1969
Exhibition organised by the Ukiyo-e Society of Japan.

Tokyo Nihombashi Mitsukoshi. *Shoki nikuhitsu ukiyo-e byōbu*, 東京日本橋三越 初期肉筆浮世絵屏風 Exh. cat., 1969

Kaneko Fusui. *Ukiyo-e nikuhitsu meihin gashū*, 金子孚水 浮世絵肉筆名品画集. Tokyo, Gabundo, 1969
Catalogue of the Kobayashi Wasaku, 小林和作 Collection of Ukiyo-e paintings.

Narazaki Muneshige (ed.). *Zaigai hihō 3: Nikuhitsu ukiyo-e*, 楢崎宗重 在外秘宝3 肉筆浮世絵. Tokyo, Gakken, 1969
Major study of Ukiyo-e paintings in Western collections, chiefly in USA, including some from the Boston Museum of Fine Arts and Freer Gallery collections.

Nagasaki Kenritsu Bijutsu Hakubutsukan. *Nikuhitsu ukiyo-e bijinga ten*, 長崎県立美術博物館 肉筆浮世絵美人画展. Exh. cat., 15–30 March 1969

Tokyo, Gotō Bijutsukan. *Nikuhitsu Katsushika Hokusai ten*, 五島美術館 肉筆葛飾北斎展. Exh. cat., 16 Dec. 1969–12 April 1970
124 paintings, drawings and books by Hokusai, including some material from Obuse whose authenticity is doubtful. Text by Kaneko Fusui.

1970

Kobe, Sannomiya Sogō. *Kinsei shoki fūzokuga meisaku ten*, 神戸三ノ宮そごう 近世初期風俗画名作展. Exh. cat., 13–25 March 1970
Twenty-six examples of genre screens.

Tokyo, Tōbu Hyakkaten. *Fūzoku byōbu meihin ten*, 東京東武 風俗屏風名品展. Exh. cat., 9–21 June 1970
Forty-one examples (illustrated) of early genre screens in an exhibition organised by Nihon Fūzokushi Gakkai, 日本風俗史学会. Some collectors' names given.

Toyama Kenritsu Bijutsukan. *Nikuhitsu ukiyo-e to kamen ten*, 富山県立美術館 肉筆浮世絵と仮面展. Exh. cat., 10–27 Oct. 1970.

Narazaki Muneshige and Yoshida Teruji. *Nikuhitsu ukiyo-e*, 楢崎宗重／吉田暎二 肉筆浮世絵. Tokyo, Kōdansha, 1970
133 colour plates and 100+ figures of Ukiyo-e paintings. No collectors' names given.

Hillier, Jack. *Catalogue of the Japanese Paintings and Prints in the Collection of Mr & Mrs Richard P. Gale*, 2 vols, London, Routledge & Kegan Paul, 1970
Includes about sixty genre and Ukiyo-e paintings, now in the collection of the Minneapolis Institute of Arts. Provenance given where known.

Hillier, Jack. *The Harari Collection of Japanese Paintings and Drawings*, 3 vols, London, Lund Humphries, 1970–3
Vol. 1 100 genre and Ukiyo-e paintings and drawings; vol. 2 184 paintings and drawings by Hokusai and pupils and Hiroshige; vol. 3 other schools. Provenance given where known.

1971

Narazaki Muneshige, 'Kabu yūen zu', 楢崎宗重 歌舞遊宴図. *Kokka*, 国華 938 (1971), 23–4.

Jenkins, Donald. *Ukiyo-e Prints and Paintings: The Primitive Period, 1680–1745*. Chicago, Art Institute, 1971
An exhibition which admirably integrated early prints and thirty-four paintings, mainly from USA collections.

Haifa, Tikotin Museum of Japanese Art. *Exhibition of Genre Paintings*. March–May 1971
Thirty-one examples, all illustrated, of genre and Ukiyo-e paintings from the Tikotin Collection.

1972

Tokyo, Idemitsu Biijutsukan. *Shoki fūzokuga to nikuhitsu ukiyo-e ten zuroku*, 出光美術館

初期風俗画と肉筆浮世絵図録. Exh. cat., 7–30 Jan. 1972

Tokyo Hagurodō. *Ukiyo-e nikuhitsu meihin ten*, 羽黒堂 浮世絵肉筆名品展. Sales exh., 18–23 Apr. ?1972
Hagurodō sales exhibition held at Tokyo, Nihombashi Mitsukoshi, in the year of its 300th anniversary. 237 items of varying quality.

Tokyo Ueno Matsuzakaya. *Nikuhitsu ukiyo e shūsaku ten*, 東京上野松坂屋 肉筆浮世絵秀作展. Exh. cat., 11–16 Jan. 1972
Thirty-six genre screens and Ukiyo-e paintings selected by Narazaki Muneshige and exhibited to commemorate the sixtieth anniversary of the Ukiyo-e Society of Japan.

Tokyo Suntory Bijutsukan. *Kambun bijin*, サントリー美術館 寛文美人. Exh. cat., 19 Feb.–19 March 1972
Thirty-seven paintings of beauties dating from around the Kambun era (1661–73). Collectors' names given.

1973

Tokyo Shinjuku Isetan. *Nihon no bijinga ten*, 東京新宿伊勢丹 日本の美人画展. Exh. cat., 23–28 Jan. 1973
Seventy-two examples of paintings of beauties through the Ukiyo-e tradition to the twentieth century from the Fukutomi Tarō, 福富太郎 Collection.

Stern, Harold P. *Ukiyo-e Painting*, Washington, DC, Freer Gallery of Art, 1973
117 important genre and Ukiyo-e paintings and drawings from the collection of the Freer Gallery of Art described in detail by Harold Stern. An international symposium on Ukiyo-e painting was held in conjunction with this exhibition.

Aoki Shinsaburō. *Ukiyo-e tekagami*, 青木進三郎 浮世絵手鑑. Tokyo, Ōtsuka Kōgeisha, 1973.

Narazaki Muneshige (ed.). *Kinsei fūzoku zukan*, 楢崎宗重 近世風俗図巻. 3 vols, Tokyo, Mainichi Shimbunsha, 1973–4
Vol. 1 gives complete reproductions (with commentary) of handscrolls by Moronobu; Itchō (2); Chōshun; Eishun; Suiō; Eishi. Vol. 2 not examined. Vol. 3 contains handscrolls by Matabei (3); Moronobu; Chōshun (2); Itchō (3); Kyōden; Masayoshi.

1974

Kamakura Kokuhōkan. *Ujiie ukiyo-e korekushon*, 鎌倉国宝館 氏家浮世絵コレクション. Kamakura, 1974
Very important collection of seventy-three Ukiyo-e paintings. Another edition was published when the collection was exhibited at the Osaka Shiritsu Bijutsukan, 15 Apr.–8 May 1977.

Tokyo, Hagurodō. 'Ukiyo-e nikuhitsu meihin ten', 羽黒堂 浮世絵肉筆名品展. *Kyūbi*, 求美 20 (summer 1974), 107–225

Sales exhibition at Tokyo, Nihombashi Mitsukoshi, 13–18 Aug. 1974. 363 items (145 illustrated).

1975

Tokyo, Hagurodō. *Ukiyo-e nikuhitsu ten*, 羽黒堂　浮世絵肉筆展．Sales exh., 11–16 March 1975
Hagurodō sales exhibition held at Tokyo, Shinjuku Mitsukoshi. 173 Ukiyo-e paintings.

Narazaki Muneshige. 'Hishikawa Moronobu hitsu hokurō oyobi engeki zukan ni tsuite', 楢崎宗重 菱川師宣筆北楼及び演劇図巻について *Kokka*, 国華 980 (June 1975), pp. 9–12

Nagoya, Meitetsu. *Nikuhitsu ukiyo-e meihin shū*, 名古屋名鉄　肉筆浮世絵名品集．Exh. cat., 29 Aug.–3 Sept. 1975
Exhibition of 179 Ukiyo-e paintings from the Shibatsuji Yasukichi Collection organised by the Fuji Art Co., Tokyo.

Tokyo Gotō Bijutsukan. *Genroku no ukiyo-e*, 五島美術館　元禄の浮世絵．Exh. cat., 17 Oct.–24 Nov. 1975
Illustrations of fifty-seven paintings, mainly by Moronobu and Itchō.

1976

Kikuchi Sadao. *Idemitsu Bijutsukan sensho 9: Nikuhitsu ukiyo-e*, 菊地貞夫　出光美術館選書 9 肉筆浮世絵．Tokyo, Idemitsu Bijutsukan 1976
Essay about the history of Ukiyo-e painting with ninety-five small black and white illustrations (collectors' names given – many of the paintings from the Idemitsu Gallery's collection); then sixty-two larger plates (some in colour) of the major paintings.

Tokyo Suntory Bijutsukan. *Kinsei fūzokuga*, サントリー美術館　近代風俗画．Exh. cat., 16 Nov. 1976–23 Jan. 1977
An exhibition divided into two parts: genre scenes set in landscapes; and scenes of everyday life and pleasures. Includes some important examples of genre and Ukiyo-e painting.

Chiba, Sogō. *Hishikawa Moronobu ten*, 千葉そごう 菱川師宣展．Exh. cat., 12–17 March 1976
Fifty-five paintings and twenty prints by Moronobu and his school. No collectors' names given.

1977

Osaka Shiritsu Bijutsukan. *Ujiie korekushon o chūshin to shita nikuhitsu ukiyo-e*, 大阪市立美術館 氏家コレクションを中心とした肉筆浮世絵．Exh. cat., 15 Apr.–8 May 1977
100 Ukiyo-e paintings; seventy-three from the Ujiie Collection (1974) and twenty-seven from miscellaneous other collections. No collectors' names given.

Tokyo Ikebukuro Mitsukoshi. *Nikuhitsu ukiyo-e meihin ten*, 東京池袋三越　肉筆浮世絵名品展．Exh. cat., 14–19 June 1977
Catalogue of the Kaneko Fusui, 金子学水, Collection by Kaneko Fusui and Aoki Shinsaburō, 青木進三郎．

Brandt, Klaus J. *Hosoda Eishi 1756–1829*. Stuttgart, K. J. Brandt, 1977
Catalogue raisonné of Eishi and pupils' prints and some (perhaps half?) of their large *oeuvre* of paintings. Brandt was forced to rely on illustrations in old catalogues as the source for many paintings. Hence he was not able to be as critical in his categorising of forgeries as one would have hoped. See review by Roger Keyes in *Andon*, 3 (1981), 84–7; 4 (1981), 114–20.

Kaneko Fusui. *Nikuhitsu ukiyo-e shūsei*, 金子学水 肉筆浮世絵集成 2 vols, Tokyo, Mainichi Shimbunsha, 1977
Ukiyo-e paintings in Japanese collections. Vol. 1 includes 285 paintings illustrated in colour; vol. 2 has 208 paintings in black and white, Ōtsu-e, and a special 'fakes' section of seven items (including some forgeries by the Yata family from the 1930s).

1978

Mizuo Hiroshi. 'Gion saireizu byōbu', 水尾比呂志　祇園祭礼図屏風 *Kokka*, 国華 1010 (1978), 29–36
A pair of Kanō screens from *c.* 1650 showing the Gion Festival in Kyoto.

Tokyo, Kinryūzan Sensōji. *Ema zuroku*, 金龍山浅草寺　絵馬図録．Tokyo, Kinryūzan Sensōji, 1978
Fifty-six votive plaques preserved at the Asakusa Kannon Temple, Tokyo, including important examples by Ukiyo-e artists.

1979

Lane, Richard. *The Early Shunga Scroll*. Tokyo, Gabundō, 1979
Bilingual text of articles extracted from the journal *Ukiyo-e* for the years 1963–78. Important *shunga* (erotic) handscrolls from the seventeenth and early eighteenth centuries.

Tokyo Hagurodō. *Ukiyo-e nikuhitsu meihin ten*, 羽黒堂　浮世絵肉筆名品展．Sales exh.. 23–28 Oct. 1979
Hagurodō sales exhibition at Tokyo Ikebukuro Mitsukoshi; 206 Ukiyo-e paintings and drawings.

Gulik, Willem R. van. 'Scroll paintings in the Von Siebold collection', in *A Sheaf of Japanese Papers*. The Hague, Society for Japanese Arts and Crafts, 1979
Genre and Ukiyo-e paintings (fifteen illustrated) from the Siebold Collection, acquired before 1826.

Kuhne, Hellmut. 'Some notes on an early theatrical byōbu', in *A Sheaf of Japanese Papers*. The Hague, Society for Japanese Arts and Crafts, 1979

Nara, Kenritsu Bijutsukan. *Zōhin zuroku daini-shū: kaiga-hen I*, 奈良県立美術館 蔵品図録第二集　絵画篇 1. Nara, 1979
About sixty illustrations of Ukiyo-e paintings and related portraits, some ex-Yoshikawa Kambō, 吉川観方, Collection.

1980

Tokyo, Shinjuku Odakyū. *Nikuhitsu ukiyo-e no hana: Utagawa-ha no zembō ten*, 東京新宿小田急 肉筆浮世絵の華　歌川派の全貌展．Exh. cat., 4–16 January 1980
127 Utagawa and twentieth-century *bijin* paintings and Utagawa prints. No collectors' names given.

Florida, Loch Haven Art Center. *Urban Beauties and Rural Dreams: Japanese Art from the Mary and Jackson Burke Collection*. Exh. cat., 8 Jan.–10 Feb. 1980.

Nishinomiya, Ōtani Kinen Bijutsukan (eds). *Ōtani Takayoshi korekushon: Nikuhitsu ukiyo-e meihin kan*, 西宮市大谷記念美術館　大谷孝吉 コレクション肉筆浮世絵名品鑑．Tokyo, 3/1980
111 important Ukiyo-e paintings (in colour) formerly in the collection of Kanda Raizō (see Tokyo, Nihombashi Mitsukoshi, 1962).

Tokyo, Tabako to Shio no Hakubutsukan. *Kinsei fūzokuga byōbu*, たばこと塩の博物館 近世風俗画屏風．Exh. cat., Oct. 1980
Seventeen examples of early genre painting (illustrated in colour). Collectors' names given.

Hillier, Jack. *Japanese Drawings of the 18th and 19th Centuries*. Washington, DC, International Exhibitions Foundation, 1980
Travelling exhibition of 142 items, including many Ukiyo-e preparatory drawings and small paintings.

Link, Howard. *Japanese Genre Paintings from the Kyūsei Atami Art Museum*. Exh. cat., 1980
Thirty-one genre and Ukiyo-e paintings from this major collection, with catalogue entries and historical introduction by Howard Link. The exhibition toured the Los Angeles County Museum and Honolulu Academy of Art.

Ukiyo-e shūka, 浮世絵聚花．18 vols, Tokyo, Shōgakkan, 1980–5
This series is devoted mainly to eighteenth-century Ukiyo-e prints in collections worldwide. However, vol. 9 includes a number of Ukiyo-e paintings formerly in the Gale Collection, now in the Minneapolis Institute of Arts. Vol. 16, devoted to the Freer Gallery Ukiyo-e paintings, has as its basic text a Japanese translation of Stern's catalogue of 1973, supplemented by Narazaki in the case of paintings which were not in the 1973 exhibition.

Narazaki Muneshige (ed.). *Nikuhitsu ukiyo-e*, 楢崎宗重　肉筆浮世絵．10 vols, Tokyo, Shūeisha, 1980–2
By far the most significant publication concerning Ukiyo-e painting to date. The colour plates are well reproduced and the works selected are generally of unquestionable authenticity. Narazaki brings together a team of leading connoisseurs to write commentaries, and signatures and seals of each painting are reproduced. Biographical essays about groups or individual artists are separate from the catalogue entries, allowing the authors to concentrate their comments specifically on each painting. However, one regrets that no attempt was

made to include a provenance for each painting, and – even more importantly – issues of authenticity remain almost completely unaddressed. The volumes are awkwardly divided up and there is no index, making it hard to find works by a given painter. A large number of outstanding paintings have been left out, and an additional ten supplementary volumes could easily be published without compromising the high standard of quality of the paintings contained. But the way forward for Ukiyo-e studies now is undoubtedly to put together *catalogues raisonnés* for each artist.

Genshoku ukiyo-e daihyakka jiten,
原色浮世絵大百科事典. 11 vols, Tokyo,
Taishūkan, 1980–2
Another *vade mecum* for Ukiyo-e scholars, organising a vast amount of information in an imaginative way that allows access according to a variety of criteria. Although still dominated by Ukiyo-e prints, this encyclopaedia also contains much information pertinent to the study of paintings. A detailed index permits easy use.

1981

Kobayashi Tadashi. 'Sakura-gari yūrakuzu byōbu',
小林忠. 桜狩遊楽図屏風. *Kokka*, 国華 1041
(1981), 32–40
The author reunites a pair of genre screens of the Kan'ei era now divided between the Brooklyn Museum and Yawata Yōtarō Collection, Tokyo.

Tokyo, Ōta Kinen Bijutsukan. *Kōnoike korekushon uchiwa-e zuroku 1: Ukiyo-e hen*, 太田記念美術館
鴻池コレクション扇絵図録1 — 浮世絵編.
Exh. cat., Aug. 1981
101 fans painted by Ukiyo-e artists, formerly in the collection of the Kōnoike, an Edo-period Osaka merchant family.

Chiba, Kenritsu Bijutsukan. *Nikuhitsu ukiyo-e ten*,
千葉県立美術館 肉筆浮世絵展. Exh. cat.,
12 Sept.–14 Oct. 1981
Ukiyo-e paintings from the Yamaguchi Keisaburō, Nagano Hōji Collections, etc.

Paris, Galerie Janette Ostier. *Le dessin japonais XIIIe-XIXe siècles*. Exh. cat., 1981
161 paintings and preparatory drawings of various schools, including Ukiyo-e.

Nuremberg, Galerie Sorko. *Kunisada: Zeichnungen*,
1981
Preparatory drawings by Utagawa Kunisada (1786–1864).

1982

Tokyo, Shōgakkan (eds). *Kinsei fūzoku zufu*,
小学館 近世風俗図譜. 13 vols, 1982–4
An excellent series, profusely illustrated, with text written by a wide range of leading scholars in art history and cultural history.

Kobayashi Tadashi. *Kan'ei Kambun-ki no nikuhitsuga: Edo no bijinga*, 小林忠
寛永・寛文期の肉筆画 — 江戸の美人画.
Tokyo, Gakken, 1982

A comprehensive collection of Kambun and earlier *bijin* paintings, grouping them into stylistic lineages with detailed comments on the costumes worn.

Amagasaki, Sōgō Bunka Sentaa. *Bijinga no kyōen: nikuhitsu ukiyo-e ten*, 尼崎総合文化センター
美人画の競艶 — 肉筆浮世絵展. Exh. cat.,
2 June–3 July 1982.

Atami, MOA Bijutsukan (eds). *Meihin zuroku: fūzokuga ukiyo-e hen*, MOA 美術館 名品図録
風俗画・浮世絵篇. 1982
Fifty-four genre and Ukiyo-e paintings and forty-one prints from this superb collection.

1983

Nagata Seiji. 'Nikuhitsu ukiyo-e: sono hensen to shuyō gaha', 永田生慈 肉筆浮世絵 —
その変遷と主要画派. *Kobijutsu*, 古美術 65
(Jan. 1983), 4–25.

Okami Masao and Satake Akihiro. *Hyōchū rakuchū rakugai byōbu: Uesugi-bon*, 岡見正雄・佐竹昭広
標注洛中洛外屏風・上杉本. Tokyo, Iwanami
Shoten, 1983
A monograph devoted to the famous pair of *rakuchu rakugai* screens formerly in the possession of the Uesugi family.

Shibui Kiyoshi (ed.). *Nikuhitsu ukiyo-e bijinga shūsei*,
渋井清 肉筆浮世絵美人画集成. 2 vols,
Tokyo, Mainichi Shimbunsha, 1983
The bulk of the catalogue comprises the Hirano Seikichi Collection, some of which has now entered the Azabu Museum, Tokyo. Vol. 2 is devoted entirely to Hokusai and his school.

Tokyo National Museum. *Exhibition of Japanese Paintings from the Collection of the Museum of Fine Arts, Boston*. Exh. cat., 1983
Includes choice items from what must be one of the largest collections of Ukiyo-e paintings in the world.

Nakamura Tanio. 'Boston Bijutsukan zō Bigeroo-shi kizō no nikuhitsu ukiyo-e bijinga gun',
中村渓男 ボストン美術館蔵ビゲ
氏寄贈の肉筆浮世絵美人画群. *Kobijutsu*,
古美術 66 (Apr. 1983), 4–22
A review article of the *bijin* paintings in the Boston Museum exhibition listed above.

Fujinomiya, Fuji Bijutsukan. *Nikuhitsu ukiyo-e bijinga ten*, 富士宮市富士美術館
肉筆浮世絵美人画展. Exh. cat., 2 Oct.–
27 Nov. 1983
Seventy-eight Ukiyo-e paintings from the Hirano Seikichi Collection.

Clark, Timothy. 'Some thoughts on the connoisseurship of Ukiyo-e painting, including an account of the Shumpōan forgery incident', unpublished M.A. thesis, Harvard University, 1983.

1984

Nagoya, Matsuzakaya. *Nikuhitsu ukiyo-e meisaku ten*, 名古屋松坂屋 肉筆浮世絵名作展.
Exh. cat., 4–11 Jan. 1984
Sixty-one high-quality Ukiyo-e paintings. Some collectors' names given. Introduction by Narazaki Muneshige and excellent commentaries by Tanaka Tatsuya.

Tokyo, Azabu Bijutsukan. *Kaikan kinen ten: nikuhitsu ukiyo-e Azabu Bijutsukan*, 麻布美術館
開館記念展 — 肉筆浮世絵麻布美術館.
Exh. cat., 1984
Inaugural exhibition of a specialist Ukiyo-e painting museum containing more than 2,000 works collected by Watanabe Kitarō.

Tokyo, Suntory Bijutsukan. *Ishoku no Edo kaiga: Amerika Puraisu korekushon*, サントリー美術館
異色の江戸絵画 — アメリカ・プライス
コレクション. Exh. cat., Sept.–Nov. 1984
Exhibition of the Joe Price Collection, including 14 Ukiyo-e paintings.

Nara, Yamato Bunkanan. *Kokuhō Matsura byōbu*,
大和文華館 国宝・松浦屏風. Exh. cat.,
5 Oct.–11 Nov. 1984
Highly focused exhibition setting the famous Matsura screens and other genre paintings in the context of women's fashions and accessories of the early seventeenth century.

Tokyo Kokuritsu Hakubutsukan. *Ukiyo-e*,
東京国立博物館 浮世絵. Exh. cat., 16 Oct.–
25 Nov. 1984
Major showing of the Matsukata and other collections held at the Tokyo National Museum, including many important Ukiyo-e paintings.

Tokyo, Azabu Bijutsukan. *Azabu Bijutsukan dayori*,
麻布美術館 麻布美術館だより
(periodical). 1984–7
A newsletter/exhibition list published regularly by the Azabu Museum of Ukiyo-e Painting which finally ran to twenty-one issues and included important articles by Tanaka Tatsuya on Hishikawa Ryūkoku (nos 6, 7); Katsukawa Shungyō (no. 9); Izumi Shuichi (nos 10, 11); Katsukawa Shunkō (nos 15, 16, 17); Takao Shōroku (no. 18); Kitao Masayoshi (nos 19, 20, 21).

Baden-Baden, Staatliche Kunsthalle. *Aus der fliessend verganglichen Welt*. Exh. cat., 15 July–9 Sept. 1984
143 preparatory drawings and small paintings, many of the Ukiyo-e school, from the Gerhard Schack Collection.

Lee, Sherman E. *The Sketchbooks of Hiroshige*, 2 vols, New York, George Braziller, 1984
Reproductions of two sketchbooks containing fifty small paintings by Hiroshige in the Crosby Stuart Noyes Collection in the Library of Congress, Washington, DC.

1985

Kobayashi Tadashi. 'Kampū yūrakuzu byōbu',
小林忠　観楓遊楽図屏風. *Bijutsushi*, 美術史
118 (Apr. 1985), 171–4

Obuse, Hokusai Kan. *Nikuhitsu Katsushika Hokusai*,
小布施北斎館　肉筆葛飾北斎.1985
Catalogue of the Hokusai paintings owned by the
Hokusai Museum established at Obuse in Nagano
Prefecture in 1976. Some of the works undoubtedly
date from Hokusai's several visits late in his career
to his patron, Takai Kōzan, who lived in Obuse
(including four splendid ceiling panels for festival
carts), but many have been acquired subsequently
from unrelated sources.

Tokyo, Ōta Kinen Bijutsukan. *Ōta Kinen Bijutsukan
shozō nikuhitsu ukiyo-e meihin ten*, 太田記念美術館
太田記念美術館所蔵肉筆浮世絵名品展.
Exh. cat., Apr.–May 1985
Catalogue by Nagata Seiji. Important showing of
167 paintings from the museum's rich and comprehensive holdings.

Tokyo, Ōta Kinen Bijutsukan. *Nihon Ukiyo-e
Hakubutsukan shozō nikuhitsu ukiyo-e meihin ten*,
太田記念美術館　日本浮世絵博物館所蔵
肉筆浮世絵名品展. Exh. cat., June 1985
Following on from the above exhibition a similarly
impressive selection of 100 paintings from the Sakai
Collection at the Japan Ukiyo-e Museum in Matsumoto was displayed at the Ōta Museum in
Tokyo.

Matsumoto, Nihon Ukiyo-e Hakubutsukan (JUM).
Nikuhitsu ukiyo-e senshū, 日本浮世絵博物館
肉筆浮世絵撰集. 2 vols, Tokyo, Gakken, 1985
In conjunction with the above exhibition a de luxe
volume was published containing a larger group of
351 paintings from the Sakai Collection, reproduced in colour with details of signatures and seals
and commentaries by various authorities.

Tokyo, Ōta Kinen Bijutsukan. *Katsushika Hokusai
ten*, 太田記念美術館　葛飾北斎展. Exh. cat.,
Oct. 1985
Epoch-making exhibition of 756 prints, paintings
and books by Hokusai organised by Nagata Seiji.
The ninety paintings included many of the best
examples from Japanese collections.

Osaka, Kokusai Kōryū Bijutsu-shi Kenkyūkai
(eds). *Tōyō bijutsu ni okeru fūzoku hyōgen*,
国際交流美術史研究会　東洋美術における
風俗表現. 1985
Proceedings of the International Symposium of Art
Historical Studies on the subject of 'The Represent-
ation of Genre in East Asian Art'.

1986

Tokyo, Azabu Bijutsukan. *Azabu Bijutsukan
shūzōhin zuroku*, 麻布美術館
麻布美術館収蔵品図録. Exh. cat., Feb. 1986
Fifty-four of the most important Ukiyo-e paintings
in the Azabu Museum Collection.

Kyoto, Kokuritsu Hakubutsukan. *Shimabara Sumiya
no bijutsu*. 京都国立博物館　島原角屋の美術.
Exh. cat., Feb. 1986
Exhibition of paintings and artefacts from the
Sumiya, a house of pleasure in Kyoto founded in
the middle of the seventeenth century.

Link, Howard. 'Pleasure House Screens', *Honolulu
Academy of Arts Journal*, vol. IV (1986), 49–67

Kyonan, Hishikawa Moronobu Kinenkan.
Hishikawa Moronobu Kinenkan zuroku,
鋸南町菱川師宣記念館　菱川師宣記念館
図録. Tokyo, Gabundō, 1986
Catalogue of the collections of the memorial
museum to Moronobu located close to his birthplace in Chiba Prefecture. Includes 46 paintings.

Kyonan, Hishikawa Moronobu Kinenkan. *Mizuta
korekushon zuroku*, 鋸南町菱川師宣記念館
水田コレクション図録. Exh. cat., Apr. 1986
Exhibition of the Mizuta Mikio Collection of
Ukiyo-e paintings and prints from the Mizuta Art
Museum, Seijō University.

Tokyo, Azabu Bijutsukan. *Azabu Bijutsukan kenkyū
kiyō*, 麻布美術館　麻布美術館研究紀要.
Issues 1 (spring 1986) and 2 (autumn 1986)
A short-lived bulletin of the Azabu Museum which
ran to only two issues. No. 1 contains biographical
studies of Hōtei Gosei and Nomura Yoshikuni. No.
2 contains articles on an album of letters and paintings collected by Ōta Nampo and studies of a votive
panel painting by Kiyoshige.

Tokyo, Waseda Daigaku Engeki Hakubutsukan.
Kabuki ema ten zuroku, 早稲田大学演劇博物館
歌舞伎絵馬展図録. Exh. cat., 12 Nov.–
8 Dec. 1986
Comprehensive scholarly catalogue of an exhibition
of sixty-eight votive plaques of Kabuki actors. One
sculpture of *saruwaka kyōgen* figures dates from
1664, but the oldest painted panel is otherwise from
1725. There is a complete listing of known panels
arranged by prefecture.

1987

Narazaki Muneshige (ed.). *Nihon no bijutsu, nos
248–250: Nikuhitsu ukiyo-e*, 楢崎宗重
日本の美術第248号～第250号 ― 肉筆
浮世絵. 3 vols, Tokyo, Shibundō, 1987
Excellent general introduction to history of Ukiyo-e
painting. Vol. 1 (Kambun-Hōreki) introduces 122
paintings, many previously unpublished, with text
by Asano Shūgō; vol. 2 (Meiwa-Kansei) contains
ninety-eight paintings, with text by Nagata Seiji;
vol. 3 (Kansei-Meiji) contains ninety-eight paintings with text by Nagata Seiji.

Victoria, Art Gallery of Greater Victoria. *Figure
Painting of the Edo Period, With an Emphasis on
Ukiyo-e Painting*. Exh. cat., 1987
Twenty-eight paintings from the Nakanishi Bunzō
Collection.

Tokyo, Ōta Kinen Bijutsukan. *Katsushika-ha,
Utagawa-ha o chūshin to shita shita-e ten*,
太田記念美術館　葛飾派・歌川派を中心と
した下絵展. Exh. cat., 2 June–24 July 1987
Important exhibition of 189 preparatory drawings
of the Katsushika and Utagawa schools, including
items from the Nagase Collection.

Nagoya, Matsuzakaya. *Shinsen ukiyo-e nikuhitsu
ten*, 名古屋松坂屋　新撰浮世絵肉筆展.
Exh. cat., 8–13 Oct. 1987
Sales exhibition of fine Ukiyo-e paintings held by
the Sumishō Gallery, Tokyo.

Narazaki Muneshige. 'Teisai Hokuba hitsu go-
sekku zu', 楢崎宗重　蹄斎北馬筆五節供図.
Kokka, 国華 1107 (Sept. 1987), 26–31.

Narazaki Muneshige (gen. ed.). *Hizō ukiyo-e taikan*,
楢崎宗重　秘蔵浮世絵大観. 13 vols, Tokyo,
Kōdansha, 1987–90
A major series on Ukiyo-e paintings and prints in
the principal European collections, with commentaries by a range of leading scholars. The index
volume lists 400–500 paintings spread among the
various collections.

1988

Sendai-shi Hakubutsukan. *Azabu Bijutsukan shozō
nikuhitsu ukiyo-e meihin ten*, 仙台市博物館
麻布美術館所蔵肉筆浮世絵名品展. Exh.
cat., 11 June–17 July 1988
104 major paintings from the collection of the
Azabu Museum.

Jenkins, Donald. 'Paintings of the Floating World',
in Cleveland Museum of Art (eds), *A Private
World: Japanese and Chinese Art from the Kelvin
Smith Collection*. Exh. cat., 14 Sept.–13 Nov.
1988, pp. 6–40
Essay about Ukiyo-e painting, introducing sixteen
examples from the Kelvin Smith Collection, Cleveland Museum of Art.

Tokyo, Idemitsu Bijutsukan. *Nikuhitsu ukiyo-e*
('Ukiyo-e paintings'), 出光美術館　肉筆浮世絵.
By Naitō Masato, 内藤正人, 1988
Important scholarly catalogue of this major collec-
tion. 162 paintings illustrated in colour with details
of signatures and seals.

Leiden, Rijksmuseum voor Volkenkunde.
Drawings by Kuniyoshi. Exh. cat., 1988
Catalogue by Matthi Forrer of 113 preparatory
drawings and related prints by Kuniyoshi in the
collection of the National Museum of Ethnology,
Leiden.

1989

Tokyo, Azabu Museum of Arts and Crafts. 'Fashion
of Edo': Women's Dress in Ukiyo-e Paintings,
麻布美術工芸館　江戸のふぁっしょん.
Exh. cat., 14 June–2 July 1989
Inaugural exhibition in the new Azabu Museum of
Arts and Crafts tracing changing women's fashions
in the Edo period using textiles and Ukiyo-e
paintings.

Naitō Masato. 'Katsukawa Shunshō no nikuhitsu bijinga ni tsuite', 内藤正人
勝川春章の肉筆美人画について. *Bijutsushi*, 美術史. No. 125 (March 1989), 57–81
Excellent article which lists all paintings by Shunshō known to the author and proposes a convincing chronology of the development of Shunshō's painting style, based in part on a detailed analysis of changes in signature and seals.

Tokyo, Itabashi Kuritsu Bijutsukan. *Nikuhitsu ukiyo-e meihin ten*, 板橋区立美術館
肉筆浮世絵名品展. Exh. cat., 8 Apr.–7 May 1989
Good selection of 130 Ukiyo-e paintings, many not previously introduced. Some collectors' names given.

Kumamoto Kenritsu Bijutsukan. *Imanishi korekushon meihin ten I*, 熊本県立美術館
今西コレクション名品展 I. Exh. cat., 17 Oct.–26 Nov. 1989
Includes seventy-five Ukiyo-e paintings, the first selection from the newly discovered collection of the late Imanishi Kikumatsu. Well reproduced in colour with details of signatures and seals and careful commentaries by Asoshina Yasuo.

1990

Clark, Timothy. 'Paintings by Hokusai in the British Museum', *Orientations*. Vol. 21, no. 8 (Aug. 1990), 37–44

Tokyo, Mainichi Shimbun (eds). *Kiyossone to kinsei Nihonga sato-gaeri ten*, 毎日新聞社
キヨッソーネと近世日本画里帰り展. Exh. cat., 16 Aug.–4 Sept. 1990
Includes fifty-two Ukiyo-e paintings from the Chiossone collection, many already introduced in *UT*, vol. 10 (1987).

Kumamoto Kenritsu Bijutsukan. *Imanishi korekushon meihin ten II*, 熊本県立美術館
今西コレクション名品展 II. Exh. cat., 5 Oct.–4 Nov. 1990
Includes a further twenty Ukiyo-e paintings from the Imanishi collection.

Nagata Seiji. *Hokusai bijutsukan*, 永田生慈
北斎美術館. 5 vols, Tokyo, Shūeisha, 1990
Summum of Nagata's researches on Hokusai, integrating well paintings, drawings, books and prints. The five volumes are arranged by subject-matter.

1991

Tokyo, New Ōtani Bijutsukan. *Maboroshi no ukiyo-e bijin-tachi*. ニューオータニ美術館
幻の浮世絵美人たち. Exh. cat. by Uchida Kinzō, 21 May–30 June 1991
Inaugural exhibition of 111 Ukiyo-e paintings from the Ōtani Collection in a purpose-built gallery inside the New Ōtani Hotel, Tokyo.

London, Richard Kruml. *Japanese Paintings* (cat. no. 24). 1991
Sales catalogue of thirty-eight Ukiyo-e and other, mainly Shijō school paintings.

Kumamoto Kenritsu Bijutsukan. *Imanishi korekushon meihin ten*, 熊本県立美術館
今西コレクション名品展 III. Exh. cat., 8 Oct.–17 Nov. 1991
A further selection of 106 Ukiyo-e paintings from the Imanishi Collection.

NOT DATED

Ukiyo-e shū, 浮世絵集. n.p., n.d. (c. 1910s–20s)
Photographs of Ukiyo-e paintings. Collectors' names given, such as Kuwabara Yōjirō, Takeoka Toyota *et al.*

Nasu Royal Museum of Art. *Ukiyo-e nikuhitsu meisaku shū*, 那須ロイヤル美術館
浮世絵肉筆名作集. ?Exh. cat., n.d. (c. 1980s)
100 examples from the important collection of this specialist Ukiyo-e painting museum.

ALTERNATIVE NAMES OF ARTISTS

Akabane: Keisai
Amano: Sei'ei
Andō: Hiroshige, Isshō
Aoigaoka: Hokkei
Aoigazono: Hokkei
Arisaka: Hokuba

Baihōken: Eishun
Baiōken: Eishun
Baisuiken: Eishun
Baiyūken: Katsunobu
Bōkanshi: Suiō
Bokutei: Tsukimaro
Bukiyō Matabei: Kunisada
Bunkadō: Sukenobu
Bunshi: Moromasa

Chōbunsai: Eishi
Chōkōsai: Eishō
Chōkyūsai: Eizan
Chōōrō: Kuniyoshi
Chōsetsusai: Tsunemasa
Chōyōdō: Anchi
Chōzaemon: Chōshun
Chūrin: Shunchō
Chūrinsha: Shunchō

Daikei: Settei
Denzō: Kyōden
Dewaya: Ando
Dokuyū(?): Eishi

Eishōsai: Chōki
Enshimbō: Shumman
Entaisai: Utamaro

Fuchōan: Kunisada
Fuchō Sanjin: Kunisada
Fude no Ayamaru: Utamaro
Fujiwara: Eishi, Isshō, Koryūsai
Furuyama: Moromasa, Moroshige
Fūsen Ichiin: Eisen
Fusenkyo Iitsu: Hokusai

Gakutei Sanjin: Gakutei
Gakyōjin: Hokusai
Gakyō Rōjin: Hokusai
Gansuisha: Yoshiteru
Genshichi: Ando
Genshinka: Kiyomine
Genzō: Toyokuni II
Gepparō: Kunisada
Getchi Rōjin: Hokusai
Getsugetsudō: Moromasa
Gikōsai: Sessai
Ginsetsu II: Katsushika Hokuga
Go: Hokkei
Gogaku: Gakutei
Gorōhachi: Hokuba
Gosei: Hōtei Hokuga
Gosotei: Toyokuni II
Gototei: Kunisada
Gummatei: Hokusai

Gyokuō: Yoshitoshi
Gyokuōrō: Yoshitoshi
Gyoshi: Miyagawa Shuntei

Hachiemon: Hokusai
Hakushōken: Matsuno Chikanobu
Hanabusa: Kunisada
Handen Shakyo: Yoshitaki
Hanekawa: Chinchō
Hanji: Shinsai
Hanjirō: Shinsai
Hara: Kunitoshi
Haruhiro: Koryūsai
Haruji: Hidemaro
Harunobu: Eishun, Gakutei
Hasegawa: Eishun
Hashimoto: Chikanobu, Hokusai II
Hatsugorō(?): Hokkei
Hidejirō(?): Eitaku
Hirazawa: Kuniaki
Hishikawa: Morofusa, Morohira, Moronaga, Moronobu, Moroshige, Ryūkoku
Hitofushi Chizue: Shumman
Hōgyoku: Yoshitaki
Hokkatei: ?Eisen
Hokubaiko: Kunisada
Hokunen: Yoshiteru
Hokutei: ?Eisen
Hōkyō: Gakutei
Horikawa Tarō: Gakutei
Hoshino: Hokuba
Hōshū: Fujimaro
Hosoda: Eishi
Hōtei: Hokuga
Hyakurin Sōri: Hokusai

Ichiesai: Toyokuni II
Ichigyosai: Kunihisa
Ichijusai: Kunitsuru
Ichimyōkai Hodoyoshi: Kuniyoshi
Ichiōsai: Kuniaki, Yoshiume
Ichirakusai: Eisui
Ichirō: Gakutei
Ichiryūsai: Hiroshige, Toyoharu, Toyohiro, Toyokuni II
Ichiunsai: Kuninaga, Kunitoshi
Ichiyōsai: Kunisada, Toyokuni I, Toyokuni II, Yoshitaki
Ichiyōtei: Yoshitaki
Ichiyūsai: Hiroshige, Kunisada, Kuniyoshi
Iitsu: Hokusai

Ikeda: Eisen
Ikkaisai: Yoshitoshi
Ikkakusai: Hashimoto
  Chikanobu
Ikusa: Kuniyoshi
Inagaki: Tsurujo
Inoue: Katsushika
  Hokumei
Inransai: Eisen
Insai Hakusui: Eisen
Ippitsuan Kakō: Eisen
Ippitsusai: Bunchō
Ippōsai: Kuniaki
Ishōsai: Yanagawa
  Shigenobu
Isoda: Koryūsai
Issensai: Eitaku
Itchinsai: Yoshiteru
Ittai: Kunisada
Ittensai: Yoshitaki
Iwakubo: Hokusai
Iwasa: Katsushige,
  Matabei
Iwase: Kyōden

Jibukyō: Eishi
Jintarō: Kyōden
Jitokusai: Sukenobu
Jitokusō: Sukenobu
Jōsen: ?Ando
Jūbei: Yanagawa
  Shigenobu
Jueidō: Yoshitaki
Jūemon: Hiroshige
Jūgasei: Shunchō,
  Shunshō
Jun: Tsukimaro

Kaburagi: Kiyokata
Kadō: Eitaku
Kaei: Eishi
Kaigetsudō: Anchi,
  Ando, Dohan,
  Doshin, Doshu,
  Doshū
Kaisai: Yoshitoshi
Kakei: Shungyō
Kakō: Hokusai
Kakusensai: Shungyō
Kameji: Kiyomine
Kankun: Suiō
Kansetsu: Tsukimaro
Kansetsusai:
  Tsukimaro
Kan'unshi: Ando
Kaō: Gyokusen
Karan: Shigemasa
Karyōsai: Katsushika
  Hokuga
Katsukawa: Hokusai,
  Shunchō, Shun'ei,
  Shungyō, Shunkō,
  Shunshō, Shunshō
  II, Shuntei
Katsumiyagawa:
  Shunsui
Katsura: Munenobu
Katsushika: Hokuga,
  Hokuitsu, Hokumei,
  Hokusai, Ōi
Kawamata:
  Tsunemasa,
  Tsunetatsu,
  Tsuneyuki
Kawamura: Hokusai
Kayanosuke: Kuninaga
Keikōsai: Hokuitsu
Keikōtei: Hokuitsu
Keisai: Eisen

Ken'ichi: Kiyokata
Kichibei: Moronobu
Kichisadō: Shunchō
Kichizaemon: Shunchō
Kida: Settei
Kiheiji: Isshō
Kikuhen: Kyōden
Kikukawa: Eiji, Eizan
Kikumaro: Tsukimaro
Kikutei: Gyokusen,
  Kyōden
Kindō: Settei
Kin'emon: Hokkei
Kinraisha: Kunisada
Kinsai: Yanagawa
  Shigenobu
Kintaisha: Hokusai
Kiō: Kunisada
Kisai: Hiroshige II
Kishō Tengō: Keisai
Kitagawa: Fujimaro,
  Hidemaro,
  Tsukimaro, Utamaro
Kitao: Keisai, Kyōden,
  Shigemasa
Kiyomitsu II: Kiyomine
Kiyotaka: Toyonaga
Kobayashi: Eitaku
Kōchōrō: Kunisada
Kodamaya: Eizan
Kōen: Gakutei
Kōga: Gyokusen
Kohensai: Isshō
Koizumi: Eisen
Kōkasai: Fujimaro
Kokushunrō: Eisen
Kondō: Katsunobu,
  Kiyoharu, Kiyonobu
Konsei: Eisen
Kōzandō: Shumman
Kubo: Shumman
Kubota: Shumman
Kukushin: Hokusai
Kumayoshi: Toyokuni I
Kunisada Sha
  Toyokuni: Kunisada
Kurahashi: Toyokuni I
Kutokusai: Shun'ei
Kuwagata: Keisai
Kyokurōsei: Shunshō
Kyōsai: Hokkei
Kyōya: Kyōden
Kyūzan: Gakutei

Magosaburō:
  Kuniyoshi
Maki: Bokusen
Mangorō: Eizan
Manji: Hokusai
Manjirō: Hōtei Hokuga
Mankichi: Eizan
Mannō: Shinsai
Mansuian: Toyokuni II
Maruya: Gakutei
Masakatsu: Koryūsai
Masaki(?): Toyoharu
Masanobu: Kyōden,
  Settei
Masateru: Shunshō
Masayoshi: Keisai
Masayuki: Shinsai
Matsui: Shunshō II
Matsuno: Chikanobu
Migaru no Orichika:
  Kyōden
Minamoto: Settei
Mitsutaka: Hokuba
Miura: Eitaku
Miuraya: Hokusai

Miyagawa: Chōki,
  Chōshun, Chōsuke,
  Isshō, Shunsui,
  Shuntei
Mokuen: Utamaro
Mori: Bunchō,
  Gyokusen
Moriyoshi: Miyagawa
  Shuntei
Mugino Orochimaro:
  Keisai
Mugyo: Eitaku
Mumei'ō: Eisen
Murasakiya: Utamaro
Museishi: Suiō
Myōnosuke:
  Katsushika Hokuga

Nakai: Yoshitaki
Nakajima: Hokusai,
  Yoshiume
Nandaka Shiran:
  Shumman
Nanzan: Gakutei
Naoyoshi: Hashimoto
  Chikanobu
Nishikawa: Sukenobu,
  Suketada, Terunobu
Nishimura: Shigenaga
Nobuyuki: Katsushika
  Hokuga
Noriya: Yoshitaki

Ogawa: Tsukimaro
Okabe: Gakutei II
Okada: Gyokuzan
Okajima: Toyohiro
Okazaki: Ando
Okazawa: Ando
Okumura: Masanobu
Onokichi: Gakutei

Raishin: Hokusai
Raito: Yanagawa
  Shigenobu
Reisai: Hokushi
Rekisentei: Eiri
Rinsai: Yanagawa
  Shigenobu
Ririn: Shunshō
Rojinsai: Settei
Rokurokuan: Shunshō
Rokusaburō:
  Tsukimaro
Ryōsa: Gakutei
Ryūen: Kuniyoshi
Ryūkaen: Shinsai
Ryūryūkyo: Shinsai
Ryūsai: Hiroshige
Ryūshō: Hiroshige II

Sabanaya: Eizan
Sadaoka: Gakutei
Saihōsha: Kuniyoshi
Saitō: Shungyō
Sakunojō: Moronaga
Samuru: Kyōden
Sanjirō: Keisai
Sankō: Keisai, Shunchō
Sankōdō: Gyokusen
Santō: Kyōden
Santōan: Kyōden
Sasaki: Yoshitaki
Satonoya: Yoshitaki
Seichōken: ?Kiyoshige
Seiryūken: Kiyomine
Seisai: Kyōden
Seisei Rōjin: Kyōden
Seiseisai: Kyōden

Sekiyō: Utamaro
Sekkoku: Kuniyoshi
Senjin: Shunshō
Sen'ō: Toyoharu
Senryūsai: Toyoharu
Sensai: Eitaku, Kyōden
Senshin: Kuniyoshi
Sensuke: Tsukimaro
Sesshin: Suiō
Shibata: ?Kaō, Zeshin
Shien: Fujimaro,
  Shunchō
Shigenobu: Hiroshige II
Shigeyoshi: Eisen
Shihō: Fujimaro
Shikasai: Fujimaro
Shikei: Keisai
Shikōsai: Hokuitsu
Shin(?): Baiyūken
  Katsunobu
Shin'emon: Toyoharu
Shinkadō: Gakutei
Shinkurō: Moromasa
Shinkyūdō: Gakutei
Shinobugaoka:
  Utamaro
Shinshichirō:
  Moromasa
Shinten'ō: Settei
Shinzō: Shungyō
Shisen: Tsukimaro
Shisendō: Gyokusen
Shisui: ?Ando
Shitatsu(?): Tsukimaro
Shitomi: Kangetsu
Shōbei: Koryūsai
Shōgorō(?): Hokkei
Shōjirō: Toyoharu
Shōju: Toyoharu
Shōnosuke: Kiyomine
Shōrinsai: Hidemaro
Shōsadō: Shumman
Shōshin(?): Keisai
Shōsuiken: Eishun
Shōtei: Hokuju
Shōzō: Kunisada
Shūei: Sessai
Shūen: Hokuba
Shūjirō(?): Eitaku
Shunkō: Shunshō II
Shunkōsai: Hokushū
Shunkyokudō:
  Chōshun
Shunkyokusai:
  Hokumei
Shunrō: Hokusai
Shunshunsai: Hokuba
Shunshuntei: Hokuba
Shusen: Fujimaro
Sodō: Gyokusen
Sogan: Isshō
Sogo: Kyōden
Sokatei: Yoshitoshi
Sōri: Hokusai
Sugawara: Gakutei
Sukezaemon:
  Gakutei II
Sumida: Kunisada
Sumie: Buzen
Sūshi Toyokuni:
  Kunisada
Suzuki:
  Harunobu,
  Hiroshige II,
  Hokusai II,
  Yanagawa
  Shigenobu

Tachibana: Sei'ei

Taigirō: ?Hokusai II
Taiso: Sessai,
  Yoshitoshi
Taito: Hokusai
Taito II: Hokusen
Tajimaya: Toyoharu
Takamasa(?):
  Gyokusen
Takeda: Eishun
Takeshiba: Genkei
Taminosuke: Eishi
Tamura: Suiō
Tanaka:
  Kyōsensai,
  Masunobu,
  Yoshiteru
Tange: Settei
Tansei: Shunchō
Tanseidō: Shunchō
Tatsumasa: Hokusai
Tatsuyuki: Hokkei
Teisai: Hokuba
Tetsuzō: Hokusai
Toenrō: Hokusen
Tōensai: Kanshi, Kaō
Tōi: Settei
Tōjirō: Toyohiro
Tokimasa: Hokusai
Tokitarō: Hokusai
Tokitomi: Eishi
Tokubei: Hiroshige
Tokusen: Eitaku
Tokutarō: Hiroshige
Tomikawa: Fusanobu
Torii:
  Kiyomasu I,
  Kiyomine,
  Kiyomitsu,
  Kiyonobu I,
  Kiyoshige
Toriyama: Sekien
Tōshien: Shunchō
Toshinobu: Eizan
Tōsuke: Yoshiume
Tōtei: Hokushi
Totoya: Hokkei
Toyoaki: Utamaro
Toyohara: Hashimoto
  Chikanobu
Toyokuni II (actually
  III): Kunisada
Toyokuni segare
  Toyoshige:
  Toyokuni II
Toyoshige: Toyokuni II
Toyoshige II:
  Kunitsuru
Tsuchimochi
  Ninsaburō: Hokusai
Tsuguzane: Keisai
Tsukioka: Sessai,
  Settei, Yoshitoshi
Tsunejirō: Yoshitaki
Tsutsumi: Tōgetsu,
  Tōrin I, Tōrin III

Uegaki: Hōryū
Ukyō: Sukenobu
Umon: Gyokusen
Uoya: Hokkei
Utagawa:
  Hiroshige,
  Kuniaki,
  Kunihisa,
  Kuninaga,
  Kunisada,
  Kunitoshi,
  Kunitsuru,
  Kuniyoshi,

Toyoharu,
Toyohiro,
Toyokuni I,
Toyokuni II,
Toyonaga,
Yoshiiku,
Yoshiteru,
Yoshitoshi,
Yoshiume
Utashige: Hiroshige
Uzaemon: Sukenobu

Wada: Kunitsuru
Watanabe: Miyagawa
  Shuntei

Yabairō: Yoshiume
Yamadera: Katsushika
  Hokuga
Yamazaki: Joryū
Yanagawa: Shigenobu
Yasaburō: Eishi
Yashima: Gakutei
Yasubei: Shumman
Yasugorō: Kunitsuru
Yasumichi(?): Isshō
Yasunobu: Kaō
Yonejirō: Yoshitoshi
Yōsai: Gakutei
Yoshinobu: Eisen
Yoshioka: Yoshitoshi
Yoshisaburō:
  Kuniyoshi, Yoshiteru
Yoshitsuru II:
  Hashimoto
  Chikanobu
Yōshū: Hashimoto
  Chikanobu
Yōsui: Yoshitaki
Yōsuke: Shunshō
Yōtei: Gakutei
Yōzan: Fujimaro
Yūchiku: Moronobu
Yūji: Shunshō
Yūjirō(?): Shunshō
Yūsai: Shunshō
Yūsei: Kyōden
Yūsenkyo: Shinsai
Yūshidō: Shunchō
Yūsuke: Shunshō,
  Utamaro

Zen Hokusai Iitsu:
  Hokusai
Zenjirō: Eisen

INDEX